D1269759

APPLIED NUCLEAR Physics

ERNEST POLLARD, Associate Professor of Physics, Yale University . . . . . and

WILLIAM L. DAVIDSON, Jr., Research Physicist, the B. F. Goodrich Company

THIRD PRINTING

JOHN WILEY & SONS, Inc., New York

London: CHAPMAN & HALL, *Limited*

IN THE REPRINTING OF THIS BOOK, THE RECOMMENDATIONS OF THE WAR PRODUCTION BOARD HAVE BEEN OBSERVED FOR THE CONSERVATION OF PAPER AND OTHER IMPORTANT WAR MATERIALS. THE CONTENT REMAINS COMPLETE AND UNABRIDGED.

THIRD PRINTING, JULY, 1944

PRINTED IN THE UNITED STATES OF AMERICA

PREFACE

No subject in the whole of science has been studied with as much sustained interest as the transmutation of the elements. Thus it is a remarkable fact that, although men were actively pursuing this goal centuries ago, success first crowned their efforts a mere two decades back in the experiments of Lord Rutherford. However, in the intervening score of years, the searchlight of scientific investigation has been focused intently on this field of physics, and the many discoveries that have flowed from these researches have had and are still having a profound influence on the scientific activities of today even in fields foreign to physics.

Transmutation is essentially linked with the atomic nucleus, and the study of transmutation will continue to be of the utmost value in elucidating the characteristics of this smallest domain of nature. Undoubtedly this study will yield new and important theoretical ideas, and yet it is questionable that these ideas will have the influence, at least in applications to fields outside the realm of physics, that is already exerted by the technical developments in nuclear physics. The discovery of artificial radioactivity has put in the hands of chemists, biologists, and medical research workers the means of studying individual "tagged" atoms, which renders possible experiments that could not have been contemplated a short time ago. Recent years, moreover, have witnessed the discovery of reactions which liberate energies far in excess of those available by ordinary chemical means and have changed the attitude of responsible physicists toward the use of atomic power from skeptical to sanguine. These discoveries promise to play an increasingly important role in the forward march of science.

In treating the subject of nuclear physics the technical aspect is emphasized in this book. We aim at presenting the essential facts and methods of artificial radioactivity and transmutation in such a way as to be of service to the growing army of chemists, biologists, physicians, and engineers, who, though not necessarily versed in the language of physics, are using the products of nuclear physics to further their ends in their own spheres.

While eliminating entirely the elaborate theoretical approach to nuclear processes, we feel that the account we give is sufficiently thorough to make the book useful as a text in a course on artificial radioactivity and nuclear physics.

Since the task of correlating all the hundreds of recently discovered radioactive elements troubles even the research worker in this field, as many tables giving summarized information as possible are presented; and we have endeavored to include and arrange the material so as to facilitate a speedy grasp of the physics of the atomic nucleus.

We have not aimed at making this primarily a reference book, but rather one to be read for description and explanation. We have, therefore, not compiled a complete table of references, which indeed would necessitate a much larger work than this, but we have provided a small number of references which can be consulted for more detailed information.

ERNEST POLLARD
Sloane Physics Laboratory,
Yale University

WILLIAM L. DAVIDSON, JR.

CONTENTS

CHAPTER 1

ALCHEMY, ATOMS, AND RADIOACTIVITY

Transmutation is the romance subject of science. It has stirred the imagination of the responsible scientist and the cupidity of the jeweler, and it has even set the armaments maker thinking about new and more deadly explosives. One can always get the attention of the layman by referring to the subject of transmutation, and indeed it would seem as if the progress of science lacked something until at least the claim could be made that transmutation could be achieved. In this introductory chapter we propose to outline the two exciting discoveries of modern alchemy: the discovery of transmutation itself, and the far more valuable attendant discovery of artificial radioactivity, which, so to speak, dropped out of the blue sky after the entry into the new realm of "atom smashing" had been made.

Before we proceed to give an account of the modern (and only real) "philosopher's stone," it is well worth while to consider for a moment the reasoning which led so many first-rate scientists to spend their labors attempting to turn lead into gold. Not everyone realizes that Newton spent much of his time as an experimentalist in the study of alchemy, and this should alone be enough to give distinction to the early science. The reasoning of the older philosopher was fundamentally sound. He credited nature with the ability to design a wonderfully diverse universe from a few original materials, and in this he has turned out to show uncanny insight. The philosopher held that all things were constructed from the "four elements": fire, earth, air, and water. In a rather arbitrary way the constituents of various substances were assigned. Once this principle had been decided upon, the incentive to change chemical elements one into another was automatically there, for though it was admitted that the combination between the constituents in a metal, for example, was unusually strong, there was no apparent reason why some powerful influence should not be found which would break down this combination and achieve the desired result. It was just a pity that centuries of effort had managed to produce only pitifully meager results. The remarkable fact is that, even though the methods used by the early chemists seem today to be a weird conglomerate of strange admixtures and superstitious rites, the basic idea, the simplicity of nature, has been justified almost beyond belief. The ancient workers had the right ideas but the wrong building blocks, and it has taken the intervening centuries to provide us with the slow accumulation of knowledge which enables us to discover the right building blocks. Once these were found, or, as it happened, with a little luck, just before all were found, the problem of changing one element into another could be solved. With this preamble we can now proceed to see how the first transmutation was accomplished.

The building blocks of nature are neutrons, protons, and electrons. It is at one with our knowledge of nature that she achieves the most amazing diversity with incredible economy of original materials. Thus, of all conceivable methods of reproduction, the simplest way which will give the greatest diversity is the one most commonly found; and, in the same vein, the great range of chemical elements is composed of the three simple particles mentioned above: neutrons, protons, and electrons. These three particles can be thought of as mass-without-charge, mass-and-charge, and charge-without-mass, respectively. The neutron is a neutral particle of "atomic weight" 1.0089, almost the same as the atomic weight of hydrogen; the proton is a positively charged particle of weight slightly less than that of the hydrogen atom; the electron is an almost weightless negative electric charge, the charge being equal to that of the proton but opposite in sign.

These elementary particles alone are not sufficient to cause the existence of varieties of atoms: forces are necessary in addition. By far the most extensive force is the well-known coulomb force between charges, a force which causes an attraction or repulsion inversely proportional to the square of their separation. If the charges are of the same sign there is repulsion: if different, attraction. In nuclear physics these forces are called "long-range coulomb forces." Now it is a property of the inverse square law of force that a heavy charged particle, attracting a light electron, will normally cause the electron to rotate around it in stable orbits, either circles or ellipses; and the simplest conception of an atom is that it is a solar system with a positive nucleus playing the role of the sun and planetary electrons rotating around the nucleus in circular or elliptical orbits. The nucleus is heavy and contains neutrons and protons: the number of protons, which governs the charge on the nucleus, also governs the number of electrons needed to give rise to a neutral atom and so governs the nature of the chemical element. Today as the chemist or physicist thinks of the sequence: hydrogen, helium, lithium, beryllium, boron, carbon · · · he thinks of numbers of electrons: 1, 2, 3, 4, 5, 6 · · · . It is usual to denote the nuclear charge, which is the same as the number of electrons, by Z. The whole subject of chemistry is vitally concerned with the electrons outside the nucleus, and it is only rarely that the properties of the nucleus concern the chemist. The first individual to become interested in the nucleus was, as is common in pioneer thought, the pure physicist. Its properties were studied in various ingenious ways, and today we are able to say a little about the type of force which holds the constituents of the nucleus in place, much as the coulomb forces hold the electrons in place in the atom itself. One of the most powerful of the methods of studying these forces has resulted from the discovery of the technique of transmutation, a discovery which followed swiftly on the discovery of the nature of the atom as briefly described above.

We have just said that the chemical elements are characterized by the number of electrons around the nucleus, and that this number, in turn, is fixed by the charge of the nucleus. It is clear, then, that to change one element permanently into another, the number of electrons must be changed permanently. This cannot be done by knocking off or adding an electron, for then, although a great change in atomic properties occurs, the change is not lasting, for the extra electron will soon leave, or an additional one be captured, to restore the original element. The only method of effecting such a transmutation is to *change the nuclear charge*, which will automatically change the number of planetary electrons and hence the nature of the element.

When understood in this way the process of transmutation is simple enough; in practice it proves to be exceedingly difficult, chiefly for one reason, the extreme smallness of the atomic nucleus.

The average radius of an electron rotating about a nucleus is roughly 10^{-8} cm; the radius of the nucleus itself is roughly one-ten thousandth smaller, or 10^{-12} cm, a fact which has two important consequences. The first is that the nucleus is an extremely minute target: it presents an area of 3×10^{-24} sq cm to anything which seeks to alter it, an area so small that the chance of striking it is almost nil. If it were not that the number of atoms in even a small piece of matter is extremely large—say 10^{18} as a figure to think about—then the smallness of the nuclear target would finally prevent the achievement of any measurable number of transmutations. The second consequence is that the forces repelling any charged particle which is "fired" at a nucleus are tremendous, for the inverse square law of repulsion is such that at very small distances of separation extremely large forces occur. Thus at the surface of a nucleus of sodium, having a nuclear charge of **11** protons or $11 \times 4.8 \times 10^{-10}$ electrostatic unit, a force equal to $\frac{11 \times 4.8^2 \times 10^{-20}}{10^{-24}}$, or roughly 2,500,000 dynes, acts on an incoming proton. On the atomic scale this is an enormous figure. We can therefore see that the problem of permanently changing elements offers great technical difficulties at the outset.

It is small wonder, then, that the achievement of the transmutation of nitrogen into oxygen by Rutherford in 1919 ranks as one of the outstanding experiments in a century of great progress. His success was due to two technical advances: the one which enabled the con-

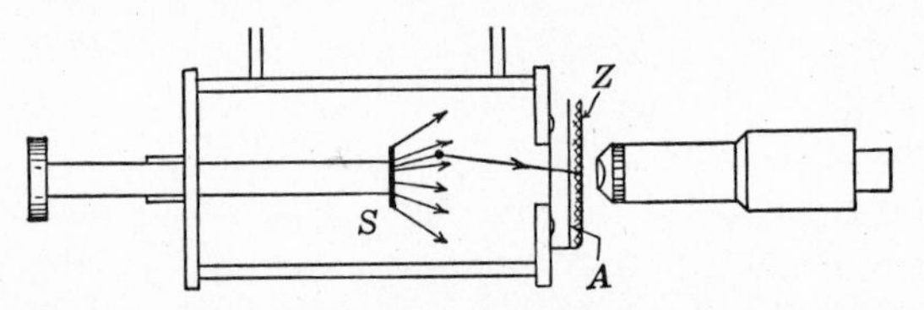

FIG. 1. Rutherford's original apparatus for the transmutation of nitrogen into oxygen. Alpha particles from the source bombard nuclei of nitrogen and cause the transmutation. At the same time swiftly moving hydrogen nuclei are set free, which traverse a considerable thickness of absorber and are detected on the scintillation screen.

centration of intensely radioactive material; the other, the discovery that crystals of zinc sulphide, and a few other substances, when observed under a microscope in a darkened room were observed to emit scintillations when struck by *single* fast-moving atomic particles. The first advance made it possible to bombard materials with a kind of atomic machine gun—radioactive "sources" emitting some ten to a hundred million doubly charged helium nuclei (alpha particles) per second, each alpha particle having a speed of 2×10^9 cm per sec and capable of passing through 7 cm of air or its equivalent in other materials. These high-speed alpha particles have enough energy to overcome the repulsion of the nucleus; there are sufficient numbers of them so that, in spite of an enormous waste, a few direct nuclear hits (about 100) are scored each second. The second advance, which renders possible the observation of single atoms, makes it possible to observe any transmutation products which travel swiftly enough to cause these scintillations in a zinc sulphide screen.

We are now in a position to appreciate the pioneer experiment of Rutherford, carried out in 1919. His experimental arrangement is shown in Fig. 1, and its great simplicity forms a striking contrast to present-day atom-smashing technique. S is the source of alpha particles (a deposit of Ra [B + C] on a metal disc); Z, the scintillation screen; *A*, a series of absorption screens which consist of thin mica or aluminum and can be placed between the gas in the box and the zinc sulphide screen. Now it had previously been observed by Marsden that, if the space between the source and screen were filled with hydrogen, scintillations were found which were evidently caused by some light particles, for they were stopped only by the interposition of roughly four times as much absorber as needed to stop scintillations due to alpha particles. The explanation for this was easy—the alpha particles collided with hydrogen nuclei and knocked them forward in a bat-and-ball fashion. Being four times lighter than the alpha particles their extra penetration was to be expected. The excitement began when Rutherford introduced a stream of carefully dried *air* into the space surrounding the source. The distance between the source and the screen was such that the air stopped all the alpha particles and it would thus be expected that no scintillations would appear on the screen. To Rutherford's astonishment a few feeble scintillations were observed which were definitely due to the presence of the air. A measurement of the distance traversed by the particles causing the scintillations before being stopped (their so-called range) proved conclusively that the new particles originated from some transformation of the atoms in the air and not from any impurity such as hydrogen.

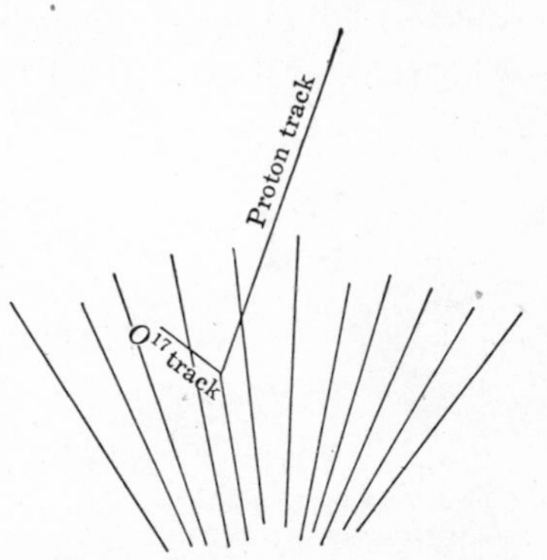

FIG. 2. Diagrammatic representation of a cloud-chamber picture showing the occurrence of a transmutation event. Of the numbers of wasted alpha-particle tracks, one is seen where the alpha particle has combined with a nitrogen nucleus with the emission of a proton. That this combination takes place is shown by the absence of a fourth track due to the spent alpha particle.

The nature of this transformation was at first not understood. It might be a shattering of the nitrogen nucleus into fragments; it might be the detachment of one piece of the nucleus; or it might be a chemical reaction in which the helium and nitrogen combined and new elements were formed. It was speedily and brilliantly proved by Rutherford that the new scintillations were caused by hydrogen nuclei or *protons*; and the nature of the process was finally conclusively established by the experiments of Blackett in the Cavendish laboratory and independently by Harkins in Chicago. A representation of a picture taken by Blackett is shown in Fig. 2. Blackett and Harkins independently undertook the laborious procedure of photographing many times a small number of alpha-particle tracks in a Wilson cloud chamber (which renders the path of ionizing particles visible by the presence of droplets of water where the ions are formed), in the hope that one photograph would show a transmutation with the expected thin, long track of the ejected hydrogen nucleus. Such an event might be a grand catastrophe, with many tracks visible, or a set of *four* tracks, one for the new hydrogen particle, one for the recoiling nucleus, one for the incident alpha particle, and one for the alpha particle afterward; or it might be a set of *three* tracks only, the alpha particle being absorbed with a new nucleus formed. It can be seen from Fig. 2 that there are only three tracks: those of the incident particle, the new nucleus, and the hydrogen particle or proton. On a greatly enlarged scale this means that what takes place is a process as drawn in Fig. 3. The black circles indicate protons: the white, neutrons. The helium and nitrogen interact in a nuclear reaction to form hydrogen and a new nucleus. The new nucleus contains eight protons and hence has a charge of eight units: it is therefore oxygen; it also contains nine neutrons and thus has a mass of seventeen units. This means that a new form of oxygen of mass 17 in place of 16 is produced and a proton is liberated. This process is represented by the nuclear reaction:

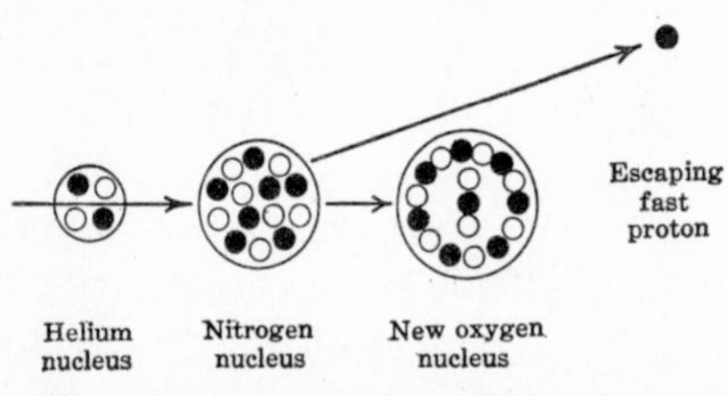

FIG. 3. Schematic representation of Rutherford's original transmutation. The helium nucleus, consisting of two protons and two neutrons, combines with the nitrogen nucleus consisting of seven protons and seven neutrons to form a rare isotope of oxygen consisting of eight protons and nine neutrons. A fast single proton is also emitted.

$$_2He^4 + {}_7N^{14} \rightarrow {}_8O^{17} + {}_1H^1$$

The symbols refer to the chemical element; the superscripts indicate the mass of the particular element, and the subscripts refer to the nuclear charge. Notice that both mass number and charge balance on each side. Since the symbol automatically implies the nuclear charge, the subscript is unnecessary and is generally omitted; it will usually be omitted in the remainder of this book once the reader has had time to become familiar with the general scheme of reactions.

The above description of the transmutation of nitrogen and helium into oxygen and hydrogen has been given at some length, not only because of its historic importance, but also because it enables us to understand the potentialities of bombardment of nuclei. It will be noticed that the form of oxygen produced is unusual; it is too heavy by one unit, or in other words it contains an extra neutron. We are led to inquire whether a nucleus of a given charge (i.e., a given chemical element) could contain *any* number of neutrons, or have any integral atomic weight greater than its charge. In concrete terms, could not oxygen nuclei of masses 8, 9, 10, 11, 12, 13, 14, 15, 16, 17, 18, 19, 20, etc., exist in place of just 16 as observed most commonly, or nitrogen nuclei of masses 7, 8, 9, 10, 11, 12, 13, 14, 15, 16, etc., instead of the usual 14? Quite clearly, since the majority of these are not found in nature, they must be regarded as freaks and their stability would be questionable; a complete answer can be given only if the forces which hold nuclei together are understood. Of these forces we have at present only rather unsatisfactory knowledge. We do know, however, that between neutrons and protons, neutrons and neutrons, and protons and protons there exist *at small separations* very strong forces the nature of which is far from simple but which find their closest analogue in the valence forces which bind chemical atoms together. These forces determine the nature of each actual nucleus in the same way that valence forces determine that chemical compounds of any two elements may only have certain definite forms: thus carbon and oxygen can combine stably in only two ways as CO and CO_2; C_2O and CO_3 are not stable although they may have a fleeting existence and show their presence spectroscopically. The fact that such forms of nitrogen as N^{13} or N^{16} are not found in nature argues strongly that they are unstable. To create them in the laboratory would be of the greatest interest. The attempts at laboratory creation, by Irene Curie and her husband Frederic Joliot, resulted in one of the most remarkable discoveries of this century. They found that, when boron was bombarded by alpha particles and the target placed near a Geiger counter (to be described later), the target showed a gradually diminishing activity as measured on the counter. In other words, from the boron had been produced a new unstable element which gradually decayed in a manner already familiar from our knowledge of radioactivity. Curie and Joliot were able to show that the activity followed the chemical reactions of *nitrogen* and determined that the reaction taking place was

$${}_5B^{10} + {}_2He^4 \rightarrow {}_7N^{13} + {}_0n^1$$

where the symbol ${}_0n^1$ refers to a neutron. In other words, boron and helium react to form nitrogen of mass 13 and a neutron. This nitrogen is one not found in nature, and the activity indicated by the Geiger counter showed that it changes into stable carbon of mass 13 (which is found in nature) with the emission of a *positive electron.* The ejection of a positive charge thus remedies the defect that the nucleus, if it is to be nitrogen, has too great a charge for stability; its conversion to carbon with the loss of a single positive charge restores the balance and gives stability. While we are considering this case it may be helpful to state a general rule for nuclear stability: *no nucleus is stable which contains more protons than neutrons.* There is one exception to this rule, He^3, discovered in 1940 to be stable.

It will be noticed that in the primary reaction above a neutron is emitted and the resulting form of nitrogen has too great a charge for its mass. It is possible to *add* a neutron to a stable nucleus, producing one which has too little charge; such a nucleus is formed if sodium is bombarded by neutrons. The reaction which takes place is the following:

$$_{11}Na^{23} + {}_0n^1 \rightarrow {}_{11}Na^{24}$$

Here the ordinary sodium combines with the neutron to produce a new form of sodium which is too heavy by one neutron mass. This abnormal sodium is unstable since its charge is not great enough, and accordingly it will change in some manner to remedy the defect. The procedure adopted by such nuclei is to emit a *negative* electron, the loss of which automatically increases the nuclear charge by one positive charge. The heavy sodium thus becomes normal magnesium as indicated below:

$$_{11}Na^{24} \rightarrow {}_{12}Mg^{24} + e$$

where e is used to indicate a negative (ordinary) electron. It is thus to be observed that nuclei which are either too greatly charged or too heavy—or, in other terms, have too many protons or too many neutrons—are unstable: *they adapt themselves by leaving their mass constant but changing their charge by emission of either a positive or negative electron.* This method of adaptation will be discussed later; the mechanism of the process is still not completely understood, although experimental rules exist which make it possible to predict reasonably well what any given nucleus will do even if no satisfactory theory for the process exists.

Such unstable elements as N^{13} or Na^{24} were named by Curie and Joliot *radioelements.* Thus N^{13} is called radionitrogen; Na^{24} radiosodium. The astonishing development of this field of human knowledge can be gauged from the fact that since the discovery of artificial radioactivity by Curie and Joliot in 1933 the number of known artificial radioelements has increased from three to more than three hundred. Virtually every element has known radioactive forms; the majority, several such. Scarcely an issue of the publication of a physical society passes without the announcement of new radioelements, and it is probable that at least two-thirds of the known elements will very shortly be available in radioactive form suitable for chemical and biological studies. It is the potentiality of this type of research which removes nuclear physics from an academic, if interesting, domain to one of the great possible practical utility.

To summarize this chapter, we have here shown the part the nucleus plays in determining the nature of an atom; what transmutation entails, and how it was achieved; how unstable nuclei may exist and be created; what is the nature of their adaptation to become stable; and the extent of the newly discovered field of artificial radioactivity.

REFERENCES

Rutherford, Chadwick, and Ellis, *Radiations from Radioactive Substances*, Macmillan, 1930. This is still the standard work in English on radioactivity.

Rutherford, *The Newer Alchemy*, Macmillan, 1937. An interesting booklet which is excellent for introductory reading.

Karl K. Darrow, "The Nucleus," *Bell System Technical Journal*, **12**, 288, 1933; **13**, 102, 391, 580, 1934. A series of articles written at the most exciting stage of the development of modern nuclear physics.

CHAPTER 2

PROPERTIES OF NUCLEAR RADIATIONS

Before proceeding to describe the results of actual transmutation experiments, and at the risk of tantalizing the reader, we shall give a short account of the properties of nuclear radiations as a help for the later chapters. We also reproduce a plate, showing the tracks of electrons, positrons, protons, and alpha particles, photographed in a cloud chamber. The shrewd reader will at once note that the particle itself is never pictured but only what it does. The alpha particle and proton ionize very strongly; the electron and positron very weakly; the newly discovered mesotrons produce intermediate ionization. The neutron, neutrino, and quantum produce little or no ionization directly.

Such a picturing of nuclear radiations serves the purpose of differentiating ionizing from non-ionizing radiations, but it is of no use unless coupled with a clear understanding of the nature of each radiation. We will therefore begin by subdividing the radiations into two categories, material and non-material. (Even this division is hard to make.)

The material list is headed by the *proton*, the nucleus of a hydrogen atom, having a single positive charge equal to that of the electron (4.80×10^{-10} esu), a mass of 1.660×10^{-24} gram, or on the scale of atomic weights, with neutral oxygen as exactly 16, a weight of 1.0076. The proton, like any heavy charged particle, possesses the remarkable feature of a well-defined path in any material. This total path is spoken of as its *range*, and the range varies with the energy of the proton very rapidly but according to no simple law. The ranges of protons of energies from 1 to 20 Mev are given in Table 1. The definite range is a simple matter to explain in a general way: a heavy charged particle loses on the average 60 electron volts of its energy for every ion it produces and hence will produce very nearly the same number of ions for the same initial energy. Since a heavy particle is hardly deviated from its path (except by rare close collisions with nuclei) this constant amount of ionization means a constant distance

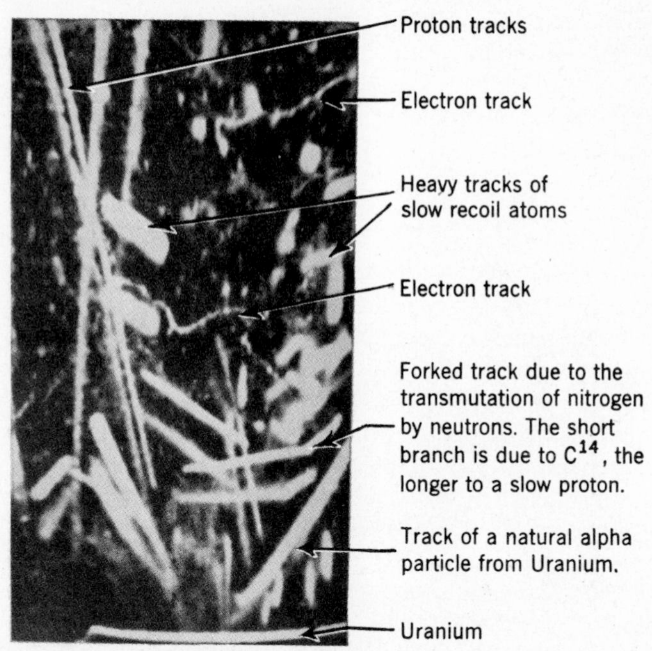

I. Reproduction of a cloud-chamber photograph, by Dr. I. A. Getting, showing the effects of a neutron source on the air and water vapor gas mixture. The track of a natural alpha particle from uranium is also visible.

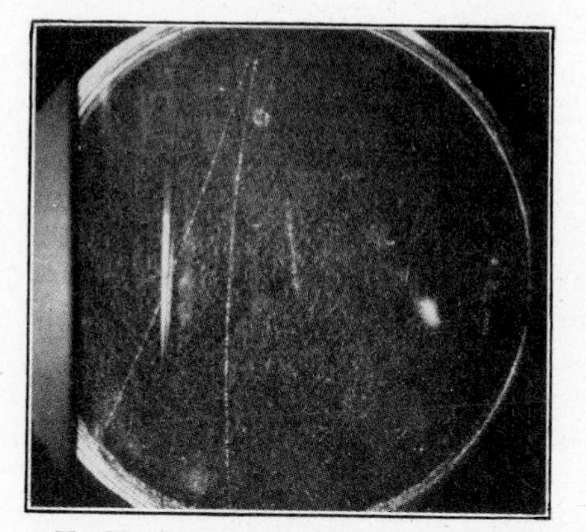

II. Cloud-chamber photograph, by Dr. J. C. Street, of a pair of electrons moving in a magnetic field.

III. Photograph, by Dr. R. Sard, of a mesotron traveling through several layers of absorption.

PLATE I

traveled. The distance traversed is not simply related to the initial energy because a fast proton does not ionize so readily as a slow one.

Second on the material list is the *neutron.* This is an uncharged particle, virtually equal in mass to the proton; though actually slightly heavier, being of atomic weight 1.0089. It produces no primary ionization but may be detected by the fact that in collisions with charged nuclei it will impart energy to them and these secondary moving nuclei will ionize and be detectable. A neutron can, at best, give up all its energy to a hydrogen nucleus, giving rise to a proton whose range will measure the energy of the original neutron. Collisions with heavy nuclei cause relatively little transfer of energy from neutron to nucleus: the amount can be calculated by methods used in elementary impact problems. A useful figure to remember is that, *on the average,* a neutron retains 1/2.7 of its energy after a single collision with a hydrogen nucleus.

Neutrons and protons together comprise all nuclei, and hence combinations of the two in all imaginable forms can be considered as nuclear particles. Of these, two will be selected for mention: the *deuteron* and the *alpha particle.* The *deuteron* is a proton plus a neutron held together by a strong force. Its importance lies in the fact that it can readily be accelerated by a cyclotron and that it is a potent agent in causing transmutations. The *alpha particle* is a nucleus of helium, or two protons and two neutrons held together extremely tightly. It is also readily accelerated in a cyclotron to enormous energies and in addition is of interest since natural radioactive elements emit alpha particles in amounts which just barely permitted the discovery of transmutations to be made.

The third components of the material list are electrons, positive and negative. Of these, only the negative is permanent, the positive ultimately changes, giving birth to two quanta of gamma radiation. The electron is the fundamental atom of electricity; that its charge is labeled negative is pure accident. The mass of the electron is small compared to the proton and neutron, being 1/1840 that of the proton. This small mass renders the properties of the electron considerably different from those of the proton, first because it is easily deflected (or "scattered") in collisions with nuclei, thus causing its path to be tortuous; second because it is less effective in disturbing the electrons in atoms, thus reducing the ionization per centimeter; and third because it is easily deflected in a magnetic field. The small mass of an electron also means that at high energies its velocity is very close to that of light and so, according to the theory of relativity, its mass is greater according to the relation

$$m = \frac{m_0}{\sqrt{1 - (v^2/c^2)}}.$$

where m = its new mass.
m_0 = its "rest" mass.
v = its velocity.
c = the velocity of light.

An electron from B^{12}, for example, having an energy of 12 Mev has a velocity of 0.99 that of light and a mass roughly 24 times its rest mass. This fact, of changing mass, must be remembered in making calculations about electrons and their motions.

Positive electrons, or positrons, are similar to electrons in all respects but two, the sign of their charge and their longevity. Within a fraction of a second a positron always diappears, if any material is near, and in its place two gamma quanta appear. There is a close relation between the frequency of the gamma-ray quantum and the rest mass of the positron, namely:

$$m_0c^2 = E = h\nu$$

where E is the "energy" of the quantum, ν its frequency, and h is Planck's constant. This interesting relation will be discussed shortly.

The positive and negative *mesotrons* or *mesons* should be mentioned here. They are positive and negative electrons possessing an abnormally high mass; they are unstable, and, though they may one day play an important role in explaining nuclear forces, they are, for the purposes of this book, mainly of academic interest, being observed only in cosmic radiation. When the supercyclotron is built and energies of more than 100 Mev can be imparted to nuclei, the mesotron may become more commonplace. Until then it has no practical application. The mesotron is considered more fully in the Appendix.

There are just two types of non-material nuclear radiation. The first is *gamma* radiation. This is generally classified as electromagnetic radiation of very short wavelength (and hence high frequency) so that officially one is expected to imagine gamma rays as trains of waves in which a varying electric and magnetic field is propagated through space. In actual fact this picture is almost wholly inapplicable in nuclear physics. The frequency of the gamma rays is so high that their behavior is almost entirely understood by considering them as quanta of energy such that $E = h\nu$. This quantum of energy, like the neutron, is itself undetectable, but fortunately a gamma ray has three very strong methods of interaction with matter which make its detection relatively simple. In the first place, a collision with an electron will project the electron in the original direction of the quantum according to the ordinary rules of impact (the quantum being considered to have a momentum $h\nu/c$, where c is the velocity of light). In this way the electron can acquire enough energy to ionize and be detected. Also, the maximum energy of these projected electrons is a measure of the energy of the gamma-ray quantum striking them. This phenomenon, known as the *Compton effect* (the electrons are known as Compton recoils), is the most common method of interaction between gamma rays and matter.

The second method of interaction is the *photoelectric effect.* The quantum communicates all its energy to an electron in an atom, detaching it completely and giving it kinetic energy of motion equal to the original quantum energy less the energy of binding of the electron in the atom, which is a small correction for these energetic quanta. Again the ionization produced by the electron is the secondary effect which renders the detection of the gamma ray possible. This photoelectric effect accounts for less than one-fifth of the energy exchanges by an average gamma ray.

The third method of interaction is the strangest and most interesting. It is known as *pair production.* A short account of this is worth while. It has been noticed already that the electrons emerging from nuclei move so rapidly that their mass changes in accordance with the theory of relativity. Now if we seek to apply the theory of relativity to the motion of electrons we are bound by the requirement that, no matter what speed the coordinate system has, the laws of motion of the electron remain unchanged. This is a simple requirement, but, when mathematical expressions including both the motion of the electron and the electric field are formulated, it is found that the equations contain two solutions for the kinetic energy of the electron: one positive; the *other negative.* A moment's thought will show that negative kinetic energy does not mean anything that we actually observe, since the quantity $\frac{1}{2}mv^2$ must automatically be positive, and this presented Dirac, the formulator of this theory, with a first-class dilemma. With unusual courage, Dirac retained his theory by proposing that these states of negative kinetic energy, though not observable, still exist; they exist but are normally completely filled with electrons. Since all the possible conditions in which these negative kinetic energy electrons can find themselves are already satisfied by electrons, we can never detect any change in them and so do not notice their presence. This line of reasoning, however, does not affect a gamma ray, to which these electrons are no more than electrons and therefore capable of being influenced. By a process similar to the photoelectric effect the gamma ray may give energy to these electrons; and, if it does, an electron in a state of negative kinetic energy may acquire enough positive kinetic energy to detach it from its state of negative kinetic energy and release it. Thus a *negative electron would appear.* At the same time there would be a hole in the completely filled states of negative kinetic energy, and this hole, or absence of an electron, will appear like a positive electron except that it will vanish when the hole is filled.

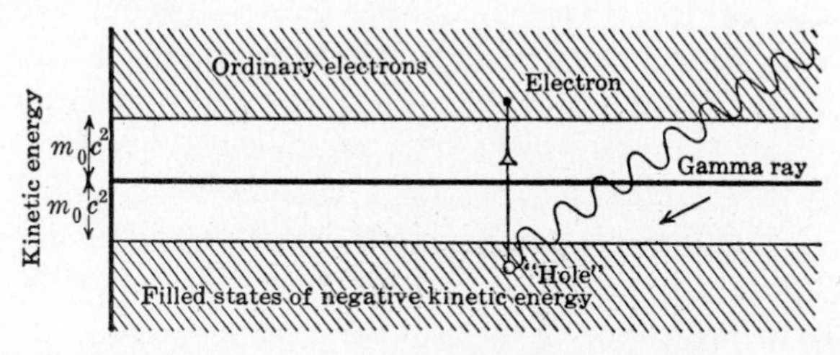

FIG. 1. Indication of the process of pair formation. The electromagnetic field of the gamma ray supplies enough energy to an electron in a state of negative kinetic energy to eject it, leaving a "hole" which behaves like an electron of positive charge.

The theory as simply outlined above lacks one important feature: we must include in the kinetic energy (whether positive or negative) the term m_0c^2 which corresponds to kinetic energy possessed by a particle in virtue of its mass alone. We can now picture all the electrons we wish to consider as in two bands, as drawn in Fig. 1. The process of pair formation is indicated schematically; notice that a pair cannot be formed unless the quantum has an energy greater than $2m_0c^2$, which is almost exactly 1 Mev.

The discovery of the positron and of the process of pair formation was one of the most startling confirmations of one of the strangest theories in science. Pairs are found only when quanta having an energy in excess of 1 Mev fall on matter; the chance of their formation increases with the quantum energy and also with the charge of the nucleus of the material from which they are derived. Thus for 3-Mev gamma rays impinging on lead, nearly one-half the energy lost by the gamma quanta is in the form of pair production. For aluminum the amount is much less, being only a few per cent.

These three processes contribute to the absorption of gamma rays in matter. To screen out gamma rays one therefore needs an inch or two of a heavy element such as lead. This is in contrast to screening neutrons which requires hydrogenous material such as water, generally at least 2 feet thick, 6 feet being much safer.

While the subject of pair production is still fresh, the reverse process of *annihilation* should be mentioned. This is the ultimate fate of every positron. The hole in the negative energy states becomes filled up by an electron from the positive energy states. This means that an amount of mass equal to two electron masses disappears, and since, if mass is annihilated some form of energy must appear, gamma radiation is evolved. This process must, however, also permit momentum to be conserved, and as there is no momentum to begin with, there must be no momentum at the end, a condition which is realized by the ingenious process of producing *two* gamma rays of equal energy, moving in opposite directions. Thus when a positron is annihilated, two quanta, of energy each equivalent to m_0c^2, are evolved. Thus any radioactive element which emits positrons also emits a secondary gamma ray, the *annihilation radiation*, whose energy is almost exactly 0.5 Mev. This phenomenon has also been observed, adding further confirmation to the theory for which Dirac received the Nobel prize.

The second non-material radiation is the *neutrino*. It is hard to avoid the witticism "non-material and non-existent" in respect to the neutrino. The neutrino is a particle which is supposed to share in the energy balance of a radioactive change; its rest mass is supposed to be zero, it is neutral, and its only possible detectable influence would be an ion pair every hundred yards or so of its path. This is too small to observe. It occupies much the same sort of place in physics that the ether did in the nineteenth century—much talked about but never observed. A new theory may dispel the actual existence of the neutrino, which is hardly true of any of the other radiations yet discussed.

Before concluding this chapter a few odds and ends should be collected. The three terms alpha, beta, and gamma rays are applied, respectively, to helium nuclei, to electrons emerging from nuclei in radioactive transformations, and to quanta. They are in decreasing order of mass and in decreasing order of absorbability. Alpha and beta rays have definite *ranges*; they may be stopped completely by relatively small amounts of materials. Gamma rays, like neutrons, can only be diminished in numbers by absorbers, never wholly cut out. The three types of absorption curve are shown in Fig. 2. The beta rays emitted from a radioactive substance are not homogeneous in energy and so are absorbed differently from electrons accelerated in a Van der Graaf machine. A definite range is always observed. In Table 1 are shown the ranges for protons, deuterons, and alpha and beta rays of various energies. The thicknesses of materials actually traversed by these rays are so small that they cannot easily be measured directly. It is very simple to express the thickness as the *mass per unit area* of a given absorber, for then accurate weighing permits an accurate figure to be given. This procedure is universal in nuclear measurements, so much so that the authors find it easier to visualize a thickness stated in milligrams per square centimeter than directly in fractions of a millimeter. It has one other advantage; it is more directly related to the fundamental absorbing process—the number of electrons encountered—than the thickness, which may vary considerably from element to element for the same range ray. This variation in actual thickness is due to the varying density of the materials, a factor which does not appear if the absorption is estimated by weighing. All the figures here given apply to aluminum as absorber.

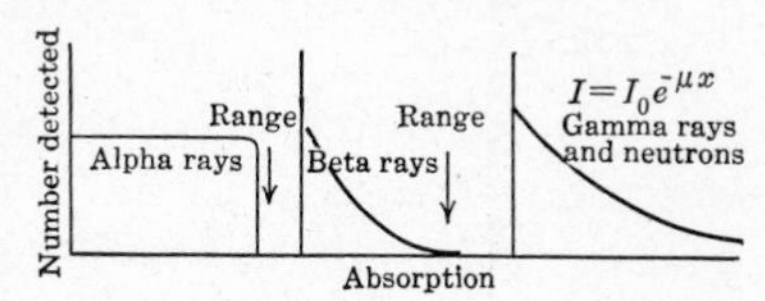

FIG. 2. Absorption curves for alpha, beta, and gamma rays and neutrons. Alpha and beta rays have a definite range; gamma rays and neutrons are absorbed exponentially.

TABLE 1

ALL RANGES IN MILLIGRAMS PER SQUARE CENTIMETER OF ALUMINUM

Energy (Mev)	0.5	1	2	3	4	5	7	9	10	15	20	30
Proton range	1.3	3.5	10.6	19.6	35.0	50.1	90.1	143.0	174.0			
Deuteron range	1.1	2.6	6.9	13.3	21.2	32.4	55.9	86.0	100.0	205.0	348.0	720.0
Alpha-particle range	0.5	0.8	1.6	2.1	3.8	5.3	8.9	13.5	15.6	39.2	50.1	102.0
Beta-ray range	111	383	926	1470	2010	2650						

In this chapter we have described the products that can be emitted from nuclei, dividing them into two categories, material and non-material. The material include protons, neutrons, positive and negative electrons, and positive and negative mesotrons; the non-material, quanta and neutrinos. The great game of composing matter must be played with these; whether any combination will work, once formed, depends on the laws of force which operate between the parts of the combination, and so on the wisdom of the choice of the constituents.

CHAPTER 3

THE DETECTION OF NUCLEAR PARTICLES

Without exception, charge and speed are required for the detection of nuclear particles. Radiation or neutrons which possess no charge must be detected by secondary effects in which they cause charged, rapidly moving particles to appear. It is thus necessary to concentrate on the effects produced by fast charged particles in moving through matter in order to understand the means by which we detect nuclear products.

Ionization. To our ordinary senses, matter, even a rarefied gas, appears continuous. This continuity is one of the most troublesome optical illusions there is. Had nature ordered things so that our eyes would focus x-rays it is likely that all modern physics would have been classical physics early in the nineteenth century and the mysteries of the atom would seem today as trite as Boyle's law. As it is, we have had to wait until experimental technique has enabled us to see how we must exert our imagination to appreciate the true nature of matter. *Matter is mostly emptiness.* Even in a solid the centers of the atoms are separated by distances a million times greater than the atoms themselves. The seeming impenetrability of a solid is due solely to the extremely powerful forces exerted by the charged atoms in the solid as soon as other charged atoms (in some foreign piece of matter such as our fist) are brought sufficiently near. If for an instant electrical charge were abolished in a championship bout the contestants would readily pass right through each other in ghostly fashion. This being so, a small, rapidly moving charge will be able to penetrate matter and, roughly speaking, it will find interference only in the electrical attractions or repulsions which it experiences.

In Fig. 1 a picture representing the passage of an electron through a gas is drawn. The electron enters at the lower left and passes near atom *A*. Although this atom is, in toto, electrically neutral, the outer portion, consisting of planetary electrons, is negatively charged, and therefore the major electrical force experienced by the moving electron is repulsion. The moving electron is deflected while atom *A* recoils as indicated. The same is true in a varying degree for other atoms such as B and C, and in each such encounter the moving electron imparts momentum to atoms in the gas, momentum which is lost from its own motion. In this way the moving electron could be brought to rest and would leave in its track a host of moving atoms.

Unfortunately such moving atoms, produced in so-called elastic collisions, are not readily detectable; if this process alone were taking place our knowledge of nuclear physics would be very slight. It may happen, however, that a very close encounter with an atom takes place, in which event there is an extremely powerful repulsion between the moving electron and the atomic or bound electron, which may receive sufficient momentum to dislodge it from the atom, a process known as ionization. Such a procedure changes the condition of the atom encountered, requires temporarily the absorption of energy, and is known as an *inelastic collision*. These inelastic collisions which result in ionization afford the means by which the detection of nuclear charged particles is effected. It is found experimentally that a swiftly moving electron produces approximately one ionized atom for each 60 electron volts it possesses, which means that an electron of 1,000,000 electron volts energy will, before it is stopped completely, produce 18,000 ionized atoms. Since the ejected electron automatically leaves a positive residue, each ionization process gives two ions, or an ion pair, and hence an average electron moving with an energy characteristic of nuclear processes can produce 18,000 ion pairs.

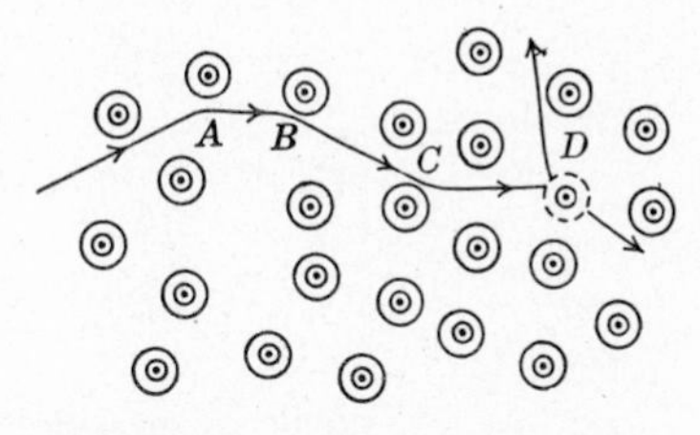

FIG. 1. Path of an electron showing repulsion when near to electrons in atoms and indicating the recoiling atoms. At A, B, C, the collision is elastic; at D an electron is detached from its atom, and an inelastic collision, here resulting in ionization, takes place.

These 36,000 charges are something we can hope to detect. It remains to consider the most expedient methods.

Direct Electrometer Detection. Before taking a look at the sensitive instruments with which the physicist is equipped to measure small electrical quantities let us express 36,000 ion pairs in electrical units. Each ion has a single electronic charge of 4.8×10^{-10} esu or 1.6×10^{-19} coulomb, so that the total is 1.7×10^{-5} esu or 5.8×10^{-15} coulomb. One glance at these figures tells the physicist that he requires instruments of very great sensitivity. Let us briefly survey the available instruments. The first is the galvanometer; it can be designed to have a current sensitivity of 10^{-12} ampere or a quantity sensitivity of 10^{-10} coulomb. Unaided, therefore, it is quite useless. The second is the electrometer. This can be made to have a sensitivity of 10^{-5} volt per division with a capacity of 10^{-11} farad. The charge it could detect, then, is 10^{-16} coulomb, and it is thus possible to detect the charge produced by an electron in ionizing a gas *directly* by means of a sensitive electrometer. In practice this method, though by far the simplest in principle, is not used for reasons to be given later in the chapter, but as it shows most simply the general arrangement of nu-

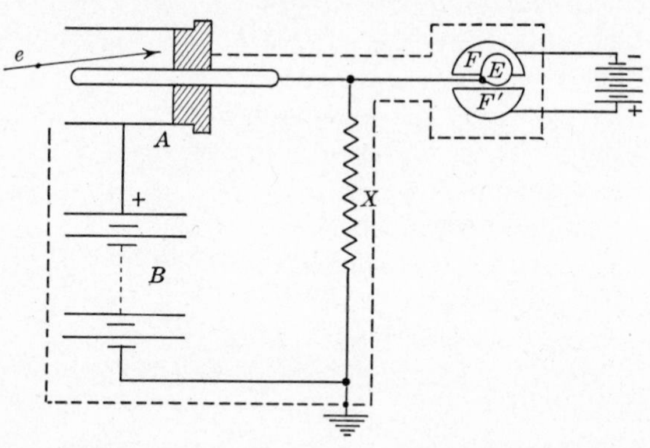

FIG. 2. Schematic diagram of ionization chamber and electrometer used for the detection of single fast nuclear particles. A is the ionization chamber with an insulated central electrode. A battery B causes the positive ions produced by the incoming fast nuclear particle e to be driven to the electrode and raise the potential of the movable vane E which is suspended by a fiber above the plates F and F'. This rise in potential causes the vane E to move.

clear detecting apparatus a diagram is given of an electrometer applied to detect single electrons.

The circuit is shown schematically in Fig. 2. The electron enters the *ionization chamber* A where it causes ions to form. The ionization chamber contains two electrodes (in this instance the outer case and an insulated central rod) between which an electric field is applied by the battery B, the circuit being completed by a high resistance X. The ions formed by the fast electron are separated by the electric field, and the plus ions are driven to the central electrode whose potential rises when it receives the charge. The central electrode is connected to a movable vane E supported by a thin conducting fiber. This vane is suspended above two plates F and F', which are maintained at positive and negative potentials by a battery, and normally the vane takes up an equilibrium position between F and F' depending on its own potential, the potentials of F and F', and the twist in the fiber. As soon as the potential of E is changed the equilibrium is disturbed and the vane swings around, its motion being observed by a mirror attached to it and a reflected beam of light. The dotted lines indicate metal casing which is used to shield all leads connected to the electrometer as the pulses caused by starting currents and so on around the laboratory can easily induce a potential of 0.01 volt, which is a hundred times larger than the effect to be observed. Screening by metal casing diminishes this "pick-up." This instrument is the "duant" electrometer, designed by Hoffmann and used in several important nuclear investigations. Attention should be given to the *A-B-X* section of the apparatus. The combination of a field driving a charge on to an electrode which is insulated except for a very high resistance is, in one or another variation, extremely common practice.

The reason for the infrequent choice of this method of detection lies in the electrometer, which is far from rugged and requires skill and experience to set up and keep operating. Since the fiber has to be exceedingly thin, the vane must move very slowly; this means that the period of the electrometer is long so that several seconds must elapse between the detections of charged particles. If our available source of fast electrons is strong so that we are never required to detect less than about a thousand incoming electrons per second, then the electroscope, which is much simpler and more rugged, can be used.

Almost everyone is familiar with the ordinary gold-leaf electroscope. Not everyone is aware that it has played a major role in the study of radioactivity. If a gold-leaf electroscope is charged, so that the leaves diverge, it will remain in that condition almost indefinitely. But if the space near the leaves is ionized the ions in the air are attracted to the charged leaves and in this way tend to neutralize their charge and cause the leaves to collapse. The leaves may be observed through a microscope of low magnification with a scale in the eyepiece and the rate of collapse of the leaves measured in terms of divisions on the scale per minute; this rate is a measure of the ionization current. The ionization current, in turn, is a measure of the number of incoming electrons. This extremely simple device has probably turned out more nuclear research data than any other instrument. It can be made reasonably sensitive by having very thin gold leaves, or more generally by using a single leaf which is repelled away from a fixed support. It does not have a linear scale, but if the timing is always carried out over the same positions of the gold leaf then it is certain that the same amount of charge has been neutralized and the differing times indicate the relative currents. If necessary an electroscope can be calibrated so as to read a current in amperes, but this is seldom necessary because it is nearly always better to compare one radioactive source with a standard source.

The Lauritsen Electroscope. The advantages of the simplicity of the gold-leaf electroscope are retained, and the advantage of greater sensitivity is added, in a beautifully simple quartz-fiber electroscope designed by Lauritsen. In the gold-leaf electroscope the force opposing deflection of the leaves is gravitation; in the Lauritsen electroscope the moving fiber is so thin and light that gravitation exerts virtually no effect on it. In place of gravitation as the restoring force the elastic force in the quartz is utilized; this is advantageous because it is possible to find an arrangement which will give a much more nearly linear

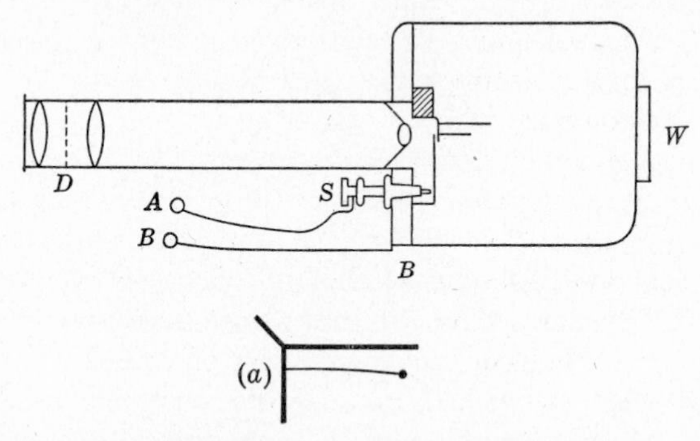

FIG. 3. The Lauritsen electroscope. (*a*) shows the detail of the metal frame and quartz fiber which is repelled from the frame when both are charged. Ionization in the space near this frame causes discharge of the frame and fiber and so a return to normal at a rate which measures the ionization current. The fiber is observed by a microscope, the illumination being through the ground-glass window *W*.

scale for the instrument. The electroscope is illustrated schematically in Fig. 3. The heart of the instrument is shown in the small diagram (*a*). It consists of a small metal frame shaped as shown, with a quartz fiber (which has gold sputtered on it to render it conducting) attached to it as indicated. The end of this fiber would be hard to see, so a little T is made on the end by fastening a short piece of quartz fiber, indicated in the diagram by the dot. The T is in a plane perpendicular to the paper. If this whole system is insulated by amber and a charge given to it the repulsive force between like charges will cause the fiber to bend away from the metal support. The presence of ions in the neighborhood will cause the neutralization of the charge and a return of the fiber to its original position. As the length of the fiber is only about 6 mm, an extremely small charge is sufficient to cause considerable deflection. Even so, this would be hard to see, so a microscope with a magnification of about 50 is used to view the fiber as illustrated in the main diagram. To charge the electroscope a potential is applied to the frame by pushing the spring contact *S* which is attached to a source of about 100 volts, either from batteries or from a vacuum-tube rectifier. Both the leads to S should include resistances of about 100,000 ohms to prevent any heavy currents from flowing if the fiber is out of place for any reason and is shorting to ground. The image of the T is made to coincide with the scale at D, and the passage of this image over the scale is recorded. In spite of the delicacy of the fiber, the instrument is remarkably rugged. This is because the fiber has almost no inertia and so experiences little force unless disturbed by air currents. The case effectively prevents these from being present, and the whole instrument can be carried around with no more than sensible care. If it is necessary to adjust the fiber when the instrument is installed, the adjustments should be made with a handkerchief over the nose to avoid air currents. For the same reason the electroscope should be installed in some location where the temperature is reasonably uniform as convection currents may make the T ride off the scale. The most likely sources of temperature irregularities are the light used to illuminate the fiber, and the vacuum-tube rectifier. These must be kept at a little distance from the instrument. The scale is nearly but not quite linear; it is still necessary to carry out the timing over the same scale divisions at each observation. The sensitivity is such that a millicurie at a distance of a meter produces a motion of about five scale divisions per minute, and the background in the absence of radiation is about the same number of divisions per hour. If time is available it is possible to detect as few as ten electrons per minute.

Application of Vacuum Tubes: the "Linear Amplifier." If we return to our survey of physical apparatus available to detect the ionization produced by a swiftly moving particle we find that we have to consider the vacuum tube. It proves to be a potent aid. The vacuum tube has the tremendous advantage of utilizing atomic particles themselves to detect the ionization due to other atomic particles. A stream of electrons is virtually without inertia and hence extremely susceptible to any electrical influence. It is fundamentally this fact which has made the vacuum tube practically indispensable in detecting small amounts of radiation.

Consider the circuit of Fig. 4. Here the ionization chamber, battery, and high resistance are the same as before, but in place of the electrometer the grid of a triode is connected to the central electrode. As before, the collection of charge on the central electrode causes a rise in its potential and hence a rise of the potential of the grid of the vacuum tube. This causes an increased flow of electrons *produced in the cathode* C to the plate P and from there through a resistance to the plate battery. The ionization chamber thus effects control of a separate electron stream, and with a well-designed triode the potential difference produced across R by the momentary surge of electrons to the plate can be twenty or thirty times as great as the initial rise of potential of the grid. This potential difference could be used to operate a relatively insensitive electrometer, but in practice it is far better to apply it to a second vacuum tube, and so on, until the am-

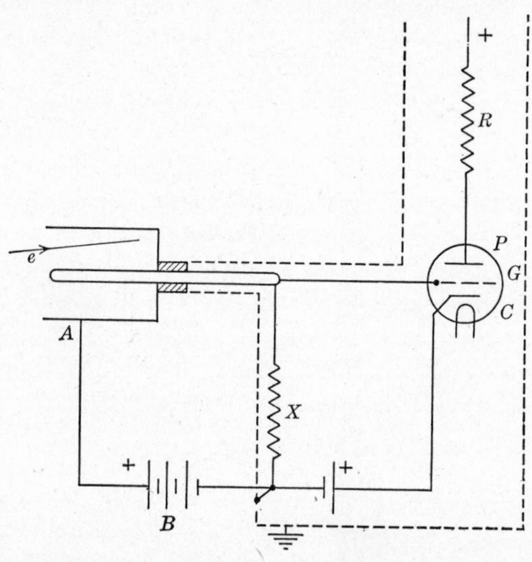

FIG. 4. Vacuum-tube and ionization-chamber arrangement. The rise in potential of the central electrode is communicated to the grid G of the triode, causing a change in the plate current and hence a relatively large potential difference across R the plate resistance.

plification of the inital pulse is a hundred thousandfold. The voltage so produced at the output is then 10 volts or so and may be detected in almost any way we please, for example by listening to the "cracks" in a loud speaker or observing the deflections of a cathode-ray oscilloscope. This is the method of the "linear amplifier," widely used in research in pure nuclear physics. Such an amplifier is not easy to operate, though far more rugged than an electrometer, and even though it affords the best method of detecting the primary ionization of a proton or alpha particle it is still not the best method for ordinary use. In fact, careful consideration shows that it is best to *change the events in the ionization chamber* to secure the simplest means of detecting the ionization due to a single particle.

The Proportional Counter. Returning to our picture of an electron moving past a series of atoms and occasionally "knocking off" other electrons in its flight, thus causing ionization, let us consider the fate of these freshly detached electrons. In the absence of a strong driving force—an electric field—they will drift around until they encounter a positive ion with which they recombine to form a neutral stable atom, and that concludes the adventure. This may be drastically altered if a strong electric field is imposed on the electrons, for then they will

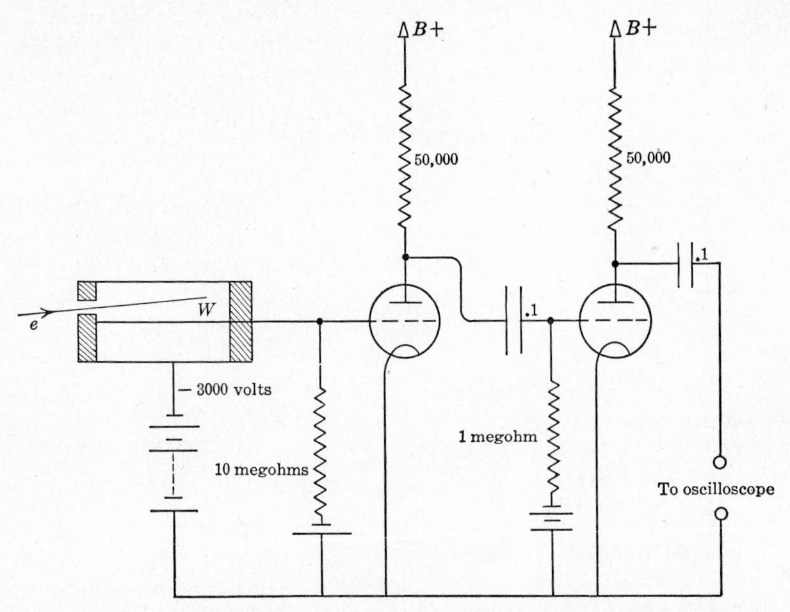

FIG. 5. *Proportional counter* with amplifier. A fine wire is stretched axially in a cylinder to which is applied a high negative voltage. The electric field near the wire is so high that it causes ionization by collision, which multiplies the charge collected by the wire many fold and renders a two-stage amplifier sufficient to operate an oscilloscope.

immediately be accelerated and in a strong enough field may acquire so great a speed before an encounter with a neutral atom that they can in their turn produce ionization. Notice that the farther they go before meeting an atom the better is this chance, for they gain speed continually until checked by meeting another atom. Now this ability to ionize will also be possessed by the electron detached in the ionization process, and so on, a very rapid accumulation of electrons taking place, which can reach a thousandfold greater number than the initial ionization. This process of *ionization by collision* is exactly what we have been seeking, for by using it skillfully we can increase the initial charge to be detected by a factor of as much as a thousand, thus reducing the amount of amplification required from a vacuum-tube amplifier to the point where a simple, stable, easily constructed amplifier will suffice for the detection of the incoming electron.

A circuit is shown in Fig. 5 which will detect single electrons very readily. The very strong field is produced in the neighborhood of a fine wire. The initial electrons are pushed toward the wire by the negative field, and, if they arrive there before they have recombined (as they will in a high field), they produce ions by collision near the wire and consequently a multiplication of charge collected by the wire. A simple two-stage amplifier is sufficient to operate an oscilloscope. If the space around the wire is partially evacuated the distance between atoms is increased and the process of ionization by collision can be made to occur for a lower applied voltage.

This is frequently done. Such a device is known as a *proportional* counter, so called because the charge collected by *W* is roughly proportional to the initial ionization. It is excellent for detecting alpha particles and protons. A modification, due originally to Rutherford and Geiger and known as the *Geiger counter*, or, sometimes, in honor of a later developer, the Geiger-Müller counter, however, supersedes it for detecting electrons. Historically the Geiger counter was devised before the proportional counter, but as it is rather more complex it is better to consider it later. The Geiger counter calls on more than the process of ionization by collision; it utilizes some of the phenomena of the discharge.

The Geiger-Müller Counter. If it were true that no available electrons resided in the metal wire or metal case then no matter how high the field applied (within some limits) there would never be more than a momentary rush of ionization following the arrival of the electron. This is not true, however. All conductors contain electrons, some of which can be extracted in various ways. If these electrons are, for some reason, pulled into the gas, then they will ionize by collision and a continuous discharge will result, maintained by fresh electrons from the metal. There are various reasons for the attraction of electrons from metal to gas; one is the fact that, in the process of recombination which is always taking place, light is emitted. In the language of modern physics we refer to this light as a number of *photons*. These photons are able to cause the emission of photoelectrons from the surface of the counter wall, and these photoelectrons can then keep the discharge going. A second reason is the hitherto neglected positive ion, which is simply the rest of the atom after the electron has been ejected. These ions are heavy, move slowly, and hardly ionize at all; but when they approach a metal, at the moment before they make contact, they exert a great outward force on electrons in the metal and may pull out several before being themselves absorbed by the metal. The nature of the surface has an effect on the number of electrons pulled out, no matter how the actual ejection is produced. If a sufficiently high field is applied between the electrodes in the counter the emission of these electrons from the walls will cause a discharge which will continue permanently so long as the voltage across the tube is kept there.

It is thus easy to see that, if a single electron arrives in a gas across which a very high field is maintained, a discharge may result in which a very large flow of current may take place. The electron thus acts as a trigger which sets off the latent discharge. Obviously such a method of detection is exceedingly sensitive. The reader will at once, however, inquire the reason why the discharge should cease, and the consideration of this matter is of great importance in understanding the operation of the Geiger counter.

If we suppose that the two electrodes are connected to a large source of power the discharge may well be maintained for an uncomfortably long time and would be quite dangerous. On the other hand, if we imagine that the two electrodes are first charged and then insulated before the "trigger" electron appears, the discharge will cease when the difference of potential between the two electrodes falls below that sufficient to cause a discharge. To make the counter sensitive again will now require the repetition of the charging and insulating process, which is obviously too elaborate. If some compromise between the dangerous maintained discharge and the self-ceasing discharge could be reached then the phenomenon of the discharge could be utilized in the detection of ionization.

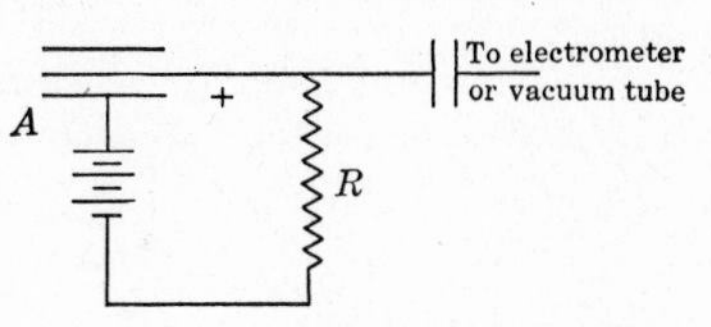

FIG. 6. *Geiger counter circuit.* There is a very high field between the cylinder and the wire of the counter *A*. An entering electron precipitates a discharge which causes current to flow in the high resistance *R* until the fall of potential across *R* reduces the potential across *A* to a point where the discharge extinguishes.

In the Geiger-Müller counter a high resistance (about 10^9 ohms) is placed in the return to the high voltage as shown in Fig. 6. The entrance of an electron then precipitates a discharge, but the resulting current must flow through *R* and in so doing sets up a fall of potential across *R* which greatly reduces the potential across the counter *A* and shortly extinguishes the discharge. The counter then gradually resumes its former condition of high tension and is ready to discharge on the arrival of a second electron. It can be seen that the high resistance fulfills the purpose of compromise as mentioned in the last paragraph and also ensures the automatic charging of the two electrodes so that the counter is in readiness for the next arrival. This automatic charging is not infinitely rapid, and a counter which employs a large series resistance will take a long time to recover after it has operated and so will only count slowly. This fact should be remembered when the operation of counters in conjunction with vacuum tubes is discussed a little later.

Since the potential of A is determined by the battery or power supply it is clear that the potential of the wire must change considerably in the above operation. In fact it changes by amounts varying between a few and a few hundred volts. The change in potential can easily be detected directly with a cathode-ray oscilloscope, or it may be converted into a current pulse by means of a vacuum-tube amplifier and detected by a counting circuit of the kind to be described later. Usually a single-stage amplifier can be used, which as often as not need not be shielded from electrical disturbances as the pulse supplied by the counter is so great that it appears very clearly above any disturbances.

The method of "quenching" the discharge is not always the same. Quite commonly a counter is filled with a mixture of gases, one of which is an organic vapor such that it forms a layer on the metal surface and prevents the ejection of electrons in sufficient amounts to maintain a discharge. In such counters the function of the resistance R is not quite the same and may actually be needed to maintain the discharge longer.

It is in place here to discuss the practical side of Geiger-counter construction. Probably no apparatus in modern physics has had more study from the technical side or appeared in more diverse successful forms than the Geiger counter. At the Massachusetts Institute of Technology the visitor is shown a Geiger counter consisting of a fork and spoon in a partially evacuated space. It works! On the other hand the reader may well intentionedly make up a Geiger counter after the best instructions and fail to make it work. The authors would like to meet the counter expert who has not at some time in his career found he has constructed a "lemon." This is, however, too much of an aside. In practice the high field near a wire or small ball is almost universally employed in counter construction, and of these the wire is found in 95 per cent of the counters.

In Fig. 7 is shown the commonest form of a Geiger counter. A tungsten wire (from 1 to 10 mils) is stretched by a tungsten spring at one end and sealed along the axis of a glass tube which also contains a thin copper cylinder with a connector sealed into the glass. The glass envelope is attached to a pumping system after the contents have been thoroughly cleaned with soap and water and dilute nitric acid. The counter is then pumped out to a very low pressure with a diffusion pump system and while on the pumps heated to outgas the metal surface. A little air can now be admitted and the heating continued to oxidize the copper slightly; the counter is again pumped out and then filled with the gas mixture chosen. Argon and oxygen is one favorite recipe, about 8 to 1 in that order, at about 5 to 10 cm of mercury pressure. Self-quenching counters made of argon and xylol in the same proportions are very satisfactory. It is important to avoid the use of any quenching compound which will react, however slowly, with the materials in the counter, for then the behavior of the counter changes with time. To set the counter in operation it is attached to a detection system and to a source of variable high potential. A source of radiation is then brought near, for example a piece of uranium glass or a luminous clock face, and the voltage is gradually increased until the counter begins to count. With counters about 2 cm in diameter and a wire of 10-mil tungsten, at a gas pressure of 8 cm argon and oxygen, the counting voltage is about a thousand. These figures are only approximate; in fact, this whole account of the construction of a Geiger counter is included more to give the reader an idea of the procedure involved than to act as a guide to actual construction. References for this are given at the end of the chapter.

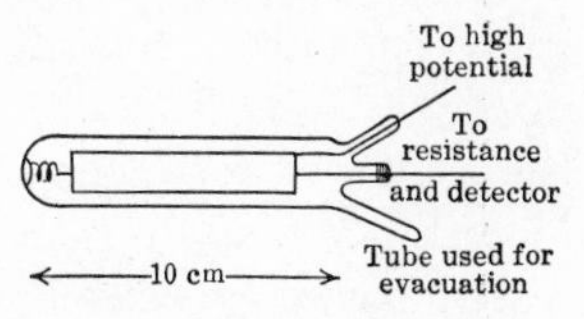

FIG. 7. Common design of Geiger counter.

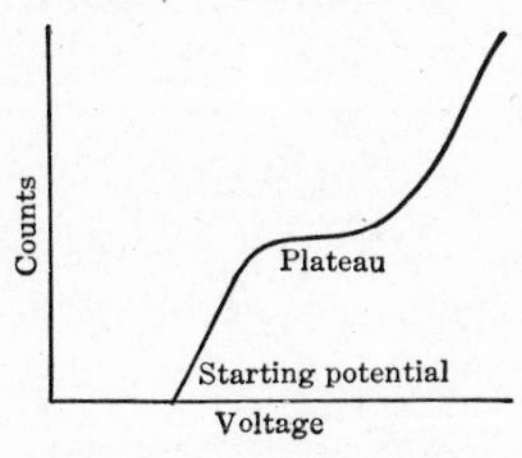

FIG. 8. Graph representing the number of counts observed when the voltage on a Geiger counter is increased. There is a definite starting potential, followed by a rise in the number counted, then a plateau, which means that as the voltage is increased there is very little change in the counting rate. After this there is a second rise.

If a counter is filled and sealed and made to operate it is very instructive to study the way in which the number of counts increases as the voltage on the counter is increased. Most counters behave as represented by Fig. 8. In this a graph of counts versus applied voltage is plotted for a counter exposed to a constant source of radiation. It can be seen that a certain starting voltage is needed before any counts at all are obtained, after which there is a steady increase in the number of counts until a more or less flat region, called the *plateau*, is reached. This plateau can be as broad as several hundred volts or may be entirely absent. Its extent depends on the value of the quenching resistance; it is generally larger when the quenching is done by vacuum-tube circuits. After the plateau there is a further rise, generally accompanied by a rise in the "background" count. This background count is due to cosmic rays and to spontaneous discharges, possibly caused by light. It is obviously advantageous to operate on the plateau, for then variations in the applied voltage are not important.

The account just given of the operation of a Geiger counter assumes that everything is favorable. It would be leaving too rosy a picture if some of the difficulties were not mentioned. In the first place there is, particularly for the inexperienced, a considerable amount of trial and error about counter construction. Of three similar counters, one may completely fail to operate for no clear reason. If, however, one thinks of the manner of operation of the counter this behavior is to be expected to some extent, for the counter must be such that it will discharge at a certain voltage when "tripped" by an entering electron and yet extinguish when the applied voltage falls by a hundred volts or so. Since the nature of the discharge in the counter depends greatly on the surface of the electrodes any dirt may or may not change the behavior of the counter in a radical way. Moreover, the gas used for filling plays an important role and must be chosen with care. There is, therefore, in the authors' opinion, no infallible set of rules which when followed will guarantee perfect operation of a counter; the proof of the pudding is emphatically in the eating. Preparation of Geiger counters is about on a par with cooking a meal; experience makes a difference. Once a counter is found which operates satisfactorily and does not contain reactive organic vapors and has no leak, it will continue to operate indefinitely. In several laboratories as many as fifty counters are in operation at one time, giving no trouble, so that they are not uncontrollably temperamental.

The background count of a counter generally depends on the area of the electrode. About 1 per minute per square centimeter of surface is not a bad guess for most counters. It can be reduced by a factor of 2 by 2 inches of lead shielding.

Vacuum-Tube Control of Geiger Counters. A very common device to quench a counter is to employ a vacuum tube. Circuits for this are shown in Fig. 9. The circuit shown in *A* is simple to understand though it is not very suitable for biological work. The high voltage to the wire of the counter is applied through a resistance which is high, but not nearly so high as the usual quenching resistance. A very high-μ tube (type 57 or 6C6) is then introduced as shown so that its plate current is supplied by the source of high voltage for the counter and its grid is at a potential of −4.5 volts unless a current flows in the counter, in which event the grid potential rises. The grid voltage of −4.5 is sufficient to prevent the flow of plate current virtually entirely so that the vacuum tube is normally without effect on the counter. As soon as a discharge starts in the counter, the cylinder becomes

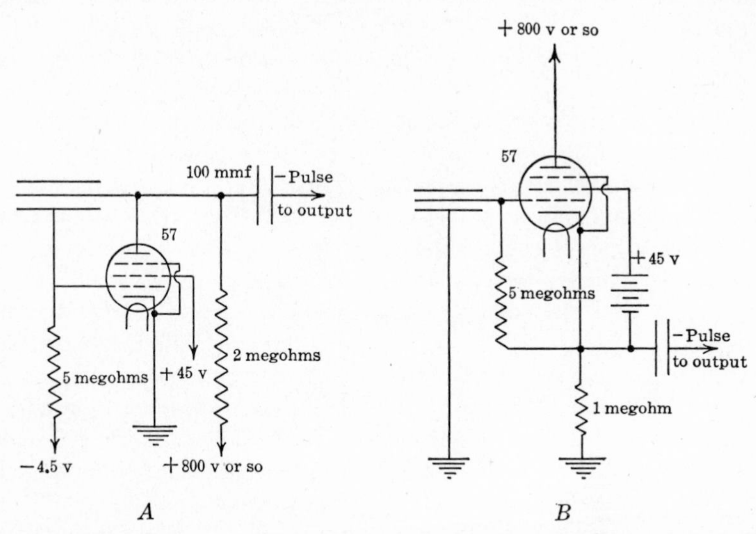

FIG. 9. Neher-Harper (*A*) and Neher-Pickering (*B*) quenching circuits. The Neher-Harper circuit acts to short-circuit the voltage on the counter; the Neher-Pickering, to break the circuit connecting the voltage to the counter. Both circuits employ external energy to extinguish the discharge. The Neher-Pickering permits the use of a grounded cylinder and so is more suitable for work where the radioactive material is likely to be in contact with the glass of the counter.

more positive so that the plate current of the vacuum tube suddenly starts to flow. The amount of current produced by a vacuum tube is far in excess of what would flow through the ordinary 10^9 ohms quenching resistance, and so the drop of potential across the relatively low resistance of a megohm or so in the plate circuit (and also the counter circuit) is plenty large enough to extinguish the counter. The vacuum tube, as it were, forcibly puts out the discharge. For work where the glass of the counter may be in contact with samples, the circuit of *B* is preferable. The principle is the same, the tube forcibly puts out the discharge, but here the voltage applied to the counter passes through the vacuum tube, which must therefore be passing plate current when the counter is awaiting the arrival of an electron. This is achieved by keeping the grid within a few volts of the plate potential by connecting it to the cathode through a fairly high resistance. The cathode is connected to ground through a 1-megohm resistance. It can be seen that when no discharge occurs in the counter the 57 tube is passing current and so the wire of the counter is virtually at the same potential as the 800 volts or so needed to make the counter operate. As soon as a discharge occurs the wire becomes negative and the 57 then passes no plate current. This means that there is no potential drop across the 1-megohm resistance, and the wire of the counter is thus virtually at ground potential so that the discharge is quickly extinguished.

The first circuit is known as the "Neher-Harper" circuit, the second as the "Neher-Pickering" circuit, in honor of their originators. It can be said that the Neher-Harper circuit short-circuits the counter voltage while the Neher-Pickering disconnects it. In both these circuits the time of recovery of the counter is much less so that faster counting is possible. This is a great advantage in many kinds of work.

The fact that the Neher-Pickering circuit permits the cylinder to be grounded brings up an important technical point about counter operation in general. If the cylinder is not grounded the contact of bodies at differing potentials with the glass case will induce potentials on the wire which may be sufficient to operate the recording mechanism. Thus, if a counter is connected so that the negative voltage is applied to the cylinder and a liquid is flowed around the counter, it will often be found that spurious counts will occur as the liquid is poured on, even after things should have settled down. If, however, the cylinder is at ground potential it acts to shield the wire and such spurious counts will be avoided. This is a small point, but the authors have known its neglect to waste much time.

Recording Equipment. Up to the present no word has been said about actual recording. For simple counting with relatively weak sources a thyratron recorder using a gas-filled 885 or 884 tube is almost universally employed. The thyratron is a three-electrode gas-filled tube which has a potential of 200 volts or so applied to its plate. If the grid is kept at a negative potential greater than roughly one-tenth of the plate potential there will be no discharge in the gas, or in other words the thyratron will not "fire." If, however, a positive pulse is put on the grid a discharge starts which is maintained by the power supply connected to the plate and which does not cease after the pulse has passed. The current passed by the thyratron depends on the nature of the tube and on the resistance in the plate circuit, but for the 884-type tube it is between 20 and 200 milliamperes in ordinary use. This is adequate to operate a high-impedance mechanical recorder or relay. The only problem is to extinguish the discharge in the thyratron after the pulse has been recorded. This cannot be done by the grid; it is necessary to bring the voltage drop between the plate of the thyratron and the cathode to less than that necessary to maintain the discharge, whereupon the tube ceases to fire and is once more under the control of the grid. One obvious way to cause this voltage drop is to make the recording mechanism break the plate circuit, and this can be done. It turns out to be rather unreliable,

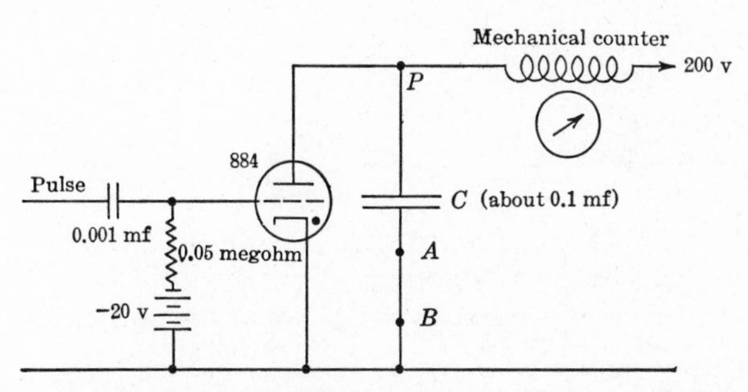

FIG. 10. *Thyratron recorder.* The positive pulse raises the potential of the grid, causing the thyratron to fire and operate the recorder. The act of recording, however, causes the condenser C to discharge and so lower the potential of the point P below that necessary to maintain the discharge, and the thyratron is extinguished. The tube is then ready to operate once more.

particularly for fast counting, and the method universally used is to short-circuit the tube by means of a condenser.

A simple circuit for this is shown in Fig. 10. The pulse is applied through the input condenser to the grid of the thyratron, which fires. The act of firing causes the condenser C to discharge and the potential of the point P to fall below the voltage necessary to maintain the discharge. The thyratron then is extinguished and is ready for operation by a fresh pulse applied to the grid. It is possible to make the operation a little more certain if an inductance is inserted between the points A and B. This inductance, together with C, forms a series oscillatory circuit and so causes the potential of P to go *below* zero, thus making sure that the thyratron is extinguished. If it happens that the thyratron readily extinguishes but the recorder does not operate, a resistance of a few thousand ohms placed between A and B will slow down the fall of potential of P and permit the discharge to continue longer and so operate the mechanism.

Such a thyratron recorder is almost instantaneous in action and its speed is limited only by the mechanical counter. For speeds of counting up to 300 per minite this simple circuit is adequate. Beyond that, various so-called scaling circuits must be used of which the simplest, the "scale-of-two" circuit devised by Wynn-Williams, is described below.

Scale-of-Two Circuit. In principle this circuit is similar to the recording arrangement just discussed except that to convey a pulse to a mechanical counter two thyratrons must have fired successively. The two thyratrons are arranged as shown in Fig. 11. The essential points are that the two plates are joined by a relatively large con-

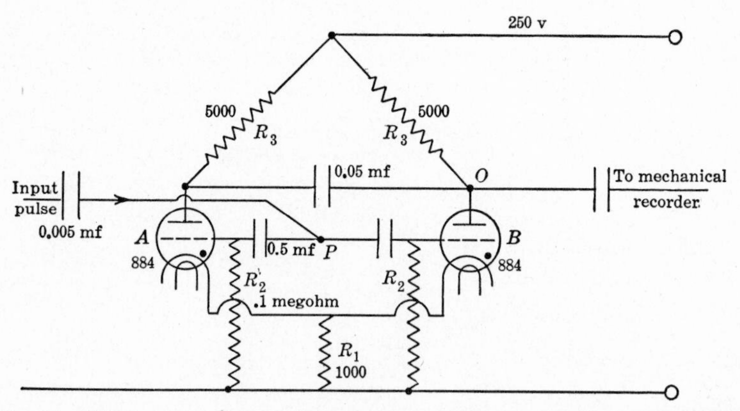

FIG. 11. "Scale of two" thyratron recorder. If thyratron A is fired it causes a current to flow through R_1 and so bias thyratron B in such a way that it is controlled by its grid. The arrival of a second pulse at P then causes B to fire, drawing so much current that the plate potential of A falls below the firing point and A is extinguished. A pulse from the point O can be made to actuate the mechanical recorder, which thus records only half the pulses.

denser and that the cathodes are grounded through a common resistance R_1 of about 1000 ohms. One thyratron always fires in such an arrangement; suppose it to be A. Then the current through A flows to the return via R_1 and keeps the grid of B negative with respect to the cathode; in other words, B does not fire. The arrival of a second pulse at P, however, gives a momentary positive bias to the grid of B, and accordingly it fires. In so doing it draws current through the condenser across the plates of the two thyratrons and drops the plate potential of A below the firing point, extinguishing A. The next pulse extinguishes B and fires A, and so on. By using a pulse from only one of the thyratrons to operate a thyratron recorder as described in Fig. 10, the mechanical counter will operate only once for each two pulses arriving. This idea can be extended to a second or third or more pairs of thyratrons, resulting in scale of four, eight, sixteen, etc., circuits. In practice it is not of much value to use simply a scale of two because the gain in usefulness is not very great. A scale of eight is needed to be of any considerable value.

One or two words of caution are in place regarding these scaling circuits. One is that they draw considerably more current than an ordinary amplifier circuit and the power supply must be designed accordingly. If care is not taken to avoid it there may be reaction from an early stage of a multiple-scaling circuit through the power supply to a later stage. Also it is wise to couple units through a vacuum tube to avoid one unit's influencing the other except as desired.

Lewis, and Stevenson and Getting, have shown that it is quite feasible to use hard vacuum tubes in scaling circuits working on the same principle. These are preferred by some and found temperamental by others. References are provided at the end of the chapter.

Counting-Rate Meters. For some purposes it is convenient to use a counting-rate meter in place of a scaling circuit. Such a meter simply reads the *rate* of arrival of the pulses, and if this rate is rapid enough the fluctuations are not very great so that a reasonably steady reading can be obtained. Such an arrangement is most convenient for photographic recording. A very carefully designed meter has been described by Gingrich, Evans, and Edgerton and tested very thoroughly by them. Their circuit is carefully arranged to provide pulses of the same size so that each count records in the same manner. These pulses are then fed into the grid of a 57 tube which is biased to give very little plate current. The pulses produce little bursts of plate current which can be read on a meter. The readings so obtained are very unsteady, but by placing a 100,000-ohm resistance in series with the meter and a 20-microfarad condenser across the two the fluctuations can be smoothed out and a reasonably steady deflection results. Time must be allowed for the condenser to become charged, which means that the meter is not as direct as might at first be supposed, but it is still more convenient than stopwatch counting. If desired, the small steady plate current can be balanced out by a potentiometer arrangement in the plate circuit. The meter must, of course, be calibrated.

Fluctuations in Counting. We have spoken above of the fluctuations in counting nuclear particles, and as they constitute a phenomenon which is inherent in all nuclear observations it is important to appreciate the nature of the random fluctuations which are met in this work. In radioactivity we may speak of certain definite figures which express the rate of decay of a substance, generally its "half-life." Such figures refer to measurements which involve the averaging of a very large number of observations of individual transitions. The actual process of the conversion of one atom of, say, radiosodium into stable magnesium takes place *at random*. It is pure chance when the individual event takes place. A very large number of such events, when averaged, will show a clear and accurate manner of decay, but the fact remains that the random nature of the individual process underlies the whole general phenomenon.

This shows up very clearly when a weak source of a radioactive substance is placed near a counting apparatus and the number of registrations in every 10-second interval is recorded. One might well record in ten such intervals the numbers 8, 5, 6, 4, 10, 7, 6, 6, 7, 3. The average is 6.2, but as high as 10 and as low as 3 can be recorded. The arrival of the "counts" is much the same as the arrival of rain-drops on a window pane. Such random fluctuations are encountered throughout atomic physics; for example, "tube noise" is due to the fluctuations in the motions of electrons in a vacuum tube, and the finite width of a spectral line is due to a similar cause. It is only in nuclear physics that the individual particles are sufficiently energetic to be individually detectable and the fluctuations show up directly instead of as a secondary effect concerned with the measuring apparatus.

Since these fluctuations are inevitable, what must one know about them? In the first place one must be wary of data taken with only a few counts. In the second place one must be prepared to accept limitations imposed on experiments by the method of counting available. In the third place one should know rough limits of error to any count which is taken.

There is one very simple and complete way of considering any one observation. This is by means of Poisson's formula. If, in a given interval, a number of particles n is counted, and if the average number arriving in a large number of such intervals is x, then the probability of the occurrence of n is given by

$$P_n = \frac{x^n}{n!} e^{-x}$$

where P_n is the ratio of the number of times n would be recorded, to the whole number of trials, if a very large number of trials were made. Now in analyzing data we wish to assume that n as observed represents the true average x. *We have no guarantee that it does*; that is the inherent uncertainty with which we must be content to live. We can, however, suppose that n is in error by a certain amount, say the permissible limit of error, and can then calculate the probability that this is so. If the probability is low we can be satisfied; if it is of the order of 10 per cent it is necessary to worry. To illustrate this method of discussion we give the probability of various errors in a count of 1000 particles. The probability is expressed as the ratio of the probability of the observed 1000 to that of the true average.*

TABLE 1

Possible "True" Count	Ratio of Probability of the Observed 1000
1010	0.9
1020	0.8
1050	0.3
1100	0.03
1125	0.01

It can be seen that a 5 per cent error is quite likely and that there is a definite chance of an 11 per cent error. In the great majority of experiments an elaborate discussion of the errors due to fluctuations is not presented, but the numbers counted and the conclusions drawn are such that there is an ample safety factor. As a rough guide one can expect a fluctuation as great as the square root of the number of particles counted in any one observation. This guide is useful because it indicates the improvement to be expected if more care is taken. Thus a count of 100 particles is fairly reliable to 10 per cent, but nearly 1000 must be counted to be fairly sure to 5 per cent. A habit the authors have formed when there is a little question of the validity of the conclusions drawn is to divide the observations into two, taking the first half of the data and comparing it with the second. If the two agree it is reassuring. By far the best procedure if there is any question regarding fluctuations is to take more data.

Coincidence Counting. The ordinary Geiger counter usually operates on a small fraction of the total ionization produced by a fast particle. The fast electron often continues right through the counter walls and is absorbed somewhere else. This fact, which is particularly evident when cosmic rays are being observed, has led to the development of coincidence counting in which the fast particle passes through more than one counter and is recorded only if it registers in both. The advantages of this form of counting are many. In the first place it is possible to ensure that the counts emanate only from one particular direction; in the second place the counter background can be

* This means that, if a large number of trials were made and the average were 1010, the count of 1000 would be obtained 0.9 times as often as the count of 1010, and if 1125 were the average, 1000 would occur 0.01 times as often as 1125.

reduced to a very small figure since the random counts in two counters will not be coincident in time and so will not cause the recording apparatus to respond. In the third place cleverly applied coincidence counting can sort out from a number of various radiations the one kind which has to be studied.

The most commonly used circuit is due to Rossi and has the advantage that it can be applied to any number of Geiger counters up to a reasonable limit, which the authors put between ten and twenty. In brief its principle is as follows: the pulse from one Geiger counter is applied to a suitable tube, say a 57, in such a way that the grid is forced strongly negative, thus preventing the tube from passing current or, alternatively, causing the tube to have an abnormally high resistance. The plate of this tube is connected to one side of a condenser which is virtually short-circuited to ground *except when the Geiger counter delivers a pulse.* A second Geiger counter is now made to feed its pulse into the condenser, which will develop no charge unless the first Geiger counter has removed the shorting resistance from the condenser. The condenser is then connected to an amplifier and recorder and will record only when two pulses arrive simultaneously. It is clear that almost any number of tubes could be placed across the condenser, which could never develop a voltage unless the grid of every tube were strongly negative. Sometimes it is desired to arrange a circuit for counting when one counter does not operate and the other does. This can be achieved by arranging a tube which is normally negatively biased across the condenser; such a tube will not prevent a potential difference from developing, but if the operation of the Geiger counter and some tube circuit causes the grid to go positive then the condenser is shorted and no signal is given to the recorder. Thus there is a record only when the counter is not operating and others are.

The circuit for straight coincidences is shown in Fig. 12. The Geiger counter and amplifying tube are shown on the left. Each of the tubes T can deliver a pulse to the tubes T_1, T_2, T_3 such as to make their grids negative and diminish the current flowing in R. If the resistance of R is 100,000 ohms and the plate resistance of each tube is also 100,000 ohms, then when all three tubes have no signal on their grids the total resistance in the circuit to the 250-volt supply is 133,000 ohms. The current flowing is roughly 2 milliamperes, and the drop of potential across R is 200 volts. If one tube receives a signal its plate resistance becomes virtually infinite; the total resistance in the 250-volt supply circuit is then 150,000 ohms, and the plate current through R is hardly altered so that the potential of the point A does not change greatly. The same is true if two tubes receive signal. However, if all three tubes receive signal simultaneously the total resistance in the circuit becomes infinite, or nearly so, and the potential of the point A, which is attached to the condenser C, rises to that of the potential of the supply, 250 volts. The output pulse in this event is so much larger than in either of the other cases that it is easy to arrange the

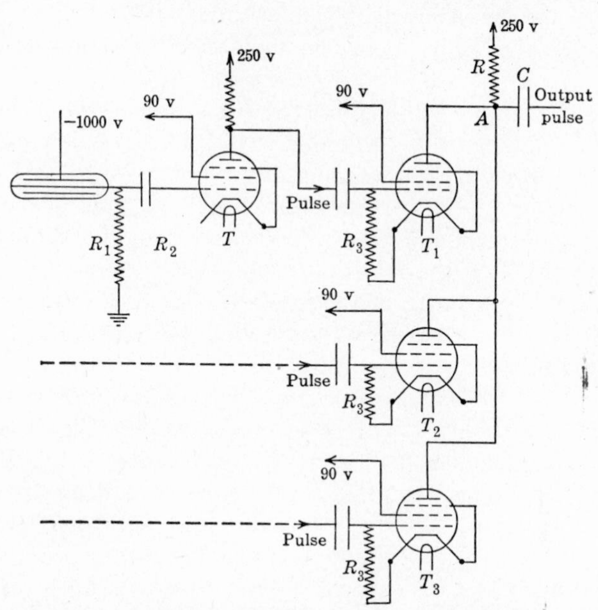

FIG. 12. *Triple coincidence circuit.* The Geiger counters deliver pulses to the three tubes T_1, T_2, T_3, such that their grids become negative and plate current ceases to flow in the resistance R. When this is so the potential of A rises and an output pulse is delivered. If any *one* tube is not blocked, enough current flows in R to keep the potential of A low, and hence a pulse is not delivered unless all three counters operate simultaneously.

recording equipment to detect only this large pulse. If the reader finds the above explanation a little involved it is easy to conceive of each tube as a low resistance short-circuiting the point A to ground. Each negative pulse on the grid acts as a switch to open each circuit, but A is nevertheless shorted unless all three switches are open at the same time.

The Cloud Chamber. The cloud chamber is almost certainly the most widely known method of detection of nuclear particles because it gives such a graphic portrayal of the path of a nuclear projectile. The familiar principle depends on the observation of C. T. R. Wilson that ions can act as centers for the formation of condensed droplets in a supersaturated vapor. He produced the supersaturated vapor by the simple process of rapid adiabatic expansion of a saturated vapor. The rapid expansion causes a fall in temperature which carries the vapor below the dew point. If the vapor is clean, particularly if it is free from dust, the state of supersaturation is maintained unless some ions are present. Droplets form about these ions and so make the presence of the ions known. By illuminating the vapor after expansion, photographs can be taken and any interesting events permanently recorded.

The cloud chamber is one of the oldest instruments in nuclear physics. It has undergone considerable development and has probably taxed more people's patience than any other piece of equipment in the whole subject. If the reader thinks for a moment of the method of operation outlined above he will soon see one disadvantage of the instrument. This is the fact that time must elapse before the cloud chamber is ready for a second expansion. The time of the expansion itself is short, and the sensitive time is about $\frac{1}{30}$ second, but 20 seconds must elapse between expansions. This means that the apparatus is only $\frac{1}{6}$ per cent efficient, and in turn this means long hours of work to secure data. Many attempts have been made to develop a "continuous" cloud chamber, and some success has been attained in finding means to produce a supersaturated state by a steady flow of one gas against a vapor. No research results have been produced yet by such equipment. A more useful technique has been to keep the cloud chamber in readiness for expansion until a particle is known to have passed through it. This seeming miracle can be accomplished only if the particle to be detected is an energetic one of the kind to be found in cosmic rays, a particle which can pass through the walls of the cloud chamber and also through a Geiger counter. The operation of this counter trips a relay which sets off the expansion. By this means the efficiency of the expansion chamber is enormously increased and the saving in film is great.

A cloud chamber for observation of alpha particles, protons, and heavy recoil atoms is not hard to construct. The expansion can be made in a volume enclosed by a rubber diaphragm which is compressed and then released. In place of water as the vapor, various alcohols can be used. They have the advantage that the "expansion ratio," the ratio of the volume after expansion to that before, is less. For air and water the expansion ratio is about 1.4, whereas with various alcohol mixtures it is around 1.2. The expansion ratio can be calculated in terms of the specific heats of the gas and latent heat of the vapor concerned. For a gas like acetylene with water vapor it rises to 1.8.

The observation of fast electrons is much harder. The expansion must be kept within close limits defined by no tracks visible and all tracks obscured by too dense a general fog. Any small trace of acid fumes will effectively prevent the operation at all, and if one talks to workers in cosmic rays one becomes aware of the existence of a cloud chamber "season," namely, the time of year when it is not too warm and humid. The observation of fast electrons by cloud chambers should not, therefore, be attempted lightly.

Expansion chambers can be operated at high pressures, up to 10 atmospheres. Such chambers are useful in measuring the ranges of protons emitted in nuclear reactions and in detecting the presence of groups. The recoil protons caused by neutrons in a gas containing hydrogen can also be detected with such equipment.

Other Methods of Detection. In the foregoing we have given an account of the more common methods of nuclear observation. Most of the work on artificial radioactive tracers is carried out with equipment which comes under the headings of the previous paragraphs. Two less commonly applied methods which deserve mention also are taken up here. The first is the *electrometer tube.*

Where fairly large samples of elements having a long half-life are to be studied it is often desirable to record the decay of a sample automatically. The counting-rate meter mentioned previously will achieve this but is not free from objections. In particular it requires the Geiger counter to retain the same sensitivity for a long run, which cannot always be depended upon. It is possible to project the fiber of a Lauritsen electroscope and photograph its position automatically at known intervals, but this requires some method of recharging the fiber periodically and is rather bothersome. If the ionization current due to a source is measured directly by means of a galvanometer it is a simple matter to take a photographic record of the galvanometer spot and the problem is solved. Unfortunately the galvanometer alone is not sensitive enough and so vacuum tubes have been applied to increase the effective sensitivity of the galvanometer and render it available. Such tubes are referred to as "electrometer tubes" because in conjunction with a galvanometer they serve the same purpose as an electrometer.

From the circuit of Fig. 13 the action of the electrometer tube can be understood. Suppose that we consider the behavior of the vacuum tube if no ionization occurs in the ionization chamber. The plate current will be determined by the grid potential, which in turn will be determined by the bias battery and the flow of grid current through the resistance X. A steady state will be reached in which a steady plate current will flow, and this plate current can be read by a galvanometer, or a battery and variable resistance can be arranged to oppose the plate current so that the galvanometer shows no deflection in this steady state. Now, if ionization occurs in A, current flows through X and the potential of the grid is changed, thus causing a change in plate current. It is commonplace for a vacuum tube to produce a milliampere of plate current for a volt change on the grid, so that a

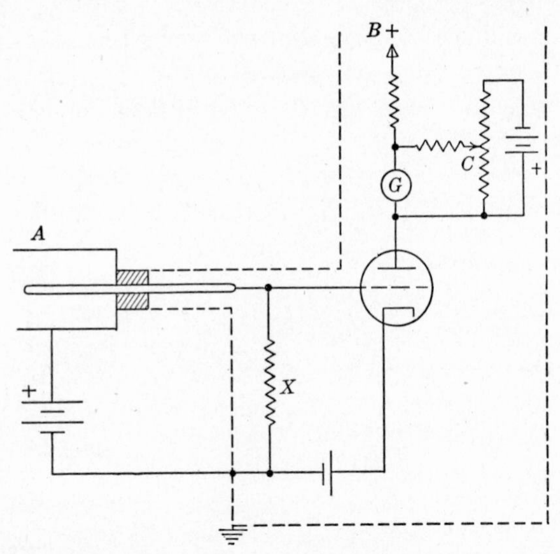

FIG. 13. *Electrometer tube.* When no ionization occurs in A only grid current flows in the resistance X and a steady grid potential results. The plate current is steady. The galvanometer G is brought to zero by the balancing circuit C. When ions are formed in A, additional current flows in X, changing the grid potential and the plate current. This change shows on the galvanometer.

change of 0.0001 volt would produce a current change of 10^{-7} ampere in the plate current; a relatively insensitive galvanometer will readily detect this amount. If the resistance X is 10^{11} ohms the current to produce the 0.001-volt change would be 10^{-14} ampere, or about 33,000 ion pairs per second. This much ionization is produced by one alpha particle per second or by 100 electrons per second. As quite small sources emit at these rates, the method of detection is amply sensitive.

The catch appears as soon as the apparatus is set up. Not only the ionization chamber, but also variations in filament temperature, plate supply voltage, electrical disturbances, and so on, will produce changes in plate current as great as those given above. It is therefore necessary to use careful shielding, a large storage battery on the filament, good heat insulation, and a steady source of plate voltage before these sensitivities can be approached. By using multi-grid tubes, compensating networks can be devised to alleviate some of these sources of disturbance, and in competent hands the electrometer tube is one of the most satisfactory methods of observation of nuclear processes. It has one interesting application in which an ionization chamber at 10 or so atmospheres is used. The increased pressure means that a large part of the ionizing path of a beta ray is spent in the chamber and the ionization current is accordingly greater. Such an arrangement will detect single electrons and is probably the best possible method of detecting very weak sources.

Finally we can consider *photographic detection.* The permanency of a photographic record, and the fact that one plate can carry a large amount of information taken from different locations at the same time, render this method of detection attractive. It has proved to be less useful (so far) in nuclear physics than other methods because of the competition of the cloud chamber and the fact that the track of a particle which ionizes heavily enough to be singly detected is so short as to require microscopic observation. However, with fine-grain plates and developer, the track of an alpha particle can be followed as a series of developed grains (around 4 per centimeter of range) in the emulsion. It is very tedious to sort these tracks out under the microscope, and for single-particle detection most (but not all) observers prefer other methods. On the other hand if the available source is quite large it is not necessary to scour the emulsion for particles of silver in line but an overall deposit can be produced and photometered in the usual way. In this manner the distribution of radiophosphorus in a bone section has been studied by placing the section above a photographic plate for several days and then developing it. The plate shows a well-marked distribution and gives information in a clear way which would have taken weeks to obtain by counting methods where individual slices would have to be counted separately. The technique of such observations is similar to that of x-ray photography.

Summary. To summarize, we can say shortly that to detect nuclear particles we detect *ionization.* This can be done directly by electrometers whose sensitivity can be pushed with difficulty to detect single particles. If 100 times the ionization of a single particle per minute is to be detected it can be done directly with the Lauritsen electroscope, which is about the most useful general-purpose instrument in radioactive work available. By means of tube amplifiers either single particles (high-gain amplifier) or steady ionization currents (single electrometer tube) can be observed. The latter is very well adapted to photographic recording. Use of a high electrostatic field and ionization by collision renders the detection of single electrons easy. The most widely used instrument, however, is the Geiger-Müller counter, which is generally associated with auxiliary circuits for recording, including scaling and coincidence circuits. The nature of fluctuations in counts is important to realize. Rough guides for estimating errors due to them are given. The cloud chamber and photographic recording are two methods of importance, the former in nuclear research, the latter in an increasing range of application to applied problems.

REFERENCES

STRONG, NEHER, CARTWRIGHT, WHITFORD, and HAYWARD, *Procedures in Experimental Physics*, Prentice-Hall, 1938. This is excellent as a general reference about most of this chapter.

C. C. LAURITSEN and T. LAURITSEN, "A Simple Quartz Fiber Electrometer," *Rev. Sci. Instruments*, **8**, 438 (1937). This gives a short adequate account of the Lauritsen electroscope.

JOHN R. DUNNING, *Rev. Sci. Instruments*, **5**, 387, 1934; E. A. JOHNSON and A. G. JOHNSON, *Phys. Rev.*, **50**, 170, 1936; P. A. MACDONALD, *Physics*, **7**, 265, 1936. These three papers cover the subject of the linear amplifier.

C. G. MONTGOMERY and D. D. MONTGOMERY, "Geiger-Mueller Counters," *Journal of the Franklin Institute*, **231**, 447 and 509. A full and accurate account of the subject with references.

N. S. GINGRICH, ROBLEY D. EVANS, and HAROLD E. EDGERTON, "A Direct Reading Counting Rate Meter for Random Pulses," *Rev. Sci. Instruments*, **7**, 441, 1936.

H. R. CRANE and J. C. MOUZON, "Simple Design for a Cloud Chamber," *Rev. Sci. Instruments*, **8**, 351, 1937.

L. A. DUBRIDGE and H. BROWN, *Rev. Sci. Instruments*, **4**, 532, 1933; D. B. PENICK, *ibid.*, **6**, 115, 1935; WHITFORD in STRONG, etc., *Procedures in Experimental Physics*, p. 418. These cover the subject of electrometer-tube set-up. If it is desired to eliminate batteries, the necessary technique is given in a letter by ANDERSON, LAWSON, and WEIL, *Rev. Sci. Instruments*, **10**, 511.

W. G. SHEPHERD and R. O. HAXBY, "A Scale of Eight Impulse Counter," *Rev. Sci. Instruments*, **7**, 425, 1936; E. C. STEVENSON and I. A. GETTING, "A Vacuum Tube Circuit for Scaling down Counting Rates," *Rev. Sci. Instruments*, **8**, 414, 1937.

CHAPTER 4

METHODS OF ACCELERATING ATOMIC PARTICLES

The simplest and one of the earliest methods developed for producing the high voltages necessary for transmutation work is a streamlined version of the age-old electrostatic machine. Inasmuch as no ion source giving more than a few hundred microamperes of ions has been perfected, the power actually utilized in the production of the most intense available beams is relatively small. This means that, although the accelerating device must develop a high voltage, no large current capacity is necessary. These requirements are admirably suited to the capabilities of an electrostatic generator. Van de Graaff was the first to recognize the possibilities of such a mechanism, and the present-day electrostatic apparatus as applied to atomic projectile work is a direct outgrowth of his development research and bears his name.

A description of the largest machine of this type ever constructed will serve to illustrate the principles of operation. This apparatus was originally assembled at Round Hill, where an airship hangar served as its home. Later a special building was constructed on the campus at the Massachusetts Institute of Technology, where it is now in operation in a modified form. In the Round Hill installation two large metal spheres, each 15 feet in diameter, were mounted 40 feet in the air on insulating pillars. It is pictured diagrammatically in Fig. 1. A wide endless belt, of silk or paper, driven by motors and pulleys, runs from the floor up inside each sphere. A transformer-rectifier set produces a voltage of 20 kilovolts. Positive electricity is sprayed on one of the moving belts by a sharp-pointed metal comb, and negative electricity is similarly put on the other belt. These belts then carry the charges up into the interior of their respective spheres, where a similar metal comb takes the charge from each belt. The comb is connected to the sphere itself, and the collected charge is transported to the outside of the sphere. That this is what must happen can be seen, at least qualitatively, when one recalls the well-known fact that like charges repel. This means that each unit of electricity forming the charge will endeavor to take up a position in the conductor as far removed from all other charge as possible. Obviously this condition is established when all charge rests on the outside surface of the conducting sphere. As a result of this, no charge ever accumulates on the comb connected to the sphere since it is in the interior, and hence, regardless of how much charge rests on the exterior, the charge sprayed

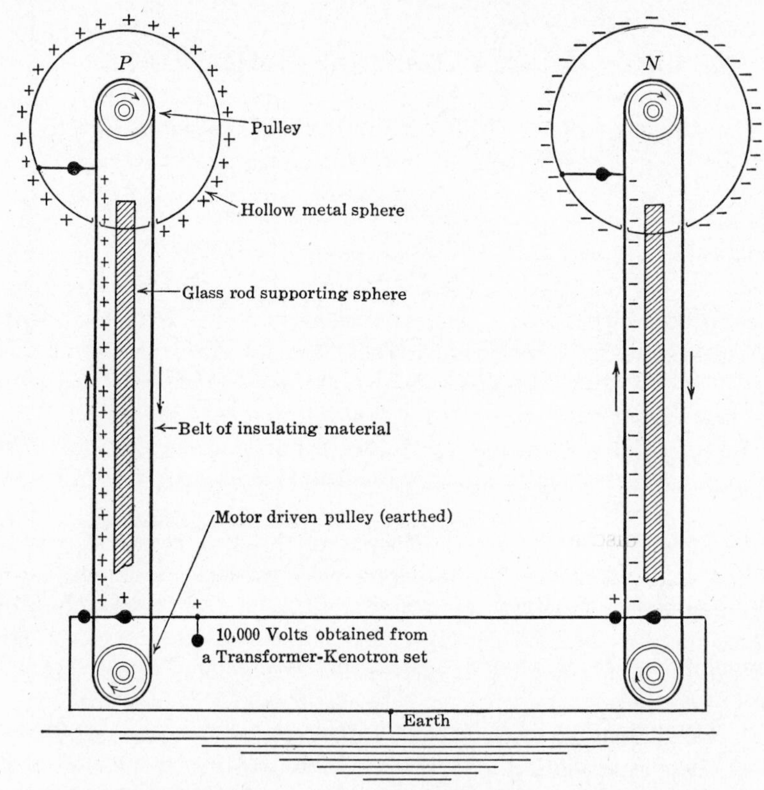

FIG. 1. Schematic diagram of the Round Hill high-voltage installation.

on the belt below will always be taken off above. Thus, as more electricity is sent up the belt, the potential of the sphere rises until the charge lost to the air through corona discharge equals that coming up the belt. To make this equilibrium voltage as high as possible it is desirable to have wide belts and run them as fast as is practicable.

Another trick is employed which doubles the amount of charge separated in any one revolution of the belt. This is brought about by having the descending belt carry an equal quantity of charge opposite in sign to that which the ascending portion carries. It is accomplished in the following manner. The rising belt carries a positive charge which was sprayed on below. On reaching A the sharp-pointed collector acquires a charge from the belt much as a vacuum cleaner sucks up dirt from a carpet. As this insulated collector assumes a higher and higher positive potential, negative electricity is attracted to the pointed rod C, of Fig. 2, which is connected to the sphere. It is then sprayed on to the descending belt. Thus each revolution of the belt is twice as efficient in charging the sphere as when the conventional scheme is used.

With this huge apparatus it was found possible easily to charge one sphere positively to well in excess of 2.5 million volts, and the other to a roughly equal negative potential. Now, by connecting an evacuated tube between the two spheres, ions produced at the positively charged sphere could be accelerated down the tube to an energy in excess of 5 Mev. These ions, which are nothing more than atoms with one or more electrons removed, are ionized in a discharge tube, into which gas, composed of the proper atoms, is continually admitted at a low pressure. A small hole drilled in the discharge tube allows the ions to emerge into the accelerating tube, where they are whisked down the tube towards the target. Figure 3 shows the accelerating tube in place. A short description of this tube is quite in order, since it is a common feature of all ion accelerators with the exception of the cyclotron.

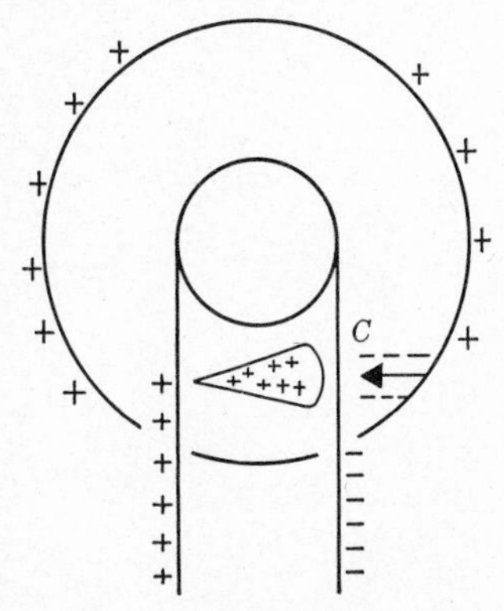

FIG. 2. Method of increasing belt efficiency by carrying negative charge down as well as positive up.

The tubular "doughnuts" are connected to metallic cylinders placed inside the accelerating tube, and through these cylinders the ion beam moves. These doughnuts carry a corona discharge from one sphere to the other, thus making for a uniform voltage gradient along the tube. The cylinders are separated by gaps and act as lenses to focus the ions toward the target. Figure 4 provides a close-up view of a section of the tube. In actual practice there is a potential difference of several hundred thousand volts between each pair of doughnuts, and consequently the same holds true for each pair of inner cylinders to which the doughnuts are connected. The electrical lines of force between adjacent cylinders follow the pattern indicated. Ions moving through these electrodes are constrained to move along the lines of force and as a consequence are confined mainly to a path near the center of the tube. The reason for this is obvious. In moving across the gap from the interior of one cylinder to the next the particle gains in energy an amount proportional to the voltage difference between the cylinders. This gain in energy results in a corresponding gain in velocity (K.E. =

FIG. 3. View of the accelerating tube in place between the spheres of the Round Hill generator. (Photograph by Dr. L. C. Van Atta.)

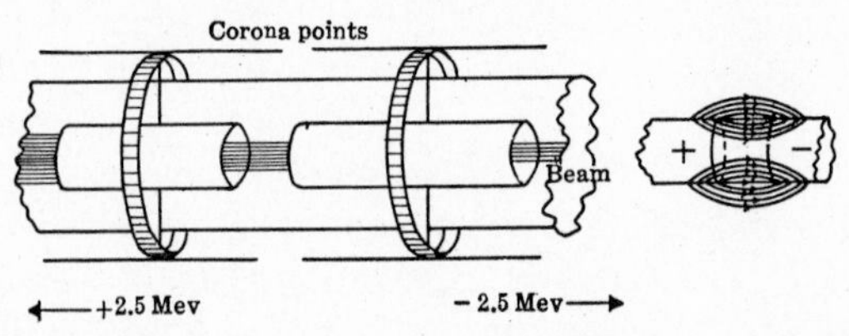

FIG. 4. Action of corona rings and points in distributing potential and focusing the beam. The small diagram shows the lines of force between the two sections. This field acts as an electrostatic lens.

$\frac{1}{2}mv^2$), which means that the velocity of the particle entering the second cylinder is much greater than the velocity it had when emerging from the first. Now, the faster a particle is moving in an electric field, the smaller the effect which the field can have in deflecting it. One might visualize this in a non-technical way by arguing that a "slow" ion stays at any one place longer than a "fast" one and thus gives the field a longer time in which to act. Hence it is evident from the previous diagram that the focusing effect exerted on an ion moving off center during the first half of its path across the gap will be greater

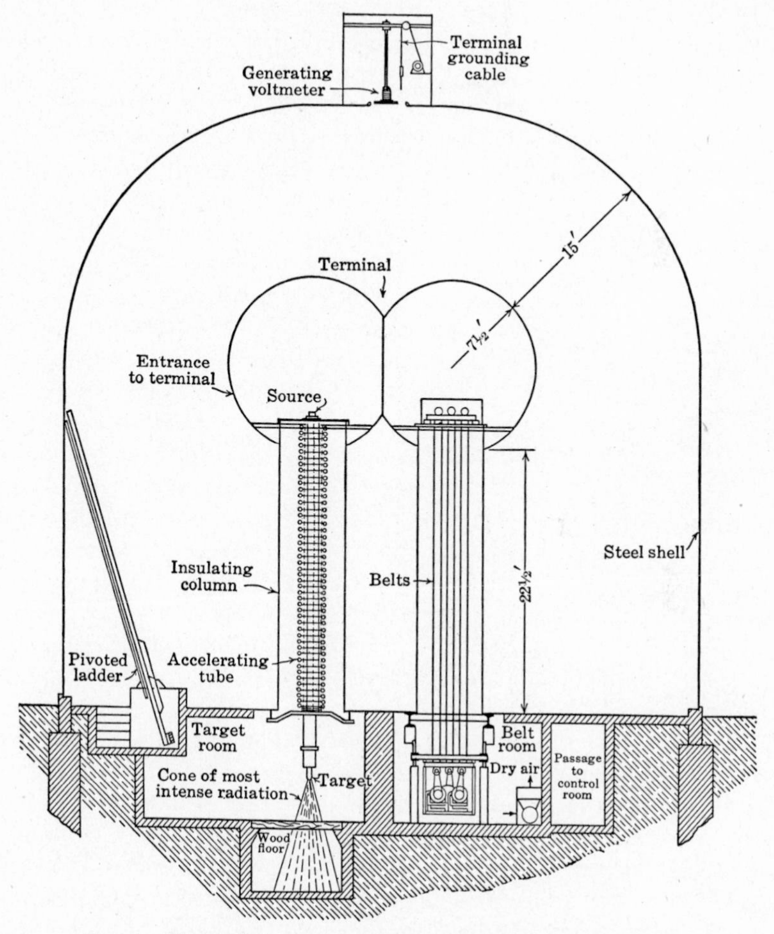

FIG. 5. Diagram of the Cambridge, Massachusetts, installation.

than the defocusing effect experienced by the now faster ion during the second half of its journey between electrodes. This focusing action is so effective that, after careful adjustments have been made, the ion beam may have a cross section no larger than a dime. This facilitates the preparation of concentrated samples of radioactive materials.

It was originally thought that the interior of one of the spheres would be the safest place for observers, as it is field-free. However, the neutrons given out in almost all bombardments make it unsafe. In the new installation at the Massachusetts Institute of Technology the two spheres are joined and charged as a single unit. A cross section of the new arrangement is shown in Fig. 5. A modified form of the Van de Graaff type of accelerator was pioneered by Tuve, Hafstad, and Dahl at the Terrestrial Magnetism Laboratory of the Carnegie Institution at Washington. This apparatus proved very successful for voltages up to 1.2 million.

If it were possible to view the ion beam under a superpowerful microscope we should notice that in general the beam would be composed of two types of projectile, one component being single particles and the other a number of dumbbell-shaped double particles. If hydrogen gas had been admitted to the discharge tube the single particles would be protons and the pairs would consist of molecular hydrogen ions. The molecular ion is in reality two protons which share an electron. Since both types of projectile forming the beam possess effectively a unit positive charge, the kinetic energy given to each after passing down the accelerating tube will be the same. This requires that the molecular ions move with approximately seven-tenths the velocity of the protons. The impact upon striking the target splits each doublet ion into two protons. These "Johnny come lately" protons possess only half the energy of those which traveled the length of the tube as such. As a consequence of this, two different energies are effective in producing transmutations when a target is exposed to the beam. For many experiments it is necessary that monokinetic particles strike the target. This can be accomplished by superimposing a magnetic field at right angles to the path of the beam. In such a field the molecular ions will be deflected somewhat less than protons, and the initial beam will be separated into two parts, one composed only of molecular ions, the other of protons alone. The target can thus be placed so as to intercept whichever fraction is desired.

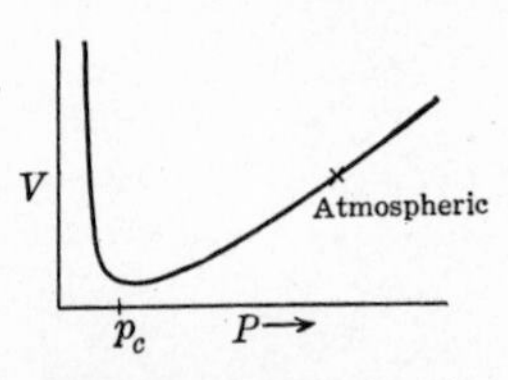

FIG. 6. Graph showing the relation between the breakdown potential between two objects in air and the pressure. Provided that a critical pressure is exceeded, the breakdown pressure increases rapidly as the pressure is increased.

The limiting voltage that can be placed on the sphere of an electrostatic-type apparatus is essentially measured by the breakdown potential difference between it and surrounding objects at ground potential. A graph showing how the breakdown voltage between two objects varies with the air pressure is given in Fig. 6. It is clear from the curve that one can increase the ultimate voltage obtainable in either of two possible ways: (*a*) by evacuating the surrounding space to a point well below the critical pressure p_c; (*b*) by increasing the pressure to several atmospheres.

The latter possibility has proved to be the more practicable, and several installations which operate under pressures up to 10 atmospheres are now completed or in the process of completion. Foremost of the workers in this phase of high-voltage machines has been Herb at the University of Wisconsin. A sectional view of his apparatus is shown in Fig. 7. The entire unit is enclosed in a steel tank built to withstand a pressure of 100 pounds per square inch. The sphere

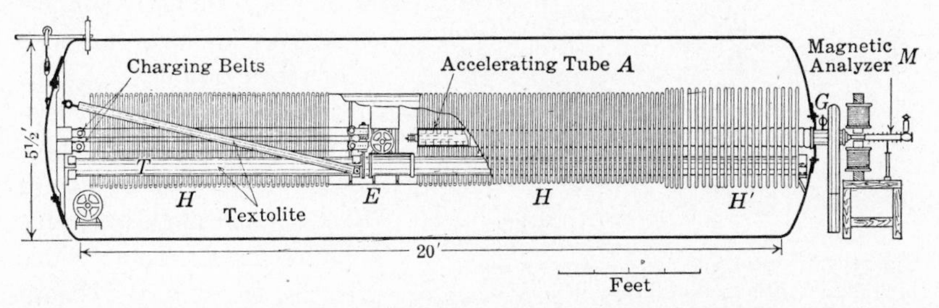

FIG. 7. Schematic diagram of Herb's pressure electrostatic generator. The hoops *H* ensure a uniform potential distribution along the length of the accelerating tube, on the one hand, and the charging belts on the other. This equipment is cheap and compact, and can develop about 2.5 million volts.

which usually serves as a high-potential electrode is replaced by the metal cylinder *E* which is supported on the "textolite" cylinder *T*. The hoops *H* are of aluminum tubing spaced $\frac{9}{16}$ inch apart. These hoops permit the flow of a small leakage current from the high-voltage electrode *E*, thus ensuring a uniform potential gradient from *E* to ground and discouraging sparking to the wall of the tank. The electrode is charged by the system of belts illustrated. The accelerating tube is of conventional design. At atmospheric pressure the highest working voltage with this apparatus is about 500 kilovolts. However, at 8 atmospheres air pressure the usable voltage is 2.1 Mev. Later investigations have shown that even larger voltages (2.4 Mev) are obtainable when CCl_4 or CCl_2F_2 vapor is introduced into the tank.

By using three separate high-voltage electrodes, and various other improvements, Herb, Turner, Hudson, and Warren have recently been able to push the voltage attained as high as 4 million, in apparatus contained in a very modest basement research room. The final development of this form of acceleration has not yet been reached; probably 10-Mev particles will be obtainable in this way.

Voltage-Multiplication Methods. Parallel with the development of belt accelerators has been the scheme first used by Cockcroft and Walton in England for obtaining high voltages. With their machine they were the first to produce a transmutation with artificially accelerated particles. Their method depends on the process known as voltage multiplication, first worked out by Greinacher. The basic idea whereby this may be accomplished can be understood from Fig. 8. Suppose that the battery supplies a voltage V. C_1 is connected across the supply and is always charged to a potential difference V. Now, by throwing the double-pole switch to the left, C_2 is placed across the

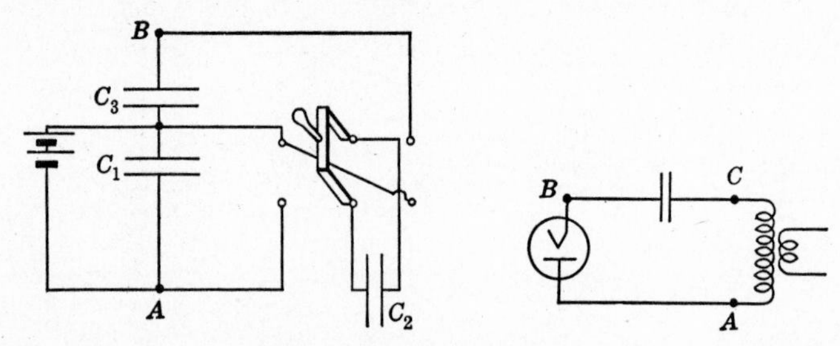

FIGS. 8 and 9. The principle of voltage multiplication. By successively throwing the switch from left to right the voltage across AB can be built up to double that of the battery.

supply and is also charged to a potential difference V. Throwing the switch now to the right will connect C_2 and C_3 in parallel. Almost immediately C_2 will divide its charge with C_3, and if $C_3 = C_2$ the common voltage across them will be $V/2$. Note that C_3 is charged in such a direction that the voltage across AB will be the numerical sum of that across C_1 and C_3. After the first charging of C_3 the voltage across AB is $3/2V$. Again the switch is thrown to the left, and again C_2 attains a potential difference V. On switching to the right C_3 is now charged to a potential difference $\frac{3}{4}V$. Now the potential difference between A and B is $1\frac{3}{4}V$. After repeating this procedure a number of times the voltage across AB will, for all practical purposes, be equal to $2V$.

This method, though quite simple, is not practicable where the final voltage must be of the order of a million volts and where current must be supplied by the output. The method actually adopted by Cockcroft and Walton utilized, instead of a battery, a transformer with an output voltage of 200,000 volts. Instead of mechanical switches, large thermionic diodes were employed. Their completed apparatus was capable of quadrupling the voltage supplied by the transformer, and furthermore the final voltage was steady, not alternating.

To understand the actual arrangement consider the circuit of Fig. 9. Assume that the transformer supplies a peak voltage E. When A is at the positive peak of a cycle the diode becomes conducting and the condenser is charged, B coming to the same potential as A, that is, $+E$ relative to C. On the subsequent half cycle A drops to a potential $-E$ below that of C, and hence across AB there is a momentary voltage difference of $2E$. After still another half-cycle A and B return to the same potential. Thus the voltage across AB varies between zero and

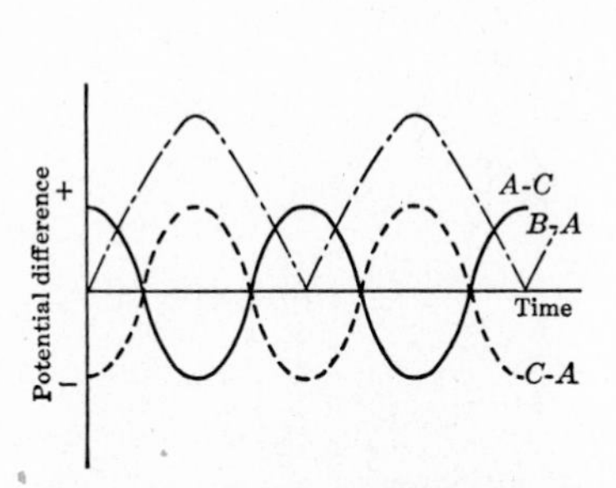

FIG. 10. Graphs showing the variation of potential difference between various points of the circuit of Fig. 9. The potential drop across the rectifier can reach double that given by the transformer.

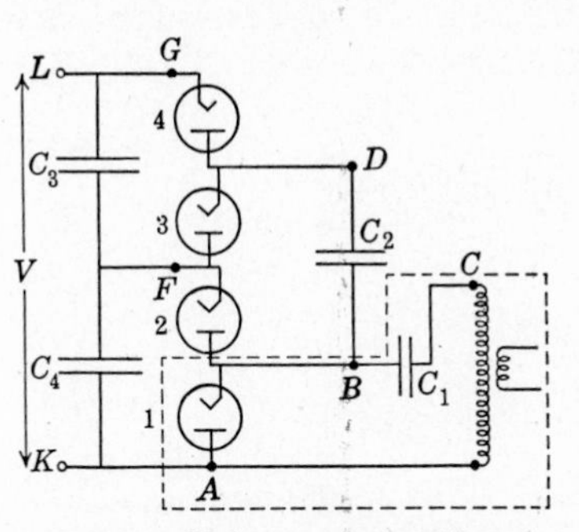

FIG. 11. Voltage quadrupling circuit employed by Cockcroft and Walton.

$2E$. Graphically, what happens to the voltage across AC, BA, and CA as time progresses is plotted in Fig. 10.

To complete the picture additional apparatus is needed as shown in Fig. 11. The broken line isolates the unit we have just discussed. As the voltage across BA approaches $2E$ the plate of diode 2 is at a much higher potential than the filament (the filament is originally at the same potential as A) and hence it conducts, the condenser C_1 sharing its charge with C_4, and the potential of B and F both reach a value E above A. Now as the cycle proceeds (see graph) the potential at B becomes less as referred to A, and D likewise becomes less. This means that F is at a higher potential than D and as a result diode 3 becomes conducting, C_4 thus sharing its charge with C_2 until both F and D are at the same potential. This is the state of affairs until the potential difference across BA begins to rise again on the next cycle. Consequently the potential of D relative to A also rises since the potential of D is the potential difference across C_2 plus that across BA. Since the potential of F relative to A does not change at the moment, and furthermore since F and G are at the same potential, it is clear that the potential of D will rise above that of G and cause C_2 to share charge with C_3 through diode 4. This is the fundamental process involving the transfer of charge from one condenser to the next, and it is repeated over and over again. Since C_4 retains part of the charge given it on the first cycle by C_1, when diode 2 again becomes conducting the charge transferred will put F at a higher potential than it was after the previous cycle. Obviously, if no losses are present, after several cycles an equilibrium condition is reached and the potential across C_4 will approach $2E$. A similar statement holds for C_2 and C_3,

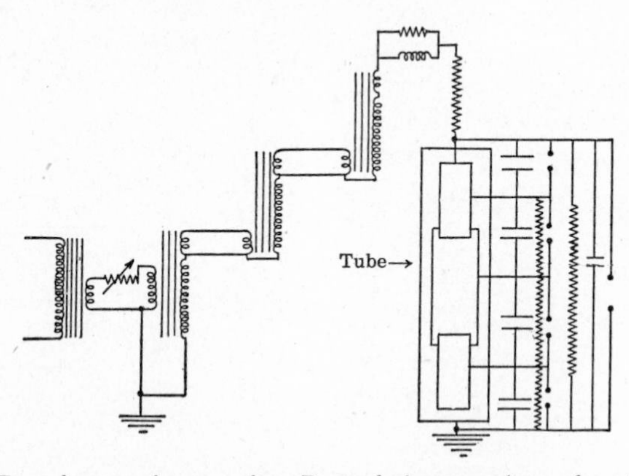

FIG. 12. Transformers in cascade. Part of the secondary of each transformer operates the primary of the next, until high voltages are built up. The tube is in three sections with the voltage applied from a divider as shown.

and hence across KL will be developed a voltage $4E$. If a load is drawn the voltage will be somewhat less than $4E$ by an amount depending on both the magnitude of the load and the capacity of the condensers used. At high voltages there is always a certain amount of corona loss, and of course a slight amount of power is needed for accelerating the ions. Cockcroft and Walton found that the current drawn from the rectifiers was slightly greater than half a milliampere. The actual voltage multiplication in their installation was found to vary between 3 and 4. To complete the apparatus an accelerating tube similar to the one described previously is connected across KL.

Early in the game of atom-smashing Lauritsen and his associates modified a high-voltage x-ray installation at the California Institute of Technology to serve as an ion accelerator. The essentials of this machine are shown in Fig. 12. Four transformers are linked in cascade as indicated, a portion of each secondary exciting the primary of the following stage. Thus the secondary of each transformer operates at a root mean square (rms) voltage of 250,000 above that of the preceding stage. This means that the fourth transformer will be raised to a potential 1,000,000 volts above ground. Notice that the successive stages require increasingly greater insulation with respect to ground to prevent breakdowns. The voltage is applied to the accelerating tube in four stages as shown. This assists focusing and permits the use of a longer tube, which is less liable to insulation breakdown. The one major disadvantage with this arrangement is that the voltage is not constant but alternates between 1,000,000 volts positive and negative. Consequently, positive ions will be accelerated only during the positive half-cycle and not all of them will have the full million electron volts of energy. This means a lower efficiency for transmutations than would result from an equal number of ions accelerated in a 1,000,000-volt constant-voltage apparatus. In addition to this, any electrons present in the free state will be accelerated throughout the negative part of the cycle, and these on striking the target will give rise to penetrating x-rays which can prove quite troublesome. Nevertheless, many valuable experiments have been carried out with this apparatus, and it seems especially suited to work involving a Wilson cloud chamber. Crane has completed a similar installation at the University of Michigan. He uses a shutter in front of the target, controlled so as to open only during the peak of the positive voltage cycle, thus obtaining bombardments by ions of the maximum energy only.

Apparatus for Producing High-Energy Ions without High Voltages. Perhaps the above heading sounds somewhat incongruous. If so, please recall that all the accelerators discussed so far have been of the direct type. By this we mean that the final voltage given the ion is equal to that generated by the apparatus. Several methods have been suggested whereby a large resultant ion voltage might be obtained by successive applications of a much smaller voltage. Inasmuch as such a scheme would eliminate most of the serious insulation difficulties present in all direct-type installations the method has much to recommend it. The simplest type of apparatus utilizing this method is the linear multiple accelerator, first demonstrated by Wideroe and developed in America by Sloan and Lawrence. The name aptly describes the operation of the apparatus.

The main features are shown schematically in Fig. 13. By means of a fixed potential E_0, ions formed at S are drawn into the first of several coaxial cylinders, which are enclosed in an evacuated container. Alternate cylinders are connected to the ends of a coil which is inductively coupled to the tank circuit of a high-frequency oscillator. An alternating potential of several thousand volts is thus produced across the gap between the cylinders. The ions present in the first gap during a favorable half-cycle will be accelerated across the gap. By choosing proper values of potential, cylinder length and spacing, and oscillator frequency, the ions can be made to pass through successive gaps at the proper moment to receive additional accelerations, each of which adds an increment of energy to the ions. As the particles gain in velocity it is obviously necessary that the successive gaps be spaced a correspondingly greater distance apart.

The great disadvantage of this apparatus is that, with the radiofrequencies currently obtainable, unreasonably long tubes would be

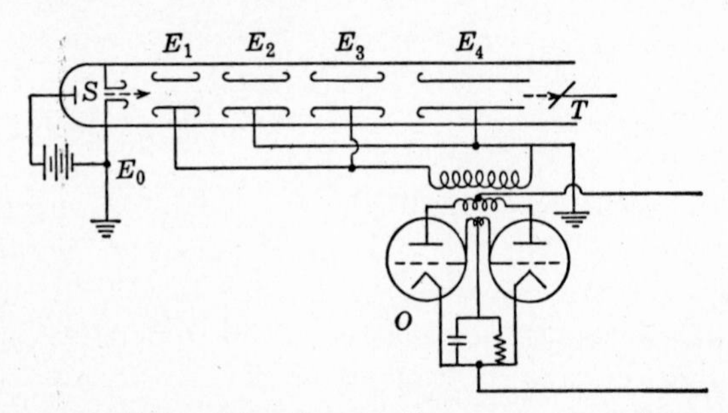

FIG. 13. Linear multiple accelerator. In this apparatus a radiofrequency voltage is impressed on alternate cylinders, whose lengths are carefully adjusted. An ion which is accelerated from E_0 to the first cylinder is also accelerated in the next gap, since the time of transit of the first cylinder is just that of a half-cycle. The equipment becomes too long and requires too much power for the development of voltages in excess of a million.

needed to produce light ions of energies in excess of a million electron volts. By using 36 accelerating cylinders Sloan and Coates were able to obtain singly charged mercury ions of almost 3 Mev, although the ion currents were very small. Such heavy atoms are not efficient in causing transmutations since in a collision with a nucleus a large portion of the energy is spent in setting the target nucleus in motion and thus only a small fraction is available for transmutation.

The development of a similar apparatus has been undertaken with some degree of success by Beams and his co-workers at the University of Virginia. However, instead of a high-frequency oscillator, Beams energizes his cylinders with a voltage sent along a loaded transmission line, the cylinders being attached to the line at points such that the voltage surge and the ions will progress at the same velocity.

The Cyclotron. The most ingenious and satisfactory device employing the principle of multiple accelerations is the *cyclotron*, the invention of Lawrence of the University of California. For this work he was awarded the Nobel prize in physics for 1940. Deuterons of 17 Mev and alpha particles of 34 Mev, by far the most energetic particles yet accelerated artificially, have been produced with his latest machine. It is almost certain that the mammoth new cyclotron now under construction at Berkeley will produce ions with energies in excess of 100 Mev. The heart of the cyclotron consists of a large circular vacuum chamber, inside which are placed two hollow semicircular elec-

FIG. 14. View of the vacuum chamber of the Berkeley 37-inch cyclotron. (Photograph by Dr. D. Cooksey.)

trodes called "dees" because each is shaped like a capital D. These dees are situated with their straight edges about an inch apart, the unit forming an approximate circle when viewed from above. Figure 14 shows a view of the chamber. The dees are coupled to a powerful source of radiofrequency current, usually through the intermediary of a coupling link called a quarter-wave line. This line matches the impedance of the radiofrequency output to that of the dees, thus permitting optimum power transfer. The dees form the high-voltage end of the quarterwave line.

In the center of the vacuum chamber, below and between the two dees, is mounted a tungsten filament, to furnish electrons for the purpose of ionizing the gas in the chamber. The whole chamber is placed between the pole faces of a large electromagnet capable of producing a field in the neighborhood of 16,000 gauss.

The operation is as follows:

The chamber is evacuated to a pressure of approximately 10^{-6} mm of mercury by several stages of diffusion pumping, backed by a mechanical roughing pump. Gas of the atoms to be accelerated is then allowed to flow into the cylinder until the pressure rises to about 10^{-4} mm of mercury. Electrons from the filament are compelled by the magnetic field to travel in tight helices to a water-cooled copper block situated just above the dees and directly over the filament. These electrons may be driven off the filament by floating it at several hundred volts negative potential. In the upward passage the electrons ionize the atoms of the gas by collision, thus forming a cone of ions in the center of the chamber. Let us focus our attention on one of these ions at the moment it is formed and follow its subsequent motion.

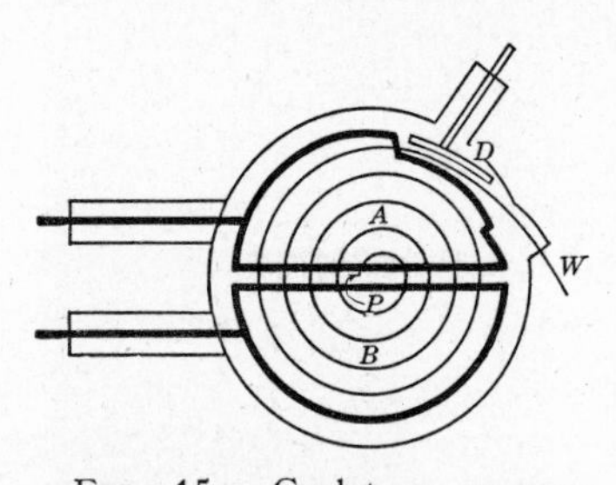

FIG. 15. Cyclotron vacuum chamber. The ion, starting at P, follows a spiral path under the influence of successive accelerations across the gap between A and B, the two dees, and a magnetic field perpendicular to the plane of the motion. It is deflected by the deflector plate D and can emerge through a window W.

Assume that, at the moment it is formed at P (Fig. 15), dee A is at the negative voltage peak of the radiofrequency cycle and hence dee B at the positive voltage peak. The ion, being positively charged, will be drawn over to A and will pass into the hollow interior, acquiring a small velocity. It is a fact that the interior of a charged conductor is a region of field-free space. This follows from the result we reached previously; namely, that no charge can reside on the interior of a conductor. If there is no charge inside, no lines of electrical force can originate or end there, and the above statement is obviously correct. So, once inside the dee, the ion is unaware of the charge or change of charge on that dee. However, the magnetic field *does* act on the ion, exerting a force on it at right angles to its direction of motion. The mathematically minded reader will immediately see that this force will result in the ion moving in a circular path, and it does. If, by the time the ion has completed a semicircle, the dees have reversed charge, the ion will again be accelerated across the gap and enter the interior of B. Each time it passes from within one dee to the other the ion gains an increment of kinetic energy equal to its charge multiplied by the voltage difference between the two dees. This difference may be as high as 250,000 volts at the peak of the cycle. For successful operation of the supercyclotron under construction at Berkeley, the voltage difference must be about a million.

One may calculate the radius of the path at any moment by equating the magnetic force on the ion to the mass times acceleration. In cgs units the force can be shown to be equal to Hev [1], while the mass times acceleration is mv^2/r [2]. Here

H is magnetic field strength (electromagnetic units).
e is effective charge on the ion (electromagnetic units).
v is linear velocity of ion.
r is radius of curvature of ion path.
m is mass of ion.

Since by definition the angular velocity ω is v/r, the mass times acceleration can be expressed by the equivalent form $m\omega^2 r$ [3]. Combining equations 1, 2, and 3 we find:

$$r = \frac{mv}{eH} \qquad [4]$$

$$\omega = \frac{eH}{m} \qquad [5]$$

The whole fundamental theory of the cyclotron is contained in equations 4 and 5. From 4 we observe that, the greater the velocity, the greater the radius of path the ion traverses. Thus as the ion gains energy (and consequently velocity, since K.E. $= \frac{1}{2}mv^2$) through continued accelerations between dees it travels in ever-widening circles until it reaches the exit slit in dee A where it is pulled to one side by a deflector plate D charged to a negative potential of 50,000 volts or so Furthermore equation 4 tells us that, since all ions passing through the deflecting system have the same radius, they have the same velocity (assuming m and e the same for all) and consequently the same energy. This implies that the beam of ions will be homogeneous in energy.

Equation 5 tells us that the angular velocity of the ions is independent of the linear velocity. In other words, *the ion requires the same time to complete one revolution whether moving near the center of the chamber or close to the periphery.* This rather unexpected result means that, if the magnetic field is adjusted so that the ion returns to the dee gap on its initial half-circle to find the charges on the dees reversed, it will continue to do so for each succeeding half-circle. Physically this condition that the time of one revolution be the same, no matter what the diameter of circle, can be understood by realizing that, the faster an ion travels, the farther it must go to complete the circle of greater radius. When the time for one half-circle is the same as that for one half-cycle, the condition is spoken of as *resonance.*

In Fig. 16 the solid line represents the variation of the radiofrequency voltage with time on dee B, the dotted line that on dee A. A singly charged ion formed near dee B at time 1 will have 50,000 electron volts of energy after its first acceleration and, if the magnetic field is in resonance, will pass across the gap next at time 1′, thus gaining an additional 50,000-electron-volt increment. If the dimensions of the cyclotron chamber and the magnetic field used are such that the emerging ions have an energy of 5 Mev an ion formed at time 1 will make 50 complete circles (two accelerations per revolution) in the chamber before emerging. On the other hand an ion formed at time 2 receives energy increments in quanta of only 25,000 volts since this represents the difference in potential of the dees when it crosses the gap at 2, 2′, 2″, etc. Hence it will have to make 100 revolutions before reaching the exit slit.

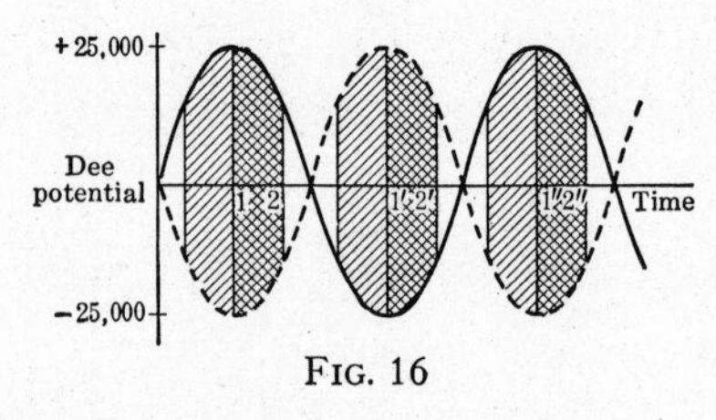

FIG. 16

Now an ion starting out from the center is in constant danger of colliding with a molecule of the gas in the chamber and thereby being lost to the beam. The greater the number of revolutions necessary for the ion to attain its final energy the greater the total distance it must travel and consequently the more likely it is to suffer a collision. In fact, for all practical purposes it may be safely assumed that no ion making more than 150 revolutions will reach the exit slit in a cyclotron of medium size. On the above basis this requires that only those ions formed when the voltage difference between dees is 17,000 and greater will be found in the final beam. Thus only ions formed during the shaded part of a cycle will reach the bombardment chamber. Consequently the particles in the final beam will come, not as a steady stream, but in a series of bursts. However, inasmuch as there will be two bursts of particles for every radiofrequency cycle, the beam current will effectively be a constant flow (20,000,000 bursts of beam per second), assuming an oscillator frequency of 10 megacycles.

Two rule-of-thumb formulas, as given by Professor F. N. D. Kurie, allow one to determine quickly the energies obtainable for the various particles in terms of the dimensions of the apparatus and working figures. These are:

$$H\lambda = K \quad [6]$$

$$E = \frac{CR^2}{\lambda^2} \quad [7]$$

	C	K
For deuterons	24	394
For alpha particles	48	394
For protons	12	187

H is the magnetic field measured in kilogauss.
λ is the wavelength of the oscillator in meters.
R is the final ion radius of curvature in inches.
E is the ion energy in Mev.

Since the electrostatic capacity of the dees is settled in the design, the shortest wavelength to which the dee system will tune is inherently fixed. Equation 6 then permits a calculation of the magnetic field necessary for resonance at this shortest wavelength. Clearly this is the maximum field value which can be utilized.

Because the exit slit is a path distance of more than 50 meters from the point where the ions are formed, at first sight it might seem as though only a small fraction of those starting out could survive such severe solid angle limitations. However, two happy circumstances prevent this fact from having more than a slightly destructive effect. The first of these, electrostatic focusing, is identical to that present in an ordinary accelerating tube which was discussed previously.

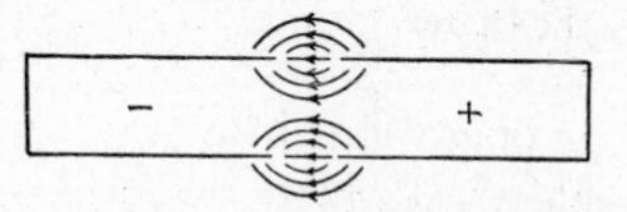

FIG. 17. Electrostatic focusing in the cyclotron. As the ion crosses the gap it gains speed and hence spends less time in the neighborhood of the gap. This means that the electrostatic force tending to drive the ion in to the median plane before acceleration is more effective than that tending to drive it away after acceleration. This produces a net focusing effect which is operative in the early stages of acceleration.

In Fig. 17 the curvature of the electrical lines of force tend to turn "off-center" ions toward the median plane over the first half of the dee gap and away from the median plane over the latter half. However, as we saw before, the net effect is toward the center, owing to the shorter time of action of the defocusing effect. It is clear that ions entering the gap while the voltage difference between dees is increasing will be acted on by a larger electric field during the latter half of the path across the gap than during the initial half. Thus the defocusing action may actually surpass the focusing effect in spite of the greater velocity of the ion. As a result we must amend our previous remark to read that only ions accelerated during the cross-hatched part of the radiofrequency cycle (Fig. 16) will be favored in reaching the exit slit.

As the amount of electrostatic focusing is proportional to the ratio of the velocity across the first half of the gap to that across the second half, and as the energy increment is constant, this type of focusing will lose its effectiveness after a dozen or more revolutions of the ion. During the later revolutions magnetic focusing is mainly responsible for converging the beam. This phenomenon may be understood by the aid of Fig. 18. The magnetic lines of force between the pole faces are shown. Toward the periphery the field has a sizable horizontal component. Above the median plane this horizontal component is directed inward; below, it is outward. By the motor rule it is clear that an ion moving clockwise as seen from above and either above or below the median plane will be forced back toward the middle by this horizontal field component. Although smaller in actual magnitude, magnetic focusing probably has a greater total effect than its electrostatic counterpart, since it is in operation throughout the whole circular path of the ion, whereas the electrostatic is operative only in the gap between the dees. So effective is the focusing in a cyclotron that the beam, after passing through the deflecting system, usually covers an area of not more than 1 sq cm.

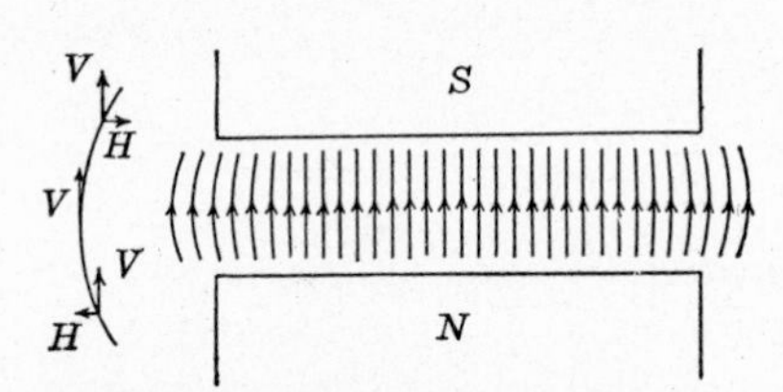

FIG. 18. Magnetic focusing in the cyclotron. The curvature of the field near the edges of the pole pieces means the existence of components of the field in the horizontal plane as shown. These components tend to keep the beam in the center.

This feature of magnetic focusing, though a great aid for beams of average and low energies, begins to be rather troublesome as soon as very energetic beams are envisaged. This is on account of the change in mass of the particle as its velocity becomes great. Thus while a deuteron of 1-Mev energy has an increase of mass over the rest mass of 1 per cent or so, a 100-Mev deuteron has a mass 10 per cent greater than its rest mass. A glance at equation 4 shows that, if we keep the frequency of rotation fixed, the magnetic field must increase as the ion travels outward. There is no great difficulty in securing this condition experimentally, but when it is secured the favorable condition of magnetic focusing is lost, for the horizontal components become reversed and the beam is defocused. At one time, when it was thought to be impossible to obtain large voltages between the dees, this fact was held to set an upper limit to the energies attainable by the cyclotron. The limit was set at about 8 Mev for deuterons. Almost before the ink was dry on the paper describing the reasons for this limit, the experimentally attained energy exceeded the predicted limit. At present the Crocker laboratory beam is about double the limit originally set. Although it is pleasant to find the gloomy predictions of theory unnecessarily dark, it must be remembered that the reasons advanced for a limiting energy are valid and they can be overcome only by using very large voltages between the dees and reducing the need for focusing of the beam. The satisfactory operation of a high-energy cyclotron is therefore bound up closely with excellent radio-frequency engineering.

A word can be added here about ion sources for the cyclotron. The first cyclotrons employed the simple filament bombardment method that we have described already, whereby most of the center of the cyclotron acts as the ion source. Such cyclotrons suffer because there is a great deal of "wild beam," i.e., beam which starts at an unfortunate point in the cyclotron and is accelerated only part way. The efficiency of such cyclotrons is low, although it is possible to use some of this wild beam by inserting probes. Livingston at Cornell first worked out the idea of an arc source of ions. A cone-shaped region is placed above the filament, filled with gas at about 100 times the pressure of the cyclotron chamber. An arc is caused in this space, and ions are allowed to emerge between the dees through a capillary. With such an ion source currents as high as 300 microamperes have been reported. Such beams represent about 5 kilowatts of power and make the cyclotron an extremely powerful tool for nuclear investigations and the preparation of radioactive sources. It is, to date, our nearest approach to the "philosopher's stone."

The Acceleration of Electrons. So far we have made no mention of the acceleration of electrons. On second thought, this fact may one day date this book more than any other feature. The reason for the apparent lack of interest in electrons is twofold. First, fast electrons, electrons with energies great enough to be interesting, are hard to produce, and second, transmutations by the heavier particles (neutrons and protons, or as it has been suggested "nucleons") have been so prolific and have provided so rich a field for research that the electron has been neglected. Actually any atom smasher that accelerates directly can be employed to give electrons of the full energy. These electrons produce very penetrating x-rays, and one by-product of atom-smasher development has been to permit the design of small x-ray equipment emitting hard x-rays for therapeutic purposes. What we would like, however, is a supply of 50-Mev electrons, and they can hardly be provided by direct acceleration.

Almost everyone who first thinks about the cyclotron asks why it cannot be used for electrons. The answer comprises two reasons. The first is the extremely high frequencies of radiofrequency power occasioned by the relatively small mass of the electron. The second is the fact that the mass of the electron is not a constant at high energies but its velocity is almost a constant. The fundamental resonance condition of the cyclotron is therefore not present for electrons. The method of Beams mentioned previously could be applied to electrons, but the effect of a transmission line on a sharp wave front is to diminish the sharpness and the electrons produced are few in number and inhomogeneous in energy. Until 1940 no successful method of multiple acceleration of electrons had been devised. In 1940 Kerst produced promising results from a device which we here describe.

A number of people have speculated upon the use of the force exerted on an electron in a changing magnetic field to accelerate the electron to great energies. Among these are Breit and Tuve, Wideröe, and Walton. The idea can be explained as follows. Suppose that we have an iron cylinder which can be magnetized by a coil of wire. Assume a copper ring enclosing the cylinder, and imagine the field increasing. Everyone is familiar with the fact that an electromotive force is set up in the copper which causes a current to flow; such an induced current is quite commonplace. Now imagine the copper ring replaced by a frictionless tube into which an electron could be introduced while the field is increasing. This electron experiences a force; in fact, it is such a force that is the basic cause of the electromotive force causing the current in the wire, and this force causes the electron to be accelerated. Now it will not matter how fast the electron is moving, or where it is; provided that it remains at the same radius from the cylinder, the force will persist. The force depends on the magnitude and rate of change of the magnetic field at the region occupied by the electron.

Suppose now that the magnetic field has a uniform rate of change for $\frac{1}{1000}$ second—a short interval of time. Suppose also, to make the matter definite, that the electric field strength exerted on the electron while the magnetic field is changing is 1 volt per centimeter. This is $\frac{1}{300}$ electrostatic unit of electric field, so that the electron experiences a *force* of $e/300$ dyne. This produces an acceleration of $e/300m$ cm per second per second, which the reader can easily verify for himself is of the order of 10^{15} cm per second per second. In $\frac{1}{1000}$ second the electron is thus readily accelerated beyond the velocity of light, if its mass remains unaltered. Actually it is well known that as the velocity approaches that of light the mass of the electron increases, so that as a rough approximation we can suppose that the electron is quickly accelerated to very nearly the velocity of light and stays at that figure for most of the $\frac{1}{1000}$ second. It will therefore travel approximately $3 \times 10^{10}/1000$ cm in the time we are considering, and this is 3×10^7 cm. Now an electron which falls this very considerable distance in a field of 1 volt per centimeter will acquire the very large kinetic energy corresponding to the charge times the field times the distance traveled, which is easily seen to be 30,000,000 electron volts. If, then, this kind of trick can be worked, the rewards will be considerable; it remains to exert a little ingenuity.

If the reader is acute he will see that ingenuity is needed to solve two problems. The first is the obvious one of the frictionless tube; the second is the problem of focusing. In the cyclotron where the ions traveled about 50 meters we pointed out the need for focusing; here we have a distance of 300,000 meters under consideration. Both these problems must be solved or the "induction accelerator" will be useless. The first is not so bad, because we know that an electron will move in a circular path in a magnetic field; all that we need is to find such a field that an electron will move in the *same* circular path while the magnetic field changes. Thus if we use electrostatic units for the charge on the electron the cyclotron equation (4) becomes

$$mv = \frac{Hre}{c} \qquad [8]$$

and if ϕ is the magnetic flux enclosed by the circular path, the tangential electric field is

$$E = \frac{\dot{\phi}}{2\pi rc} \qquad [9]$$

Now in all these considerations we must remember that the mass of the electron is not constant; that (mv), the momentum, involves both quantities as variables. If we remember this and write the momentum as p, then the second law of motion gives us

$$\dot{p} = \frac{e\dot{\phi}}{2\pi rc}$$

from which we deduce that, if in a certain time interval the flux enclosed changes from ϕ_1 to ϕ, the momentum developed will be

$$p - p_1 = \frac{e(\phi - \phi_1)}{2\pi rc} \qquad [10]$$

which combined with [8] gives us

$$H - H_1 = \frac{\phi - \phi_1}{2\pi r^2} \tag{11}$$

Now if we consider the flux due to a *uniform* magnetic field H spread over the area of the orbit, and call it A, we can write equation 11 as

$$A - A_1 = \frac{\phi - \phi_1}{2}$$

which means that the magnetic field at the orbit must be much weaker than the magnetic field at some point inside the orbit. The weak field

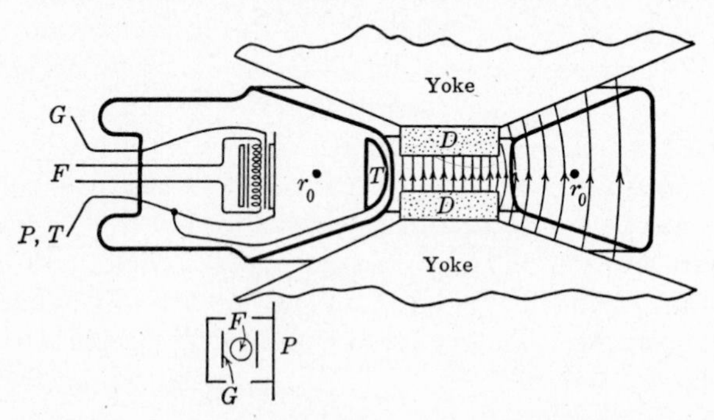

FIG. 19. The induction accelerator. Electrons are injected from a simple type of "gun" into the vacuum, which is of doughnut shape and situated in a magnetic field carefully designed for focusing. The force on the electron due to the alternation of the magnetic flux 600 times per second accelerates it until it acquires very great energy. The fact that the pole pieces DD are of dust means that they saturate early, and the beam then spirals on to the target. Over 2 Mev electrons can be produced in a very compact apparatus.

holds the orbit in its place; the strong field supplies the flux to give the correct acceleration. This condition can be fulfilled.

The problem of focusing is harder to solve. It turns out that there is a tendency for the electron to follow a path which executes a *damped* oscillation about this stable circular path, provided that the magnetic field diminishes with radius according to $H \sim 1/r^n$, where n lies between $\frac{1}{2}$ and 1.

The focusing conditions were worked out by Kerst and Serber; guided by these, Kerst constructed a doughnut-shaped vacuum chamber as illustrated in Fig. 19. The electrons are injected into the vacuum chamber from a "gun" of the type familiar in beam power tubes. The schematic structure of the gun is shown in the small figure: the filament is a spiral; the plate P is shaped as shown, and the "grid" G consists of two plates placed as drawn, which concentrate the electrons into a definite beam. The electrons then experience the influence of the varying magnetic field and go into the equilibrium orbit at r_0. There they acquire the energy due to their fall in the accelerating induction field. In order to allow the bombarding of a target the designers use, in their own terms, one of several obvious methods. This "obvious" method is the ingenious idea of making the pole pieces of iron *dust*. The dust is a mixture of air and iron, and therefore the external magnetic field when the iron is saturated is not so high as for solid iron. The field near the pole pieces therefore rapidly reaches a maximum value, while the field further out continues to increase. However, the accelerator is effective only when the whole of the field is increasing, so that, after the center saturates, the increased edge field causes an inward spiraling of the beam on to a target at T.

In order to obtain the varying magnetic field the copper windings of the magnet are made the inductive part of a resonant circuit; that is, a capacitance is connected across the windings. To maintain the oscillating current power is fed in from a 600-cycle generator through a transformer.

With the first experimental version of this accelerator a small beam of 2.3-Mev electrons was obtained. These electrons generated x-rays equivalent in amount and penetrating power to about 1 curie of radium. A larger improved version has delivered electrons of energy up to 20 Mev and much greater currents. The fact that the whole equipment is easily installed on a bench indicates that it is a miracle of compactness. It is not inherently expensive and should find a place in most laboratories engaged in nuclear physics, after it has been developed a little further.

Summary. In this chapter we have described the standard methods for acceleration of nuclear particles. These include electrostatic methods, voltage-multiplication methods, the cyclotron, and the induction accelerator for the acceleration of electrons.

REFERENCES

M. S. Livingston and H. A. Bethe, "Nuclear Dynamics, Experimental," *Rev. Mod. Phys.*, **9**, 247, 1937. This contains a short review of the methods of acceleration.

J. D. Cockcroft and E. T. S. Walton, *Proc. Roy. Soc.*, **136**, 619, 1932. An account of their acceleration apparatus.

L. C. Van Atta, D. L. Northrup, R. J. Van de Graaff, and C. M. Van Atta, "Electrostatic Generator for Nuclear Research at M.I.T.," *Rev. Sci. Instruments*, **12**, 534, 1941.

R. G. Herb, D. B. Parkinson and D. W. Kerst, "Development and Performance of an Electrostatic Generator Operating under High Pressures," *Phys. Rev.*, **51**, 75, 1937.

R. G. Herb, C. M. Turner, C. M. Hudson, and R. E. Warren, "Electrostatic Generator with Concentric Electrodes," *Phys. Rev.*, **58**, 519, 1940.

W. B. Mann, *The Cyclotron*, Chemical Publishing Company, New York, 1940. An interesting and well-written account with references.

F. N. D. Kurie, *J. Applied Physics*, **9**, 691, 1938; E. O. Lawrence and D. Cooksey, *Phys. Rev.*, **50**, 1131, 1936. Two important papers on the cyclotron. It is rather to be regretted that the generous personal distribution of information from Berkeley to those engaged in cyclotron construction has not been put on permanent record in book form.

D. W. Kerst, "Acceleration of Electrons by Magnetic Induction," *Phys. Rev.*, **60**, 47, 1941; also "New Induction Accelerator Generating 20 Mev," *Phys. Rev.*, **61**, 93, 1942.

CHAPTER 5

TRANSMUTATION

Today nearly a thousand nuclear reactions are known, an astonishing development since the first artificially induced nuclear reaction in 1919. The long-awaited flower of alchemy has broken into full blossom in two decades. This abundance of reactions calls for some systematization, correlation, and explanation; in fact, it calls for the development of the new subject of nuclear chemistry, and in this chapter we intend to present the rudiments of that subject.

In the first chapter we introduced the idea of transmutation and illustrated it by describing some of the pioneer work of Rutherford, Blackett, Chadwick, Curie, and Joliot, who employed natural radioactive sources to provide bombarding projectiles. The technique of artificial acceleration described in the fourth chapter has put transmutation on a totally different plane, for now in place of alpha particles as primary bombarding agencies we have protons, deuterons, and neutrons available in overwhelmingly greater numbers. It is not surprising that so many new transmutations have been discovered in so short a time. We intend to discuss transmutations by all these particles, as well as by neutrons and gamma rays, but first we propose to consider a feature of nuclear reactions common to all, and of the greatest importance, namely, *energy relationships in reactions.*

Suppose that we write a reaction in ordinary chemistry:

$$2H_2 + O_2 \rightarrow 2H_2O$$

The chemist is not content until he can add to this equation a term expressing the gain or loss of heat in the process, the "heat of reaction." Such an equation then reads:

$$2H_2 + O_2 \rightarrow 2H_2O + 136{,}000 \text{ calories}$$

which means that when two gram molecules of hydrogen and one of oxygen combine with water as the final product 136,000 calories are evolved. Heat may also be absorbed, and the evolution or absorption of heat is described by the self-explanatory terms exothermic or endothermic reaction. If a chemical reaction is exothermic the temperature of the molecules rises; if endothermic, the heat needed is supplied from the molecules by their fall in temperature. Temperature in turn means the energy of motion of the molecules. Now in the same way we may write an equation:

$$_3Li^7 + _1H^1 \rightarrow 2_2He^4$$

which refers to the bombardment of lithium by protons with the evolution of helium. Like the chemist we are still not satisfied until we add a term analogous to the heat of reaction, a term called (for want of a better) "nuclear energy change," and universally represented by the symbol Q. This representation has become so widely accepted that "nuclear energy change" and "Q value" are synonymous. The equation then reads

$$_3Li^7 + _1H^1 \rightarrow 2_2He^4 + Q \quad \text{(Mev)}$$

and again we keep the terms exothermic or endothermic for reactions in which Q is positive or negative, respectively.

Let us now suppose that Q is positive, or that in the reaction energy is released. Why is there this release of energy, and where is the seat of the energy whence it came? The answer is similar to the answer in chemistry. The new product is more stable than the two former constituents separately; the particles are more tightly bound together, and this means that in lithium and hydrogen separately we have a surplus of energy over the combination to form two helium nuclei. The nuclei of lithium and hydrogen are supplied by nature with energy to spare—*why* we have yet to discover, but it is so—and our setting off the reaction has liberated the energy that was already available. The energy liberated in a large Q value is the "atomic energy" that has been discussed so much in popular literature since 1920.

Balance Sheet of Mass and Energy. The reason why "atomic-energy release" is so sensational a subject is the enormous magnitude involved as soon as we consider these nuclear reactions in terms of their chemical analogues. Thus, when 4 grams of hydrogen and 32 of oxygen combine, 136,000 calories, a fair amount, is released. Yet the combination of 7 grams of lithium and 1 of hydrogen would release roughly 5 billion calories, a stupendously greater amount.* This greater release of energy per atom gives the physicist a head start on

* We should like to make it clear that the passage from nuclear reactions to their chemical prototypes should not be thought of. Chemistry is a statistical process of reactions which can go at ordinary temperatures. If temperature alone were to start nuclear reactions such as those mentioned here, millions of degrees would be needed. Possibly the centers of stars are hot enough, but not man-made materials.

the chemist, for it means that he can, by a physical measurement to be described, *predict* the energy change in any reaction whatever. He can, for example, predict that the reaction:

$$_{6}C^{12} + {}_{2}He^{4} \rightarrow {}_{7}N^{15} + {}_{1}H^{1} + Q$$

will have a large negative Q value and hence will not proceed unless the bombarding alpha particles (He^4) are extremely energetic. This physical measurement is simply *the mass of each of the atoms concerned.* According to the theory of relativity there is a relation between the mass a body possesses and its energy; to the ordinary energy must be added the quantity mc^2, where m is the mass and c is the velocity of light. Ordinarily this term appears equally before and after some change and so may be subtracted out or not even included, but where there is a heavy release of energy in a nuclear reaction *the release is at the expense of mass* and linked to it by the equivalence relation:

$$E = mc^2$$

In the years from 1922 to the present day, physicists, notably Aston, Bainbridge, and Dempster, have developed methods of measuring atomic masses with great refinement. Thus it is well known that the atomic weights of most elements are not whole numbers, a fact partially accounted for by the simultaneous presence of isotopes of different atomic weight in the same element. The entire deviation from whole numbers is not due to this cause, for accurate measurements show, for example, that the "atomic weights" of the *isotopes* Li^7, He^4, and H^1 are 7.01818, 4.00389, and 1.00813, respectively. These atomic weights refer to the masses of a specific number of atoms, the number in a gram atom, and to obtain the actual mass of a single atom of these isotopes we need to divide by the number of atoms in a gram atom. When this is done we find that the mass of a single atom of an isotope of "atomic weight" unity is 1.66×10^{-24} gram. The mass of a single atom of Li^7 is then $7.01818 \times 1.66 \times 10^{-24}$ gram. Now, if we consider the balance sheet of mass in the reaction below, where the actual masses of the atoms taking part are written in, we see that mass is not conserved.

$$\underbrace{\overset{Li^7}{7.01818 \times 1.66 \times 10^{-24}} + \overset{H^1}{1.00813 \times 1.66 \times 10^{-24}}}_{8.02631 \times 1.66 \times 10^{-24}} \rightarrow \underbrace{\overset{2He^4}{2 \times 4.00389 \times 1.66 \times 10^{-24}}}_{8.00778 \times 1.66 \times 10^{-24}}$$

The two sides do not balance; there is an excess of $0.01853 \times 1.66 \times 10^{-24}$ on the left-hand side. This is a loss of mass in each individual reaction of 3.16×10^{-26} gram. According to our energy relation

$E = mc^2$, we therefore expect a release of energy of $3.16 \times 10^{-26} \times (3 \times 10^{10})^2$ or 2.76×10^{-5} erg *per individual reaction.* Expressed in terms of the energy to accelerate an electron to the same energy this is 17 Mev. We therefore are led to expect as a result of the reaction that each helium nucleus will acquire 17/2 or 8.5 Mev as a result of the reaction, and since to a definite energy of a helium nucleus there is a definite range we expect to find helium nuclei (or "alpha particles") projected with a range of 8 cm in air, the value appropriate to 8.5 Mev. This is accurately verified, and the verification is one of the greatest triumphs of the theory of relativity.

We now have a beautifully compact means of expressing the potentialities of a nucleus for energy evolution—its mass. This fact has given great impetus to the measurement of nuclear masses, and the gradual compilation of a comprehensive table of all nuclear masses is one of the tasks that lies ahead of the physicist. To illustrate the use of masses we give here a shortened table of masses of neutral atoms: *

H^1	1.00812	Li^6	6.01690
n^1	1.00893	Li^7	7.01804
H^2	2.01472	Be^8	8.00777
H^3	3.01704	Be^9	9.01497
He^3	3.01701	B^{10}	10.01605
He^4	4.00389	B^{11}	11.01286

With these the reader can see, for example, that two deuterons may collide with the release of either H^3 and H^1 or He^3 and n^1. Both reactions are known and are very prolific. He can also see that Be^8 is almost exactly equal to two He^4's or two alpha particles. In fact, Be^8 is probably unstable for the reason that it can split up into two alpha particles. An interesting diversion is to use the table to calculate the energy release in any reaction one cares to invent and test whether the transmutation could be made to go.

For convenience in using tables of masses two conversion factors are given here:

$$0.0011 \text{ "mass unit"} = 1 \text{ Mev}$$

$$1.6 \times 10^{-6} \text{ erg} = 1 \text{ Mev}$$

Then, for example, the reaction produced when B^{10} is bombarded by deuterons to give B^{11} and a proton can be treated thus:

$$B^{10} + H^2 \rightarrow B^{11} + H^1$$

	10.01605 + 2.01472	11.01286 + 1.00812
Total	12.03077	12.02098

* A table complete, so far as is now known, is given in the Appendix.

Balance = 0.00979 on the left-hand side, indicating an energy release of 9.1 Mev. This has been observed to be the fact.

It should be noticed that the masses of *neutral atoms* are given. This is convenient for workers with mass spectrographs and is no trouble to the nuclear physicist. The electrons which must be added to a nucleus to form a neutral atom will always balance out if we neglect all electrons, with one exception, the emission of a positron. Thus, for example, in the reaction above, B^{10} has five electrons, H^2 one, making a total of six, while B^{11} also has five and H^1 one, also totaling six. Or, again, suppose that we have the recently discovered radioactive decay of C^{14}:

$$C^{14} \rightarrow N^{14} + e^-$$

C^{14} has six electrons, N^{14} seven. Now if we take the difference in mass between these neutral atoms we have already included in the balance sheet the additional electron; the fact that a fast beta particle leaves the C^{14} and an additional electron is attracted from outside to neutralize the newly formed N^{14} is immaterial. For greater clarity let us take the very simple example

$$H^3 \rightarrow He^3 + e^-$$

What actually occurs is indicated in Fig. 1 at *A*. The dotted lines indicate a vacant space to be filled by an electron. If we consider the change to be as in the figure at *B* we have included all the particles taking part quite adequately; any difference of mass will then tell us what energy is available. This energy is divided between the fast-moving beta ray and the incoming neutralizing electron, but the latter is a few electron volts only and hence may be neglected. The emission of a positron, however, is different. For example, in the reaction:

$$N^{13} \rightarrow C^{13} + e^+$$

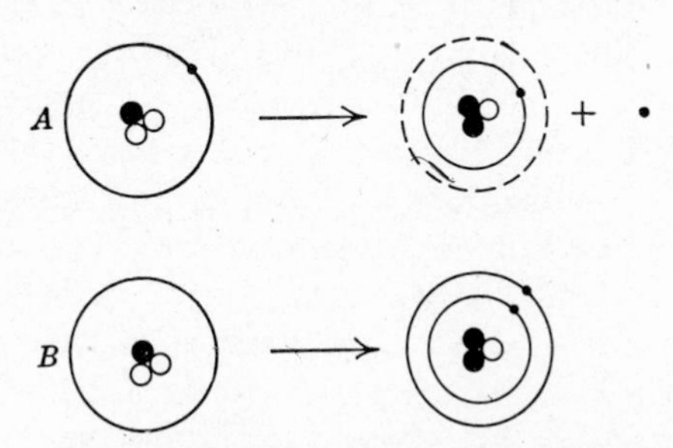

FIG. 1. The use of masses of *neutral atoms* to determine energy changes. The neutral atom formed as indicated in *B* is equivalent to the actual process in which an electron is evolved and possibly lost as at *A*.

the nitrogen has to lose first a positron and also an electron in an orbit, or pictorially the process is as shown in Fig. 2. We must therefore add two electron masses or 0.0011 mass unit to the right-hand side or else we shall predict too great an energy for the positron. It is useful to remember that this correction is 1.02 Mev or very nearly 1 Mev.

To summarize about energy relations and atomic masses, we may say that if we consider any reaction we can predict the energy release in million electron volts if we find the difference between the neutral atom masses and use the conversion factor from mass units to million electron volts. If a positron is emitted it must be treated as costing 0.0011 mass unit or 1 Mev extra.

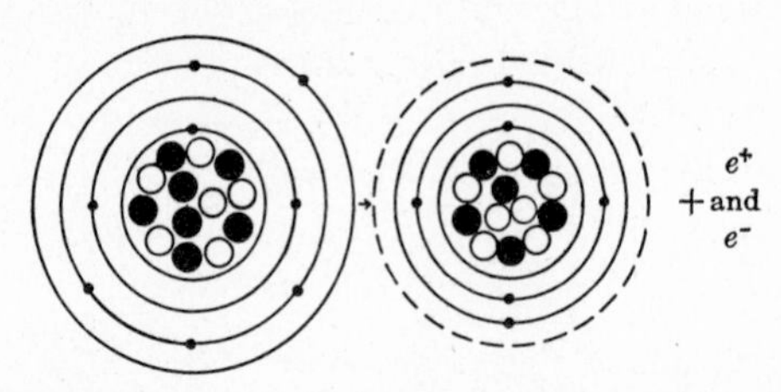

FIG. 2. The transition from radionitrogen, N^{13}, to stable carbon, C^{13}, shown schematically to illustrate the correction to be made to the masses of the neutral atoms when a reaction in which a positron is emitted is considered. The change itself ejects a fast positron, leaving an atom capable of holding one less electron. Additional mass equal to that of the positron and the electron must therefore be available to make the process go. In the balance sheet this means 0.0011 mass unit on the right-hand side.

Nuclear Reactions in General. Having seen how a nuclear physicist predicts the energy lost or gained in a nuclear reaction, let us now see how the reactions are actually made to go. We have already mentioned that an establishment equipped with a moderate-sized accelerator has available the following projectiles: protons, neutrons, deuterons, and alpha particles. In addition gamma rays also can cause transmutations One can therefore readily see that many kinds of combinations are possible and that a complete description of every reaction would need several volumes. To the person who, like the writers, recoils from such a massively detailed subject we can offer some solace. In the first place *almost any energetically possible reaction can be made to go.* It seems to be only a matter of relative yield, and yields do not vary among one another very greatly except for rather easily predictable reasons. Thus with his table of masses the reader can, if he wishes, decide for himself whether a reaction can take place and, if energy will not permit it, discard it. In the second place, since there is a close similarity between types of reactions, a little study of a few categories will be repaid by a reasonably good understanding of the whole subject of nuclear chemistry.

It is a temptation to list here a series of categories of nuclear reactions and then to spend the rest of the chapter discussing them. First, however, we should like to point out that one must keep in mind at once both the nature of the incident particle and the product ejected particle. For example, one can see that, if a deuteron (mass 2.0147) strikes a nucleus and causes a reaction in which a proton (mass 1.0081) is ejected, there will in general be a release of energy unless the bombarded and product nuclei have a distinctly unfavorable mass difference. We thus expect this type of reaction to be commonly found, and it is. On the other hand if an alpha particle (mass 4.0039) ejects a neutron (mass 1.0089) there will be an absorption of energy unless the bombarded and final nuclei have a favorable mass difference. We therefore expect this type of reaction to be less commonly found unless the alpha particles are very energetic, a conclusion which is nearly true. It is not quite true, as there is, in the lighter elements, a favorable mass difference which helps this type of reaction.

To aid in considering the in-and-out nature of a nuclear reaction a compact notation has been devised as follows. The bombarded element is placed before parentheses, the projectile just inside, the ejected particle next, and finally after the parentheses the product element. Thus Rutherford's pioneer reaction:

$$He^4 + N^{14} \rightarrow O^{17} + H^1$$

is written: $N^{14}(\alpha p)O^{17}$. The α stands for the alpha particle, p for the proton; other symbols are n for neutron, d for deuteron. This notation may or may not appeal to the reader, but it is convenient, and one soon acquires it as a sort of language. Thus our predictions, earlier in the chapter, about deuteron bombardment with emission of protons and alpha-particle bombardment with neutron emission can be said shortly: (dp) reactions generally are favorable energetically, but (αn) reactions not so much so. The common forms of reaction are: (np); $(n\alpha)$; (pn); $(p\alpha)$; (dp); (dn); $(d\alpha)$; (αp); (αn). Simple capture occurs, and it is written $(n-)$ or $(p-)$ or sometimes $(n\gamma)$ or $(p\gamma)$. More abnormal reactions are $(n, 2n)$ or (pd).

Historically the first class of reaction studied was the (αp) type. For simplicity we propose to consider neutron reactions first since neutrons are free to enter a nucleus without regard to any repulsion set up against their entry. Also, the neutron is so potent an agent in making radioactive materials that it warrants early consideration.

Neutron-Induced Transmutations. Only one element is known which will not react with neutrons. This is ordinary helium, whose great stability prohibits the creation of any other element from it by combination with a neutron unless bombarding energies greater than any available today are used. With this one exception, every element yields to neutron bombardment. By far the commonest process which results from neutron bombardment is *simple capture*, a process which may be indicated as:

$$A^{M} + n \rightarrow A^{M+1}$$

meaning that an atom A^{M} of atomic weight M has captured a neutron to form the *composite* and, in this case, also *final* nucleus, A^{M+1} of weight $M + 1$. As illustrations we may take the following, which we have chosen because the reactions can be made use of for other purposes.

$$Br^{79} + n^{1} \rightarrow Br^{80} \quad \text{or} \quad Br^{79}(n-)Br^{80}$$

$$I^{127} + n^{1} \rightarrow I^{128} \quad \text{or} \quad I^{127}(n-)I^{128}$$

$$Ag^{107} + n^{1} \rightarrow Ag^{108} \quad \text{or} \quad Ag^{107}(n-)Ag^{108}$$

$$Ag^{109} + n^{1} \rightarrow Ag^{110} \quad \text{or} \quad Ag^{109}(n-)Ag^{110}$$

All four of these reactions result in radioactive products. The first two afford convenient methods of making moderate-sized samples of two of the halogens; the second pair give radioactive silver isotopes which have rather convenient half-lives for use in detecting the presence of neutrons and measuring their intensity. If the reader is ever permitted to approach a cyclotron while it is running and quickly tests the money in his pocket with a Geiger counter, he will find that it is definitely radioactive. The radioactivity will shortly die out and should warn him that the apparently harmless apparatus is nevertheless giving him an appreciable bombardment which will before long begin to have serious effects. The radioactivity will be due to the two last reactions listed above.

This type of reaction is of some interest since it brings up the question of the mechanics of a transmutation. Almost everyone has worked out the familiar problem of two balls colliding and remaining together after collision and knows that it cannot occur if both momentum and mechanical energy are conserved. Some energy must be lost as heat. Do such considerations hold in the collision of two nuclear particles? If they do, they must clearly have a profound influence on the events in the above type of reaction where the two colliding particles stick together. The answer is yes. The reaction invariably proceeds with the emission of the necessary energy to guarantee the conservation of momentum, not as heat, as in the collision of two putty balls, but as a gamma ray. Now the reader, whether he be a physicist, or a long-suffering physiologist compelled to add one more technique to his already exacting requirements, will know that in atomic physics the emission of radiation is not a continuous process, but that a quantum of energy is emitted as one unit. This fact, that the emitted gamma ray must have *a certain definite energy*, the energy corresponding to the transition between two of a discrete set of levels in the nucleus, means that the outgoing gamma ray, which gets rid of the surplus energy, *can have only certain energy values*. Now the amount of energy to be disposed of depends on the energy of the neutron that does the bombarding. If the amount does not happen to agree with the energy corresponding to a transition in the resulting nucleus, then there is a situation which requires that one of two rigid laws break down. In this instance the laws have unquestioned validity, and the only way out is for the process of sticking to fail to take place; to the satisfaction of physicists, this is what happens. The simple capture type of reaction will go for only certain values of the energy of the incident neutrons, those for which the surplus energy exactly fits one of the gamma-ray energies the nucleus is able to emit.

The physicist does not rest content until he has the word "resonance" in every section of his subject, and here it finds its place in nuclear physics. Simple capture is said to be a resonance process: it can occur only if there is resonance between the energy of the incident neutron and the energy of one of the states of excitation of the new composite nucleus. This resonance characteristic has been verified many times. It has some important consequences, because it means that neutrons from any source will not necessarily cause the reaction to proceed and in fact the great variation in the yields of this type of reaction is to be traced to this limitation on the energy of the incident particle.

Let us follow this a little further since it will throw light on our present-day picture of the process of transmutation as well as show what to expect from this particular type of reaction. Modern theory, for better or worse, has been driven to explain phenomena in the atom by first assigning a "potential field," that is, by deciding the value of the potential energy a particle will have at any point. Reduced to its simplest terms, this means that we cannot say anything about the way a body will move unless we know what forces act upon it. The potential field, which is fundamentally related to the force acting at any place,* is used simply because it is far more convenient than force to handle in equations; there is nothing inherently abstruse in its use. The necessity of assigning this field in nuclear phenomena is about as cheerless a task as any mathematical physicist has ever

* The negative of the derivative of potential energy with respect to distance measured in any direction is the force in that direction.

had to face, as we are only just beginning to know the forces between single particles, let alone the forces in a complex nucleus. So unhappy a task is it that few theoretical physicists feel optimistic about a complete theory of the nucleus. However, this complexity leads to a certain simplicity, for the theoretical physicist "gives up" and represents the potential field of a nucleus simply by a potential "well" as in Fig. 3.

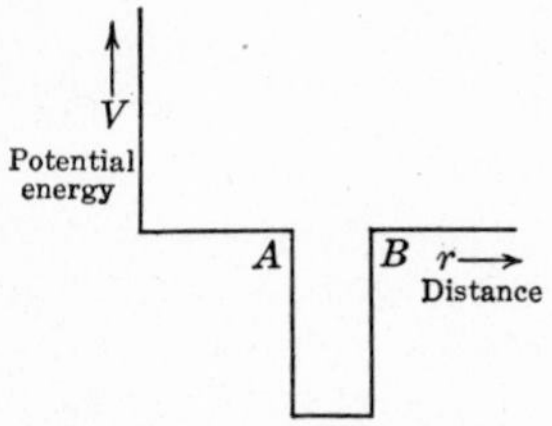

FIG. 3. The potential field of a neutron in the neighborhood of a nucleus, as represented for simple theory. The neutron experiences no force except between A and B, where very strong forces act. On the potential-energy diagram above, such strong forces are represented by a sudden drop, forming a "potential well," into which the neutron will fall. As it falls it acquires speed and can easily bounce out of the well unless some reason for its "capture" exists.

An incoming neutron is quite unaffected by this well until it is between the points A and B, when a strong attraction operates on it and it is swept into the complex of particles which comprises the nucleus it is bombarding. The reader must remember that falling into this well is not like the usually imagined accident. The neutron, in falling, acquires speed which may easily carry it up the far side of the well and so out again, without any apparent change at all. On the other hand this entry into the target nucleus is the first requirement of a transmutation and must be considered the preliminary stage. The second stage is concerned with the adaptation of the remaining particles to the new situation. For the reaction under discussion, simple capture, the new composite will be acceptable and it will "settle down" by emitting a gamma ray. We therefore picture the neutron falling into the potential well, acquiring speed which it may lose by giving it to the other particles in the nucleus, which bears this abnormal excitation for a short while and then emits a gamma ray to restore itself to a normal condition with the new neutron accepted. Or if the emission of a gamma ray is not feasible, the motion of the particles continues until a neutron has enough energy to duplicate the original energy of the incident neutron, whereupon it is ejected and no transmutation has taken place. The question of the feasibility of emission of a gamma ray turns upon whether in the particular potential well there is a permissible energy value exactly agreeing with the energy the neutron has to contribute. It turns out that all but the lightest nuclei have many available levels, so that the resonance requirement does not cause so great a limitation as might be expected. In fact, it can be said quite generally that, with the exception of He^4, any element A^M, after bombardment by neutrons from any but a very peculiar source of exactly one energy, will contain some atoms of A^{M+1}. Often A^{M+1} is not detectable as it is stable, and is not produced in sufficient amounts to be detected by ordinary means, but if A^{M+1} is radioactive, even the small proportion of transmuted material can easily be detected. This generality of neutron capture was discovered in 1933 by Fermi and his collaborators at Rome; it is one of the most important discoveries in nuclear chemistry.

Slow Neutrons. While engaged in this work Fermi found that, if the neutron source were surrounded by water, or paraffin, or any substance containing a large proportion of hydrogen, it frequently was far more efficient in producing radioactivity. Thus if silver is exposed to "straight neutrons" it becomes active. If, however, the silver and the neutron source are enclosed by paraffin about 3 inches thick, the yield is increased about tenfold. It is in fact this combination which is present when a visitor carries money in his pocket near a cyclotron, since the visitor himself is hydrogen-containing material, and the money contains the silver. Fermi was quick to see that the significant fact about the hydrogenous material was the *slowing down* of the neutrons by impact with the hydrogen. It may be recalled that after an impact with a hydrogen nucleus a neutron loses on the average 60 per cent of its energy. This has remarkable consequences after only a few collisions, as is shown in the sequence below:

Number of collisions:	0	1	2	3	6	9	12
Energy: (Mev)	5	2	0.8	0.3	0.018	0.001	0.0001

It will be seen that after only a dozen collisions the neutron has only a few electron volts energy left and that it will require very few further collisions to reduce the speed of the neutrons to that of the molecules of the water or paraffin (speeds corresponding to a few one-hundredths of an electron volt). Such neutrons would be particularly deadly in causing transmutations, for if they happened to strike a nucleus they would spend a long time in its neighborhood with a resulting excellent chance of being caught. This phenomenon of transmutation by *slow neutrons* can often be turned to great advantage and made to yield very concentrated sources of artificially radioactive elements.

The phenomenon of resonance plays an important part in slow neutron reactions, for naturally the majority of the slow neutrons will have energies at or near the energy of the molecular motion, and if it happens that an energy level is not available for this energy the reaction will not be favored. On the other hand if it turns out that an energy level is available there will be a very prolific yield. Thus it has been established that for simple capture by cadmium there is a resonance at about $\frac{1}{30}$ *electron volt* (note the small unit of energy) so that slow neutrons are readily absorbed by cadmium.* For iodine the resonance occurs at about 1 volt, and there is much less, though considerable, absorption. This accounts for the great variability of yields in slow neutron reactions and means that, though neutron bombardment can be a simple and efficient method of preparing a radioactive substance in some cases, it is relatively unsuitable in others.

Neutron-Induced Reactions with Particle Emission. Less common than simple capture, but of great importance in some cases, is the phenomenon of *transmutation with particle emission.* Such reactions are:

$$B^{10} + n \rightarrow Li^7 + He^4$$

or

$$N^{14} + n \rightarrow C^{14} + H^1$$

or

$$Si^{30} + n \rightarrow P^{30} + H^1$$

These reactions have their characteristics fixed for them by the fact that the ejected particle is charged. This has a strange consequence, which at first sight seems absurd, namely, that the charged particle, though it may be given sufficient energy to escape from the composite conglomerate, is still not free to escape. One would naturally conclude that a positive particle would be pushed away all the more easily from a nucleus, and here we are asking the reader to believe that the pushing away is to be considered as a holding in, apparently just at our whim.

This little difficulty is one we are greatly tempted to slide over and beg the reader to accept, but as we are confronted with a property of nuclei which is of the greatest importance we will take a short while to consider it. A few pages back we drew a potential "well" and said that the neutron must fall into this well to start a transmutation. Now let us suppose that it has done so and that a proton is due for ejection. We may now inquire as to the potential well appropriate to this proton and see at once that because the proton is charged it is all higher as drawn in Fig. 4*B*. Now this shape is clearly wrong, for if the proton

* It may be asked how these energies are measured. The answer reveals the ingenuity of the physicist. One way is to interrupt the cyclotron beam periodically and see how the neutron absorption is affected some distance from the cyclotron at very short times after interruption. The longer times correspond to slower neutrons, and the time after interruption can be used as a measure of the velocity of the neutron.

were outside the well it would be repelled and thus would run downhill in some potential field; in other words the volcano and crater appearance shown in *C* is correct. The reader can now see the reason for our paradox. To make a *clean* getaway the proton must somehow acquire enough energy to reach the point *T*. When it does, the repulsion will give it the energy corresponding to a fall down the slope of the volcano so that we would expect our transmutations to yield us only fast particles. This is nearly, but not quite, true. An effect, linked intimately with the property that small-scale matter is governed by the properties of waves, permits the emerging proton to "cheat." A proton of energy *less* than *T* can leak through the walls of the volcano just as light can penetrate a very thin film of gold. This "cheating," or, more elegantly, penetration of the potential barrier, means that in one sense charged-particle transmutations are favored, which is what we at first expected, but that once we have been led to expect this favoring we are to be disappointed in that the process of leaking through the potential barrier takes time; during that time the nucleus may become impatient and reeject the neutron instead.

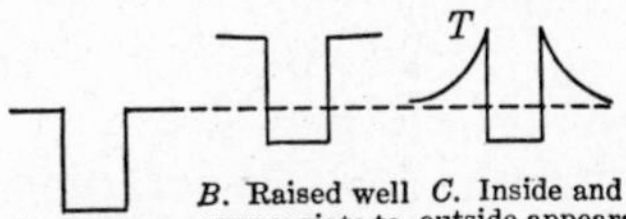

A. Neutron potential well. *B.* Raised well appropriate to a proton which does not escape. *C.* Inside and outside appearance of a proton potential well.

FIG. 4. A diagram to show how the repulsive force exerted on a proton by the protons in a nucleus modifies the appearance of the proton potential well. To be sure of escaping, the proton must have enough kinetic energy to scale the top *T*, but it can penetrate the part of the field above zero energy with a certain probability.

To shorten this account, we find that processes which require charged-particle emission are commonest in light elements where the energy required to get somewhere near *T* is small and become less and less common as the nuclear charge increases and the energy of *T* becomes greater. To achieve a particle emission from boron a slow neutron will suffice, but exceedingly fast neutrons are needed for elements such as iron. An interesting exception is *uranium*, which is so complex that it is vulnerable to a new type of process in which the whole nucleus can become drawn out into a long droplet shape and then actually blow apart by the mutual repulsion of its charged constituents. Such a process is known as "nuclear fission," and a special chapter will be devoted to it.

Before we go on to consider deuteron-induced transmutations it will be well to summarize the features of neutron reactions. The most common of these is simple capture, which is strongly resonant in nature; the neutron must have one of a set of definite energies or it will be ineffective in producing a transmutation. If one of these energies happens to occur in the region of the energies of thermal agitation, then slow neutrons, or neutrons which have collided so many times that their energy has been reduced to approximately that of the molecular motion, are very effective in producing reactions.

In the next type of process a charged particle is emitted, and here the resonance characteristic is not so important as the fact that the charged particle has to leak out of the potential barrier. The consequence is that, unless the neutrons are very energetic, this kind of reaction is not favored, except for light nuclei.

We next consider deuteron-induced transmutations, which are important because the deuteron, having a relatively large positive mass deviation, has a considerable amount of available energy and is potent as a bombarding particle. It is used more than any other in the actual manufacture of radioactive materials.

Deuteron-Induced Reactions. The deuteron is a composite of a proton and a neutron bound together tightly but not inseparably. Its mass is 2.01472, so that it will be expected to be capable of causing reactions in which energy is set free. This is the fact. There are three main types of deuteron-induced reactions: deuteron in, proton out; deuteron in, neutron out; and deuteron in, alpha particle out. In shorthand notation these are: (dp); (dn); $(d\alpha)$. The general nature of transmutation by deuterons is reasonably easy to predict. The transmutations will not proceed nearly as easily as for neutron reactions, on account of the repulsion exerted by the charge of the nucleus being hit. This repulsion creates a potential barrier which must either be overcome or penetrated (in much the same way as the emergence of a proton from a nucleus is conditional upon either surmounting or penetrating the potential barrier). This greatly limits the number of successful approaches made by a deuteron to a nucleus. Unlike neutrons, which almost all finally succeed in entering a nucleus and causing a transmutation, only about one deuteron in a million manages to do so. It may then be asked why anything but neutrons are ever used for "atom smashing"; the answer is that we have not yet developed a neutron source which does not depend on some primary reaction involving charged particles. This may not be true in a year or two, as U^{235}, if produced in sufficient amounts, could be used as a separate source of neutrons. Therefore, even though particle for particle the neutron is far more effective, the number of available neutrons is always far less than the number of available deuterons, and so deuteron reactions are, on the whole, more potent than neutron reactions in practice.

Since the repulsion by the charged nucleus is an important factor, it follows that, the more energy available to overcome this repulsion, the greater the yield of reaction product. In Fig. 5 are plotted rough values for the yield of various reactions as the deuteron energy is varied. Three reactions are chosen, each resulting in an important radioelement. The formation of radionitrogen from carbon involves comparatively little repulsion as carbon carries relatively little charge. The yield is thus appreciable at 1 Mev, rising until at 3 Mev the yield does not rise any more. The rising part corresponds to penetration of the barrier, while the flattening occurs where the deuteron has enough energy to overcome the potential barrier, after which all deuterons are equally efficient. In sodium and iron, the nuclei are more highly charged and the flattening occurs at nearly 5 and at 6 Mev, respectively. It is possible to give a rough general guide which enables the yield of any charged particle reaction to be predicted. This rule goes on the assumption that the radius r_0 of the well of the nucleus is given by the relation

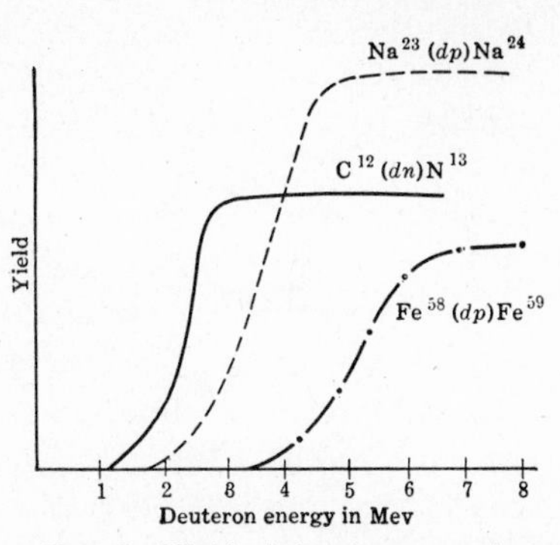

FIG. 5. Yield of the three reactions resulting in radionitrogen, radiosodium, and radioiron as the energy of the deuteron is varied. After a certain energy the yield ceases to increase. This energy is low for light elements, becoming higher for elements of high nuclear charge.

$$r_0 = 1.5 \times 10^{-13} \times A^{1/3} \qquad [1]$$

where A is the atomic weight. The energy of the top of the barrier is then equal to

$$\frac{Ze^2}{r_0} \text{ ergs} \qquad [2]$$

where Z is the nuclear charge and e the charge on an electron. (Note that this is doubled if an alpha particle, doubly charged, approaches.) For the element carbon, A is 12, so that $A^{1/3}$ is 2.29 and r_0 is 3.44×10^{-13} cm. Since Z is 6 the energy of the top of the barrier, E_T, is

$$\frac{6 \times 4.8^2 \times 10^{-20}}{3.44 \times 10^{-13}}$$

or 4.0×10^{-6} erg. This is 2.5 Mev.

Equations 1 and 2 can be combined to give the approximate formula

$$E_T = 0.9 \frac{Z}{A^{1/3}} \qquad [3]$$

for singly charged bombarding particles. (E_T is in Mev.)

Using the same method we can calculate the energy of the top of the barrier for any element we please, and having done so we are in a position to give a rough prediction of the yield for all energies of the incident particle above this value. This is done as follows. If a layer of pure substance which is equivalent in absorption to 1 cm of air is bombarded by particles of energy above the top of the barrier, the yield will be approximately one changed atom for every million bombarding particles, a figure which can vary considerably, but which is not a bad guide. If the layer bombarded is thicker than 1-cm equivalent then we must be careful about estimating the yield; for that part of the thickness which is being hit by particles of energy above the summit of the barrier we may simply add to the yield proportionally to the thickness, and for that part which is being hit by slower particles we must add less than this. We can give a rather rough estimate of the yield below the top of the barrier. The yield will fall to 50 per cent at an energy which is 60 per cent of that of the top, and to 10 per cent at an energy 25 per cent that of the top. We wish to stress that all this estimate of yield is only roughly true.

Cross Section. While we are considering the subject of the amount of material resulting from a reaction, we might define a term which is often used in nuclear physics, namely, "cross section." The reader is, of course, able to say what is ordinarily meant by the expression, but it is disconcerting to find a prolific reaction described as one with a large cross section. It is, however, a very sensible way of describing a yield of a bombardment process, since it tells us, in effect, the area of the "bullseye," which everyone knows is closely correlated with the score a marksman gets. For some reactions this area is larger than others, and those are favored. The actual value of the cross section is of more use than simply to give relative yields; coupled with a knowledge of the thickness of the target it will tell us exactly how many transmuted atoms will result. Suppose that we are bombarding an element which has a thickness equivalent to 1 cm of air. There will then be 5×10^{19} atoms in 1 cu cm, and so if the beam is spread over 1 sq cm this number of atoms will be traversed by the beam. Now if each atom exposes an area of 10^{-26} sq cm to the bombarding particles, the total area exposed to the beam is 5×10^{-7}, or roughly one-two-millionth of the total area covered by the beam. In actual fact we have only very poor estimates of the real area exposed to the particles, if, indeed, this area has any meaning, but we can arrange the area to tell us the number of particles effective in causing transmutation. In the example we have been considering, the number will be 1 deuteron in 2,000,000 fired at the element, or rather smaller than the ordinary case. The area of 10^{-26} sq cm is then called the cross section. Notice that the area of 1 sq cm that we chose is not important; we could have taken any area which happened to be covered by the beam, for the ratio of the effective area to the area covered would have remained the same.

With this explanation of cross section should go a few values to show how they run. Our best estimates of the actual area a nucleus presents to a particle vary between 3×10^{-25} and 3×10^{-24}. Ordinary cross sections for reactions in which the impinging particles are more energetic than the top of the barrier are about one-tenth of this figure. Some slow neutron reactions have cross sections of 1000×10^{-24}, a very large figure. Transmutations by gamma rays are much less—in the neighborhood of 10^{-27}. A useful figure to remember is that, for deuterons of 5 Mev hitting thick targets, the yield is about 1 transmuted atom for every 100,000 deuterons hitting the target.

Having gone over the generalities of this type of reaction let us consider a few important examples. The first is a series of reactions which yield neutrons. The simplest is the bombardment of deuterium by deuterons. The reaction is:

$$H^2 + H^2 \rightarrow He^3 + n \quad \text{or} \quad H^2(dn)He^3$$

This reaction is of great importance because it involves nuclei of very low charge and therefore proceeds at extremely small energies of the bombarding deuterons. The yield was so great when the original discovery was made by Oliphant, Harteck, and Rutherford in 1934 that it was thought to be due to extraneous x-rays until check experiments showed the actual nature of the process. The neutrons are emitted with about 2 Mev of energy and there is no accompanying gamma radiation, a fact which simplifies the interpretation of experiments made with neutrons from this as a source. If an inexpensive installation of a source of neutrons is needed, a moderate yield can be obtained by adapting a 100-kilovolt transformer to accelerate deuterons which then bombard a target of heavy ice. Sufficient numbers can be obtained to prepare fair samples of several elements for tracer work, for example, chlorine, bromine, and iodine. It has proved possible to detect the presence of neutrons when the bombarding energies are less than 10,000 electron volts.

The next two reactions to be considered are also important as neutron sources. The most commonly used neutron source is the reaction:

$$Be^9 + H^2 \rightarrow B^{10} + n \quad \text{or} \quad Be^9(dn)B^{10}$$

At bombarding energies above 1 Mev the yield of neutrons from this reaction exceeds that from any other of this type, and as beryllium is very stable to heat it forms an ideal target. It is likely that beryllium is the most-bombarded element, almost solely on account of its use in this way. The neutrons so produced are, with cyclotron deuterons of 5-Mev energy, spread out between 0 and 9 Mev. Such neutrons are fast but not the fastest that can be obtained, and they will not cause all the reactions which can be induced by neutrons, notably the type in which for the entry of one neutron two are ejected, the $(n, 2n)$ type. The fastest available neutrons are produced by bombarding lithium by deuterons; here the energy change is roughly 15 Mev, so that with 5-Mev deuterons the energy produced is nearly 20 Mev. The yield is also large, not much less than from beryllium, and so this form of neutron source finds considerable application also. The difficulty is to find a stable target which will withstand long hours of bombardment and yet contains a high proportion of lithium. If the target is well cooled, lithium itself can be used. Lithium nitride is a very stable compound.

A fourth reaction of this type should also be mentioned since it accompanies virtually every deuteron bombardment in spite of all precautions. This is the reaction:

$$C^{12} + H^2 \rightarrow N^{13} + n \quad \text{or} \quad C^{12}(dn)N^{13}$$

The presence of carbon as impurity in any material other than that which has been treated with extraordinary precautions is almost universal. It is therefore found that after removing a target from a bombardment there is always a 10-minute positron activity due to the decay of the radionitrogen formed. This activity must be considered in all experiments in which the time of working occurs soon after the bombardment. It is easily avoided, if time is available, by letting the product "age" for an hour or so, after which the amount of radionitrogen present is negligible.

Of great importance for the manufacture of radioactive elements is the type of reaction in which a proton is ejected, in shorthand the *dp* reaction. The reader will notice that, if a deuteron enters a nucleus and a proton is ejected, the whole is the equivalent of the addition of a neutron alone. Therefore the *dp* type of reaction achieves the same result as simple capture in the bombardment by neutrons. It is more favorable to use deuterons than neutrons to get the final product as they can be obtained in greater numbers, and, in general, if a radio-element of half-life not exceeding a year can be made from a prolific isotope by this reaction, it can be considered as readily available. To cite a few examples we have:

$$C^{13} + H^2 \rightarrow C^{14} + H^1 \quad \text{or} \quad C^{13}(dp)C^{14}$$

$$Na^{23} + H^2 \rightarrow Na^{24} + H^1 \quad \text{or} \quad Na^{23}(dp)Na^{24}$$

$$P^{31} + H^2 \rightarrow P^{32} + H^1 \quad \text{or} \quad P^{31}(dp)P^{32}$$

$$As^{75} + H^2 \rightarrow As^{76} + H^1 \quad \text{or} \quad As^{75}(dp)As^{76}$$

Of these the second and third have been used very extensively to produce radiosodium and radiophosphorus. The fourth gives a good yield of radioarsenic and will probably find much future application. The first reaction is at once an encouragement and a disappointment. By its means the long-sought-for long-lived radiocarbon can be made. But the carbon so formed has a half-life of about a thousand years, which is too long to permit very large samples to be made without special bombardment; and also the amount of the target C^{13} is only 1 per cent of the total. All the same, if the development of atom smashing goes ahead as it has in the last year or two the first reaction may assume considerable importance.

The above (dp) type of reaction is of interest for the particular reason that it involves a unique method for the process of the reaction. The deuteron does not have to penetrate all the way into the nucleus to cause a transmutation; it can cause one by merely getting near the repulsive field of the bombarded atom. In the repulsive field the deuteron ceases to act as a single particle. It is a composite of a neutron and a proton, only one of which experiences any effect due to the charged nature of the target nucleus. The proton is repelled away from the nucleus, while the neutron is not affected, and the result is a tendency for the neutron and the proton to separate. If this happens, the neutron is conveniently near the target nucleus and is captured by it, while the proton is sent away. The resemblance to the simple capture of a neutron is thus not merely trivial; in a real sense the process is actually such a capture, only the neutron has to be specially created from a deuteron in the neighborhood of the nucleus. This method of effecting a reaction was suggested by Oppenheimer and Phillips, and the dp type of reaction is often referred to as the Oppenheimer-Phillips reaction.

A third type of reaction has already been mentioned: the *dα* type. As examples of this we have:

$$Ne^{20} + H^2 \rightarrow F^{18} + He^4 \quad \text{or} \quad Ne^{20}(d\alpha)F^{18}$$

$$Al^{27} + H^2 \rightarrow Mg^{25} + He^4 \quad \text{or} \quad Al^{27}(d\alpha)Mg^{25}$$

The first gives a 110-minute half-life isotope of fluorine; the second gives a stable form of magnesium. This type of reaction is not of great use in preparing radioactive materials as the yield is not so great in general, owing to the higher barrier to the emergence of the doubly charged alpha particle. Nevertheless it should be considered a possible means of forming a desired radioelement.

Under the head of deuteron reactions we have considered many of the features common to reactions involving charged particles. Therefore we can consider the remaining two groups of such reactions rather more briefly. These two groups are proton- and alpha-particle-induced reactions. Since alpha particles can be accelerated in a cyclotron set up for deuterons without any change, it is not bad to group alpha-particle reactions with deuteron reactions.

Alpha-Particle Reactions. The main feature of interest about alpha-particle reactions is that they produce a considerable change in the mass of the bombarded element. That is to say, one produces an element 3 mass units away from the original element. This may be a useful method of reaching an isotope required for certain purposes. For example, one can make radioactive carbon, C^{14}, by deuteron bombardment as indicated earlier in the chapter by the $C^{13}(dp)C^{14}$ reaction, which requires bombarding the rare isotope of carbon. On the other hand, the same end product can be reached by bombarding the abundant isotope of boron, B^{11}, by alpha particles according to the reaction:

$$B^{11} + He^4 \rightarrow C^{14} + H^1 \quad \text{or} \quad B^{11}(\alpha p)C^{14}$$

If it were possible to obtain as prolific a beam of helium nuclei as a deuteron beam it would be the best agent to make this form of carbon. It is possible that such bombardment will finally prove to be the best, when better currents of alpha particles are obtained.

A second feature of alpha-particle reactions is the small mass excess of the helium atom, which it will be recalled means that relatively little mass energy is available to make the reaction proceed. This is largely compensated for by the fact that the double charge of the alpha particle enables the same cyclotron to accelerate helium nuclei to double the energy of the corresponding deuterons. To take a definite example we may consider the beams available at the Crocker Laboratory in Berkeley (as of June 1941). The deuteron beam is 16 Mev; the alpha-particle beam is 33 Mev. To the deuteron energy must be added the mass excess of 13 Mev equivalent; to the alpha-particle beam, the smaller mass excess of 4 Mev equivalent. The deuteron thus totals 29 Mev, while the alpha particle is worth 37 Mev and is thus already more able to supply energy needed to make a reaction go than the deuterons produced by the same cyclotron. This situation is not true for low-energy beams, where the deuteron is an easy winner, but it can be seen that the effectiveness of alpha-particle bombardment by a large atom smasher must not be underestimated.

Proton Groups and Energy Levels. The two commonest alpha-particle-induced reactions, as might be expected, are the αp and the αn types. The αp type is of interest as it is the oldest known type of reaction and for that reason one of the best studied. In fact, until recently no type of reaction except this one had been thoroughly studied from the angle of measuring the energy of the emitted protons. These studies are not wholly in place in a book on applied nuclear physics, but as they have formed the principal work of the authors it would be hard to omit them entirely. They are also of value in showing the place of gamma radiation in nuclear reactions. Consider, then, a well-studied reaction:

$$Al^{27} + He^4 \rightarrow Si^{30} + H^1 \quad \text{or} \quad Al^{27}(\alpha p)Si^{30}$$

If the aluminum is bombarded by, say, 7-Mev alpha particles and the ejected protons are detected by a proportional counter it is found that the protons fall into definite energy groups.

This is experimentally proved rather simply by that standard trick of twentieth-century physics, the absorption curve. If very thin foils of aluminum are prepared in various thicknesses and calibrated by weighing known areas of foil, these foils can be considered equivalent to certain definite thicknesses of "air equivalent." Thus an aluminum foil of thickness such that it weighs 1.54 mg per sq cm of area is equivalent to 1 cm of air. Now if a target of aluminum is bombarded by a beam of alpha particles from a cyclotron, for example, there will be emission of protons in all directions, starting from the region hit by the beam. A narrow pencil of these protons can be selected by a small hole covered by a foil, and the protons can be detected by a proportional counter or other means. The arrangement is illustrated in Fig. 6. The absorption curve is plotted by interposing the calibrated foils between the target and the counter and plotting the yield against the air equivalent provided by the foils. When this is done, under very good conditions, the result is rather like the full curve of Fig. 7. The number of protons detected is seen to fall rapidly at first, after which there is a plateau, followed by successive drops and plateaus until the protons are finally stopped by a thickness which is determined by their maximum energy.

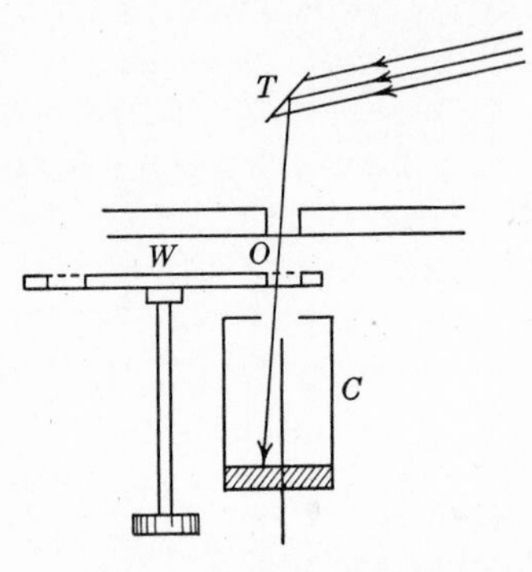

FIG. 6. Schematic arrangement for plotting an absorption curve for protons. An alpha-particle beam strikes a target T, causes the emission of protons, some of which pass through the defining opening O, and the absorbing foil into the counter C. The wheel W carries foils of different thicknesses which can be interposed in front of the counter.

Now there is a definite relation between the thickness of air which will stop a proton of a definite energy and the energy of the proton. This means that if we replot the curve of Fig. 7 against *energy* instead of against absorption we obtain something like the dotted curve of the same figure. We can go one step further and plot the number of protons between certain energy limits against the energy and get the curve of Fig. 8. It can be seen that there is a series of concentrations of numbers at certain definite energies, and when the experimental limitations are allowed for it is found that protons actually occur only *at* certain definite energies and not in between. This is quite agreeable to the modern physicist, for he at once recognizes the phenomenon of quantization, now occurring in the nucleus of the atom. The explanation of the results found is that the product nucleus (in the example given, Si^{30}) can be formed in either the ground or stable state, or in some excited state. If it is formed in the ground state, the proton which is emitted at the time of the process has all the energy available given to it (ignoring a small amount which goes to speed up the Si^{30}). If the product nucleus is formed in an excited state it holds some energy itself, and this energy is not available for the motion of the proton, which accordingly can travel a correspondingly shorter distance in the absorbing foils. The higher the state of excitation the less the energy of the proton released. The energy held by the nucleus is set free by a transition to the ground state

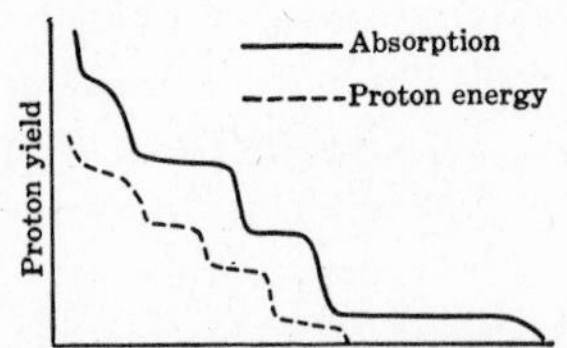

FIG. 7. Type of absorption curve found from work with the apparatus of Fig. 6. The full line is yield plotted against absorption, and the dotted curve is yield plotted against energy of proton as deduced from the absorption. Definite groups of protons can be seen.

and the emission of one or more quanta of gamma radiation. From such experiments a set of energy levels for a nucleus can be found, and the process of finding such levels for a wide variety of nuclei has just been begun.

The importance of experiments such as this is twofold. In the first place an accurate measurement of the limiting energy permits the determination of the nuclear energy change for the reaction and hence the mass difference in the process. This information, when culled from a number of reactions, allows a table of isotopic masses to be drawn up with an accuracy at least as great as that of the mass spectrograph. In the second place these experiments show conclusively the presence of discrete states of energy in the nucleus.

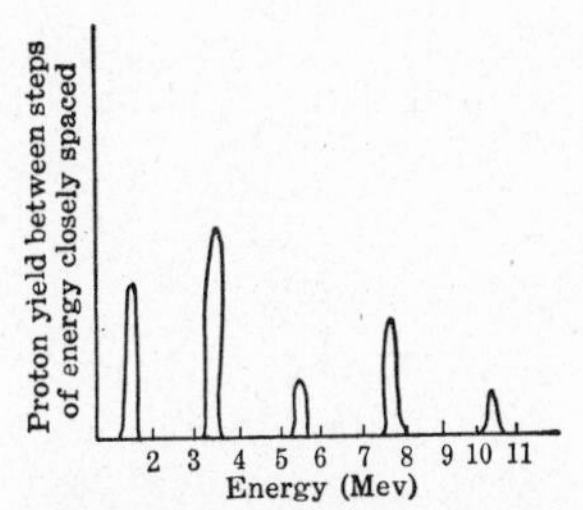

FIG. 8. Distribution curve for the protons of Fig. 7. The proton yield for a small interval of energy is plotted against the corresponding energy. It can be seen that all the protons are grouped about certain definite energy values. Those of maximum energy are formed when the product nucleus is directly produced in the stable ground state, thus liberating all the available energy for the motion of the proton. The groups of less energy correspond to the formation of the product nucleus in excited states, holding energy away from the proton and subsequently emitting it as gamma radiation.

αp and αn Reactions. To return to the discussion of the αp type of reaction, although we may give several historically interesting reactions as examples of this kind of transmutation it should be pointed out that it is of little importance in the manufacture of artificially radioactive substances. The reason is that the very nature of the reaction requires the addition of two neutrons and one proton to the bombarded nucleus, and, as the number of neutrons relative to protons is gradually increasing as we proceed towards elements of larger mass, the reaction will tend to produce stable nuclei, at least in the lighter elements. In the heavier elements this is not so true, although it still remains a type of reaction which is suitable for studying transitions between stable nuclei rather than a reaction for producing radioactivity. As examples we may choose:

$$N^{14} + He^{4} \rightarrow O^{17} + H^{1} \quad \text{or} \quad N^{14}(\alpha p)O^{17}$$

This is the pioneer reaction of Rutherford which has ushered in the whole subject of modern nuclear physics. The O^{17} is stable.

$$Ca^{40} + He^{4} \rightarrow Sc^{43} + H^{1} \quad \text{or} \quad Ca^{40}(\alpha p)Sc^{43}$$

This reaction results in the formation of a radioactive form of scandium having a half-life of 4 hours.

The *αn* type of process in which a neutron is emitted is of more practical interest. It is of some importance as the first method by which neutrons were produced, and indeed the reaction

$$Be^9 + He^4 \rightarrow C^{12} + n \quad \text{or} \quad Be^9(\alpha n)C^{12}$$

is still commonly used as a neutron source when either no better is available or for some experimental reason the whole space surrounding the source must be filled with some material under study. Such a source commonly consists of powdered beryllium into which some radon gas is mixed. A small brass container can be filled with beryllium powder, evacuated, and radon forced in before the container is sealed off. A reasonable estimate of the number of neutrons emitted by a mixture of 1 millicurie of radon and beryllium is 25,000 per second. This can easily be exceeded by almost any equipment using artificial acceleration, but it is sufficient for many purposes.

The *αn* reaction as opposed to the *αp* type increases the ratio of protons to neutrons and so tends to cause reactions which result in unstable nuclei. Historically the discovery of artificial radioactivity was made by means of this reaction. We may cite the reactions first discovered by Curie and Joliot:

$$B^{10} + He^4 \rightarrow N^{13} + n \quad \text{or} \quad B^{10}(\alpha n)N^{13}$$

$$Al^{27} + He^4 \rightarrow P^{30} + n \quad \text{or} \quad Al^{27}(\alpha n)P^{30}$$

In both these reactions the final nucleus has too much charge and relieves itself of the excess by the emission of a positron. This type of reaction generally produces positron emitters. The N^{13} is already familiar from the bombardment of carbon by deuterons and decays with a 10-minute half-life. P^{30} decays with a half-life of 2.5 minutes. Finally we come to the use of protons as the bombarding particle.

Proton-Induced Reactions. The proton was the logical particle to try in the first experiments with artificially accelerated particles. It was found to be eminently successful, as the reader knows. The pioneer work of Cockcroft and Walton, shortly followed by many others, showed that by bombarding light elements with protons a variety of reactions could be made to go. Since we are primarily interested in presenting a systematization of nuclear chemistry we do not intend to consider the historically interesting reactions but will follow the same order as for the neutron reactions and will start with *simple capture.*

The astute reader may perhaps wonder why we made such a business of simple capture for neutron bombardment, ignored it for deuteron and alpha-particle bombardment, and now return to it for proton reactions. The reason is mainly experimental. There is now some evidence for simple capture of deuterons, but in general the many products involving particle emission obscure the process of simple capture, which has to be detected by observing the emitted gamma radiation that it causes. Also the great mass excess of the deuteron means that, when it is captured, the resulting conglomerate is in a high state of excitation and in general seems to prefer to emit a particle rather than settle down by mere gamma-ray emission. This, of course, only tells us that the process is uncommon, not that it does not occur. It does tell us that it will be hard to detect. Similar experimental conditions also prevent the detection of this process in alpha-particle reactions. For both neutrons and protons the bombarding particle is elementary, and this greatly aids the detection of the simple capture process. It means that the whole reaction is simpler and so the competition from other processes is less.

The results of the simple capture of protons are of the greatest value in many research experiments. The gamma ray which is evolved after the proton has been caught is likely to be very energetic; for example, the bombardment of lithium yields a gamma ray of energy 17 Mev, far greater than the 2.6-Mev ray which is the most energetic available from natural sources. Other reactions give less energy than this, but the run of energies is around 6 Mev, which is still considerable. Since the yield of such gamma rays is great and beams of protons of several microamperes can be used, these reactions can be made to act as sources of energetic gamma rays which can, themselves, produce transmutations. One does not use gamma rays for actual manufacture of radioactive materials, but they have been of great value in sorting out the radioactivities found in elements having several isotopes. There they play a part somewhat like that of an analytical reagent in a chemical laboratory; one bombards the mixture of isotopes with, among other things, energetic gamma rays, and uses the resulting radioactivity as a sort of "precipitate" from which the true nature of the process going on can be inferred.

This is interesting enough to be exemplified here. It was found that the two isotopes of bromine, when subjected to neutron bombardment, gave *three* radioactive periods. This is not unexpected, as several kinds of reaction could take place, giving at least three different elements. The unexpected event was the fact that all three had the same chemical reactions, those characteristic of bromine itself. This meant that all three were due to simple capture, which in neutron bombardment does not change the chemical nature of the target, only the nuclear mass. Therefore more than one period was to be associated with one of the radioactive elements formed, a discovery of "nuclear isomerism." The question of which element could exist in isomeric forms could not be answered, however. Now bromine exists as Br^{79} and Br^{81}. If simple neutron capture takes place, Br^{80} and Br^{82} will be formed. If a gamma ray caused the ejection of a neutron from the two stable isotopes there would be formed Br^{80} as before and Br^{78}, a new form. It was found by Bothe and Gentner that two substances having periods of 18 minutes and 4.2 hours were present when bromine was bombarded by the gamma rays from the reaction between protons and lithium; they were also present when bromine was bombarded by neutrons. The only common product of these two bombardments is the Br^{80} isotope, which is accordingly fixed as the radioactive element responsible for the nuclear isomerism.

In addition to the evolution of an energetic gamma ray, the capture type of reaction can give rise to considerable yields of radioactive materials. To cite a simple example, the bombardment of carbon by protons causes the formation of a substance with the familiar 10-minute half-life associated with N^{13}. The reaction is:

$$C^{12} + H^1 \rightarrow N^{13} \quad \text{or} \quad C^{12}(p\text{-})N^{13}$$

The radioactivities associated with the simple capture of protons are the same as would be produced by the *dn* type of reaction on the same target. If a cyclotron is set to be in resonance for protons it can still be used to give many radioactivities produced by deuteron bombardment.

The salient feature of simple capture of neutrons was shown to be resonance. Since there is no essential difference between proton bombardment and neutron bombardment as far as the formation of a composite nucleus is concerned, it is to be expected that there will be resonance in proton bombardment. This is so. If a suitable gamma-ray detector is placed near a target of lithium bombarded by protons whose energy can be smoothly varied (as, for example, protons from a Van de Graaff generator), there is found to be no yield of gamma rays at all until the energy of the beam exceeds 440 kilovolts. At this energy the yield of gamma rays suddenly shows a marked increase, and, if the layer of lithium is thin so that it does not cause any slowing up of the protons, the yield of gamma rays falls as soon as this energy has been passed. At higher energies other resonance levels may become apparent. In simple capture with aluminum as the target, there have been shown to be thirty or more resonance levels between zero and 2.6 Mev. This rapid increase in the number of levels is expected on the present theory of nuclear structure.

After the simple capture process, the next of interest is the *pn* process in which the proton is merely exchanged for a neutron. This type of reaction has two characteristic features. The first is that the energy of the proton must always exceed a certain threshold value before the reaction will proceed. The reason for this is that the neutron is heavier than the proton and also that we are always starting with a stable nucleus in the target and producing a less-stable nucleus, which is an abnormally heavy nucleus. This twofold demand on mass requires that we supply the equivalent energy in the form of the kinetic energy of the incident particle; and also that there can be a threshold energy below which we have not supplied enough to make the reaction go. The second characteristic feature is that a positron emitting radioactive element universally results. It is a rule, which is nearly perfectly obeyed, that no two nuclei of the same mass and charge differing by only one unit can exist. In other terms, if there are two neighboring isobars, one always decays into the other. Isobars which are stable exist, but their charges generally differ by two units. Now if we put a proton into a stable element and take a neutron out, we produce an isotope which has the same mass but a charge differing by one unit from the original element. The new isotope is therefore unstable, and to return to stability it must lose charge, or emit a positron. So a laboratory which specializes in this reaction gets to regard the positron as a commonplace.

As an example of this type of reaction we may cite the formation of F^{18} from oxygen (O^{18}).

$$O^{18} + H^1 \rightarrow F^{18} + n$$

This is interesting as it indicates that the yield of this type of reaction is considerable. The amount of O^{18} present in ordinary oxygen is less than 1 per cent, and yet the yield of radioactive material is readily detectable with insensitive apparatus.

Since it is a handicap to be unable to make any installation deliver neutrons at a moment's notice, it is important to find a reaction which will give neutrons when protons are the bombarding agent. The *pn* reaction is suitable, and it is found that if beryllium is bombarded by energetic protons the numbers of neutrons are very nearly as great as if deuterons were used as projectiles. The reaction is

$$Be^9 + H^1 \rightarrow B^9 + n \quad \text{or} \quad Be^9(pn)B^9$$

The B^9 is, as expected, a positron emitter.

The last important reaction type is the $p\alpha$. There is no striking feature of this reaction, which is the reverse of the αp type. Except for the lighter nuclei, where this reaction often goes with considerable release of energy, there has been no direct study of the emitted alpha particles, and so the occurrence of the reaction is inferred from the radioactivity resulting. It is a reaction which is highly favored only at high bombarding energies as the ingoing and outgoing particles are both charged and subject to the necessity of passing through barriers. As an example we may take:

$$F^{19} + H^1 \rightarrow O^{16} + He^4 \quad \text{or} \quad F^{19}(p\alpha)O^{16}$$

Transmutation by Radiation. Only one large species of nuclear reaction now remains. It has already been mentioned while discussing the emission of energetic gamma rays from proton capture. It is the so-called *photodisintegration* process. This means transmutation by gamma rays. We have already indicated the use that can be made of this type of bombardment in assigning periods to the correct isotope, but we have not considered the general features of the reactions produced. While we were considering the pn type of reaction we called attention to the presence of a threshold energy which must be given to the proton before the reaction will go. This threshold feature is even more strongly present in photodisintegration, for the gamma ray possesses no mass of its own and must therefore achieve its results by sheer original energy. For this reason the process was not discovered until relatively recently. Ordinarily, if one takes any nucleus and removes any light nuclear particle from it, it will be found that the increase of mass needed to separate these two parts corresponds to about 9 Mev. This energy must be supplied entirely by the gamma ray, if it is to cause disruption. No such energetic gamma rays are found among naturally radioactive materials, and it was only by bombarding the relatively loosely bound deuteron that Chadwick and Goldhaber were able to show that this type of reaction could occur. They used the 2.6-Mev gamma ray from ThC′ to bombard deuterium gas and found that protons were liberated. The process is:

$$H^2 \rightarrow H^1 + n \quad \text{or} \quad H^2(\gamma n)H^1$$

Beryllium can also be split up in this way, according to the reaction:

$$Be^9 \rightarrow Be^8 + n \quad \text{or} \quad Be^9(\gamma n)Be^8$$

These two reactions actually give rise to considerable numbers of neutrons, because the gamma ray is able to cause transmutations throughout a thick layer of material, as it is absorbed by a different process from charged particles. Such neutrons are of interest in that they are all of one energy, and they are therefore a useful tool in research. The energy is determined by the energy of the gamma ray which is used and the energy needed to separate a neutron from the target nucleus. It is unique, but it cannot be controlled.

The extensive series of photodisintegrations now known came as a result of the use, by Bothe and Gentner, of the energetic radiation from lithium bombarded by protons. In general there is so great a stray neutron background from this source of gamma rays that the neutrons cannot be detected directly. Frequently, however, the result of ejecting a neutron from a nucleus produces a radioactive element which can be detected and recognized. This was done by Bothe and Gentner in reactions such as:

$$P^{31} \rightarrow P^{30} + n$$

Here the P^{30} is radioactive, emitting a positron with a half-life of 3 minutes. The process of photodisintegration differs from other methods of transmutation in that it does not call on the interaction between particles to effect a change. The fundamental force that causes the disruption is the force resulting from the action of electromagnetic radiation on the particles in the nucleus. This force is not so great as the direct force between elementary particles, and the result is that the effectiveness of radiation is rather small. We do not, therefore, expect any great commercial use to be made of this reaction; it is rather to be useful in studying the nucleus itself.

Before concluding this rather rambling chapter there are one or two oddities to be noticed. It should be mentioned that such reactions as *pd; αd; n, 2n;* have been observed in some instances. In fact, the date of this book will certainly be easy to guess in the future because we have mentioned only a few simple categories of reactions. As the available bombarding energies get higher and higher, more and more types of reaction will be discovered, and it is certain that the subject of nuclear chemistry will vie with orthodox chemistry in length and elaboration of volumes describing it. For example, if energy enough were available it should be possible to split an oxygen nucleus away from a moderately heavy element; such a reaction would then be labeled, say, $Zn^{64}(n, O^{16})Ti^{49}$. It is dangerous, of course, to prophesy in a young science, but the authors feel that, though the study of such reactions would be fascinating, their use outside nuclear physics will not be very great. The reason for this lies in another factor which should be mentioned here, the *competition between various processes.* It has probably already occurred to the reader that these different reactions may well all happen at once for the same target. Then the question arises, "Which will take place?" The answer is that there is a definite chance of all taking place at once; no process that is energetically possible is completely forbidden. On the other hand the dice may very well be loaded in favor of a certain type of transition and against another.

This feature of the chance of a process taking place is one of the great questions that the theoretical nuclear physicist has to answer. There are clearly factors entering in, but as yet no one has been able to give rules which will tell us why neutron emission is favored in one case and not another. However, if we leave out the unsolved problem of explanation, we are still able to appreciate the effect of the fact that all processes can take place. We can understand the way things behave by considering the effect observed when alpha particles bombard nitrogen. Suppose that we observe the protons produced by the αp reaction with one counter, and the neutrons due to the αn reaction with a second suitable counter. Now if the energy of the alpha particles is increased gradually, it will be found that protons are evolved in steadily increasing numbers. This is only on account of the increased penetrating power as the energy of the alpha particles increases. There is no yield of neutrons at all. As we increase the alpha-particle energy beyond the value 5 Mev it becomes energetically possible for neutrons to be evolved with the formation of F^{17}, and the neutron counter begins to register. At the same time the proton counter records a diminishing number of counts, and as the energy is still further increased the number of protons diminishes until it falls to half its greatest value. It seems as though the number of alpha particles which enter nuclei varies in a smooth manner, but that the yield of any one process may show abrupt changes as the other processes begin to compete with it.

This factor of the competition between processes makes it hard to predict the yield of any reaction.

Thus we would naturally expect that the evolution of protons from Be^9 by the $Be^9(dp)Be^{10}$ process would be great. This is not so; the yield is low. The competition set up by the very prolific process $Be^9(dn)B^{10}$ is so great that the proton yield is only a fraction of the normal value. To return to the emission of O^{16} as speculated on above. It is very likely that at these high energies there are so many competing processes that one such process will not be of any greater value than some more prosaic process which operates at low energies as well.

This chapter bids fair to be the longest in the book. It is an interesting chapter to write, but rather unsatisfactory when read over. The truth is that the important ideas in nuclear chemistry, like the importance of mass and energy, can be said rather quickly, but that the "feel" of the subject cannot be imparted so soon. It takes thought and

Summary of Reaction Types

Reaction Type	Normal Mass Change	Dependence on Energy of Projectile	Yield	Type of Radioactivity Usually Produced	Sample Reactions
n capture	Positive	Resonance	Virtually 100%	Electron	$Ag^{107} + n \rightarrow Ag^{108}$ $Br^{79} + n \rightarrow Br^{80}$
np	Slightly positive	Smooth	Large for light elements; escaping barrier to consider	Electron	$N^{14} + n \rightarrow C^{14} + H^1$ $S^{32} + n \rightarrow P^{32} + H^1$
$n\alpha$	Slightly positive in light elements; negative in heavy	Smooth	As above	Electron	$F^{19} + n \rightarrow N^{16} + He^4$ $Al^{27} + n \rightarrow Na^{24} + He^4$
$n, 2n$	Very negative	Smooth	Small	Positron	$N^{14} + n \rightarrow N^{13} + 2n$ $P^{31} + n \rightarrow P^{30} + 2n$
p capture	Positive	Resonance	Large	Positron	$C^{12} + H^1 \rightarrow N^{13}$ $F^{19} + H^1 \rightarrow Ne^{20}$
pn	Negative	Threshold: smooth increasing with energy	Large	Positron	$B^{11} + H^1 \rightarrow C^{11} + n$ $O^{18} + H^1 \rightarrow F^{18} + n$
$p\alpha$	Slightly positive in light elements; negative in heavy	Smooth, increasing with proton energy	Large	Generally stable products	$F^{19} + H^1 \rightarrow O^{16} + He^4$ $Al^{27} + H^1 \rightarrow Mg^{24} + He^4$
pd	Very negative	Smooth as above	Small	Only one case established	$Be^9 + H^1 \rightarrow Be^8 + H^2$
αn	Slightly negative in light elements; positive in heavy	Smooth	Large for elements where barrier penetration is easy	Positron	$B^{10} + He^4 \rightarrow N^{13} + n$ $Al^{27} + He^4 \rightarrow P^{30} + n$
αp	Slightly positive except some light elements	Smooth	As above	Generally stable products	$Al^{27} + He^4 \rightarrow Si^{30} + H^1$ $N^{14} + He^4 \rightarrow O^{17} + H^1$
dp	Always positive	Smooth	As above	Electron	$Na^{23} + H^2 \rightarrow Na^{24} + H^1$ $P^{31} + H^2 \rightarrow P^{32} + H^1$
dn	As above	Smooth	As above	Positron	$C^{12} + H^2 \rightarrow N^{13} + H^1$ $Be^9 + H^2 \rightarrow B^{10} + H^1$
$d\alpha$	Always positive	Smooth	As above	Generally stable products	$O^{16} + H^2 \rightarrow N^{14} + He^4$ $Al^{27} + H^2 \rightarrow Mg^{25} + He^4$
γn	Always negative	Sharp threshold	Small	Positron	$Be^9 + \gamma \rightarrow Be^8 + n$ $Br^{81} + \gamma \rightarrow Br^{80} + n$
γp	As above	As above	As above	Only observed for deuteron	$H^2 + \gamma \rightarrow n + H^1$

much discussion to become happy at the array of possibilities now presented to us. It is intended that this chapter serve, not as a compendium to all nuclear reactions, but as an ice breaker to enable the reader to join in discussion, or read the more thorough summaries either now available or shortly to be written.

There is much valid witticism at the expense of summarizing summaries. Nevertheless, we are going to summarize this chapter. As a beginning we show the table, in which the various types of reaction are listed together with the salient points of each.

The progress of a reaction is first of all conditional on a favorable mass balance; the mass of the two reacting particles plus the mass equivalent of the kinetic energy of the projectile must exceed the mass of the resulting products. Second, all charged particles must either surmount or penetrate through a potential barrier which becomes higher and thicker the greater the atomic number of the target element. Third, there will always be a competition among various possible reactions so that one cannot always predict the nature of the yield given. On these counts the deuteron is on the whole the most favorable projectile for causing transmutations, although this statement must not be interpreted as meaning that deuterons are always so. Roughly speaking, if there is no unusual competition, the yield of changed nuclei from bombardment by any particle which has enough energy to overcome the barrier will be one for every 100,000 incident particles. This figure can vary by as much as a factor of 10, and it applies only to a thick target. As the energy of the bombarding particles becomes higher with technical advance, it is likely that many new varieties of reaction will be discovered, rendering this long chapter a slender first section of a large subject. It is prophesied, however, that these reactions will be of little use in manufacturing radioactive isotopes for practical work.

We hope that a reasonable digesting of this chapter will enable the reader to master the subject of radioactivity and the production of radioactive materials, the subject of Chapter 6.

REFERENCES

M. S. Livingston and H. A. Bethe, "Nuclear Dynamics, Experimental," *Rev. Mod. Phys.*, 9, 247, 1937. An excellent compendium of information up to the date given.

Franco Rasetti, *Elements of Nuclear Physics*, Prentice-Hall, 1936. A useful book, though a little out of date and biased toward theory.

Wolfgang Riezler, *Einführung in die Kernphysik*, Bibliographisches Inst. AG, Leipzig, 1937. A first-class, compact, and practical book. Excellent as far as the date of its publication.

N. Feather, *Introduction to Nuclear Physics*, Cambridge University Press, 1936.

CHAPTER 6

RADIOACTIVITY

. . . such interchange of state,
Or state itself confounded to decay.

Radioactivity is a veritable godsend to the physicist. He is used to expatiating on a subject whose main attraction is the one thing most people resent—exactness—which seems to the listener like being pinned down all the time, and radioactivity, though it has been imbued by the press with all the mystery of relativity, is actually mostly a simple descriptive subject. The basic ideas are easy, and it takes very little familiarity with the principles to be able to predict the general behavior of any given radioactive element; only when the actual process is closely examined does the theory become unpleasant. For practical purposes such theory is not necessary.

Radioactivity in General. In the first chapter we described the extreme simplicity of the scheme of nature. Neutrons, protons, electrons, and forces—no more. We also asked and for the moment answered the question as to the way in which we could mix neutrons and protons in a nucleus. We could mix them how we liked, but nature would see to it that, after the mixture was made, the neutrons or protons would interchange until the mixture was one of her own recipes. These recipes have been standard for more than a billion years. The process of readjustment is known as "radioactivity."

Let us now take a closer look at the events taking place; in fact, let us concentrate on one example for a while. The simplest radioactive element is extra heavy hydrogen, H^3. This element was thought for a long while to be stable, but a brilliant piece of investigation by Alvarez showed that, in spite of the form book, H^3 is the wrong horse to back. He^3 is the winner. In more detail, the combination of two neutrons and one proton is less stable than the combination of two protons and one neutron. This, nevertheless, does not prevent us from being able to make a considerable number of atoms of H^3; in fact, the reaction:

$$H^2 + H^2 \rightarrow H^3 + H^1$$

is one of the most prolific known, and we can easily build up many millions of H^3 atoms.

Consider for a moment one of them. It is unstable. It wants to become He^3, which it can do at any time by changing a neutron into a proton and emitting an electron. This process is not quite so simple as it sounds, for the neutron has a certain tendency to remain a neutron, and if the difference in stability between H^3 and He^3 is not very great, the H^3 will remain such for a considerable time; but in the end it will go over. *This process, the passage from one nearly stable nucleus to one which is stable, is the underlying process of radioactivity. Every radioactive element is one which is off the beaten track; it is a freak, but a freak with the power to correct itself by changing its nature so that it returns to type.*

We can illustrate this account of radioactivity further by considering various types of carbon. In order to have a carbon nucleus only one real requirement is involved: the nuclear charge must be 6, or six protons must be present. The commonest form of carbon has six neutrons as well, making a total of twelve particles. Now let us imagine that a neutron is added; we still have carbon, but is it stable? The answer is yes, although it is not so abundant as the ordinary form. Very well, add a second neutron. We now have C^{14}, and we quickly perceive that a stable element having the same number of particles (fourteen), namely N^{14}, already exists. We therefore confidently predict that C^{14} is a freak, that it will adjust its constitution until it becomes normal, and that therefore it will change one of its neutrons into a proton, emitting at the same time an electron. In other words, we predict that C^{14} is beta-radioactive. Such is the fact.

Instead of adding neutrons we could have imagined them removed. Then on removing one neutron from C^{12} we obtain C^{11}, and again we see that the number, eleven, of particles is already taken up by stable B^{11}. We therefore predict that C^{11} is radioactive, that it will convert a proton into a neutron with the emission of a *positron*. And it is so. In the same way it can be seen that Na^{24} usurps the number occupied by Mg^{24} and so Na^{24} is radioactive; that P^{32} will decay into S^{32}, and so on. In fact, it becomes clear that, once the technique of bombardment described in the last two chapters has been developed, the number of radioactive nuclei produced will be very great, actually greater than the number of stable nuclei, but that the general nature of radioactive processes will be as simple as we have already described.

If the reader will stop here for just a moment to consider what we have said regarding the nature of radioactivity, he will see that the major idea is very simple: as simple as rolling off a log, which is after all a passage from a nearly stable state to one more stable. *This major idea need not bother him*, and it is in reality the secondary questions which now arise that may cause him trouble. Such questions concern the actual time taken to effect the change and the energy of the products of the change. We can now consider radioactivity in more detail.

Statistical Nature of Atomic Theory. Before we look more closely at the process of reversion to type it will repay the effort to consider for a moment the rules which have been found to apply to small-scale matter, such as atoms or parts thereof, and then see how they will apply to radioactivity. In the first place it has been found that it is impossible to describe the motion of electrons or protons or any small enough particles in detail. Notice, by the way, that it is not necessary to do so, for we are nearly always compelled to deal with vast aggregates of atoms, and the motion of one alone need not be followed. If we cannot follow the behavior of an electron in detail, the question arises what we can do; and the answer is that we can calculate a quantity which will evaluate the chance that an electron be at a given place at a given time, although we cannot calculate its precise path. The quantity we calculate is quite accurate and of the greatest value; in fact, it is all we need; but it must be remembered that it informs us of only a probability, not a certainty.

A little digression will show the difference between the modern outlook and what our large-scale knowledge led us to expect until this century. A careful study of Harvard men has shown that their average height is greater than that of the rest of the population. This means that if a man is known to be a Harvard man he will be expected to be taller than average, but there is no reason why any one Harvard man will be tall. In fact, if we were going to use this as a test for whether a man were a Harvard man, we would have to admit that it would not help much. On the other hand if we were presented with a party of a thousand Harvard men and asked to verify whether they were genuine, we could get real information by finding their average height and seeing if it were above the average for the country. The difference between the two outlooks can be seen from our illustration. Modern atomic physics is of service only in the statistical sense; it can give real information only when a large number of cases is considered, whereas the course of physical discovery up to the present century led us to expect that in each case we could follow what happened accurately if we only had the right theory to help us to explain the events.

Let us repeat, then, that, to describe the motion of an electron or any part of an atom, we must calculate the value of a certain function at each place and then its value will tell us what the chance is that an electron be at that place. One interesting and exciting result that follows from this kind of procedure is that in an atom an electron can have only a limited number of values of energy, the "energy levels" of the atom, and these energy levels play a vital role in spectroscopy, which has justified the method of procedure of modern physics so convincingly.

Probability and Radioactivity. To return once again to radioactivity. A neutron and a proton are supposed to be two states of the same thing, with the proviso that a neutron may change into a proton and liberate an electron at the same time. Now we may suppose that the change takes place because some force acts tending to make it occur. We do not yet presume to suppose the nature of the force; nuclear physics is still a young science; but we suppose that there *is* such a force and that it tends to make such a change. In a stable nucleus there is a balancing of these forces so that there is no net force seeking to make the change, whereas in an unstable nucleus there is a net unbalanced force which is tending to convert a neutron into a proton. All we have to do is to calculate the value of the function corresponding to the changed neutron, and this will tell us what the chance is that, at a given time, a neutron will have become a proton and a radioactive change will have taken place. Notice that all we get is the *chance.* We get no definite information about when a single atom will change. *All we can say is that there is a certain chance within a given interval of time that the neutron will take the alternative form of a proton, electron, and neutrino, and, of course, the greater this chance the more rapid is the process of radioactive decay.*

Radioactive Decay. Before we go on to consider the predictions of the theory of nuclear instability it is important to look at the main features of the manner of change just described above—a manner in which there is a certain constant probability of a change taking place in a given interval of time. Understanding of the nature of this apparently simple way of change will go a long way to help in understanding the whole nature of radioactivity.

Let us therefore first consider the meaning of the word "probability." If a certain number N of cases be considered, the probability of a certain distribution of cases is the ratio of the number in that category (say n) to the total number N, that is n/N. Thus, if we toss pennies N times, the probability of getting heads is the number of times we find heads divided by the total number of times N.

Now consider the changing of a million atoms. Suppose that during 1 second there is a probability of radioactive change of $\frac{1}{1000}$. This means that in any 1 second a fraction $\frac{1}{1000}$ of the atoms will have changed. Then 1 second after the beginning of our study of the million atoms we expect that we shall find 1000 atoms in a changed condition. This change, once made, is complete, and we are now in possession of only 999,000 atoms. (The change from stable to unstable cannot occur as there is not the energy available to make it go.) In the next second the probability is still the same, but as we now have only 999,000 atoms a slightly smaller number will change: 999, to be precise. This leaves us with 998,001 atoms, and therefore in the next second 998 atoms will go over. (Not exactly, as there is the odd one to consider, but this means only that it is likely that 998 will go.) The reader does not need to continue with this form of arithmetic; he can see that, if we let N be the number of "parent" atoms left and n the number changing in a second, then we have the relation:

$$n = \frac{1}{1000} N$$

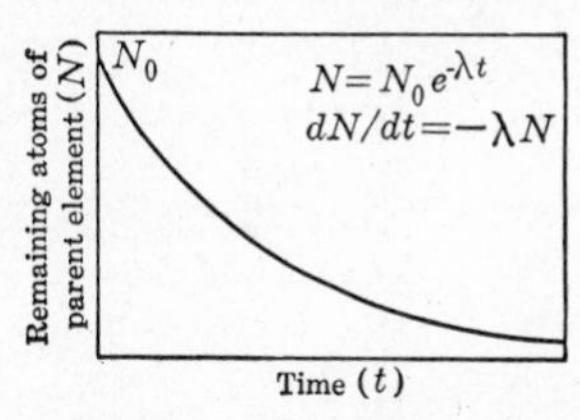

FIG. 1. Graph representing the number of atoms of a radioactive element left after different intervals of time. This is equivalent to a "decay curve." The curve corresponds to the relation $N = N_0 e^{-\lambda t}$ which is the same as $dN/dt = -\lambda N$, meaning that the rate of change is proportional to the number of atoms of the decaying element.

If we plot a graph of the number of atoms of the unstable or "parent" atoms left after different intervals of time it will appear somewhat as indicated in Fig. 1. The number diminishes rapidly at first, and then more slowly, approaching, but never reaching, zero after a long interval.

If we confine ourselves to examples of decay involving a very large number of atoms, then n, which in the above is the number changing in a second, can be considered a *rate of change*, and we can write a general relation which will determine the form of the curve of Fig. 1. This is

$$\frac{dN}{dt} = -\lambda N \quad [1]$$

The relation giving N explicitly is

$$N = N_0 e^{-\lambda t} \quad [2]$$

where N_0 is the initial number of atoms at the arbitrary starting time. The quantity λ is called the *disintegration constant* or *decay constant.* For ordinary use we can rewrite equation 2 by taking the logarithm of both sides, with the result:

$$\ln N_0 - \ln N = \lambda t \quad [3]$$

This is one of the most important equations in applied nuclear physics. It should be remembered that natural logarithms are used above, and that if common logarithms are used experimentally the value of the decay constant deduced without correction will be too small by the factor 2.30.

Equation 3 refers to the number of atoms of the parent element present, which is not usually measurable. It is far easier to observe the effects due to the radiations emitted during the actual change; this would mean observing an effect proportional to the *rate of decay* dN/dt. It follows from equation 1 that observation of dN/dt also gives us $-\lambda N$, so that we are observing a quantity which is proportional to the number of atoms present. If we put $N = \frac{-dN/dt}{\lambda}$ and $N_0 = \frac{-dN_0/dt}{\lambda}$ in equation 3 we get:

$$\ln \frac{dN_0}{dt} - \ln \frac{dN}{dt} = \lambda t$$

or if we put A_0 and A for the "activities" at the initial time and any time, respectively, these activities are directly proportional to dN_0/dt and dN/dt, so that we get the final relation:

$$\ln A_0 - \ln A = \lambda t$$

or in common logarithms

$$\log A_0 - \log A = \frac{\lambda}{2.30} t \qquad [4]$$

In Fig. 2 is shown the type of line resulting from plotting the common logarithm of the ionization current produced in a Lauritsen electroscope by a source of radiosodium against the time in hours. The sloping straight line can be seen to verify relation 4.

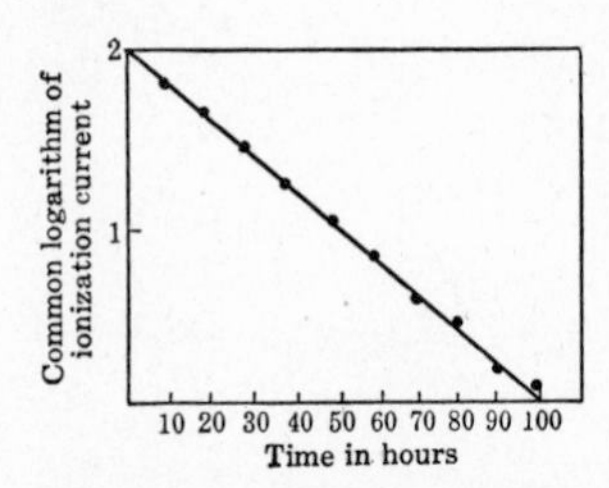

FIG. 2. Graph of the common logarithm of "activity," in this case ionization current produced in a Lauritsen electroscope by a radiosodium source plotted against the time in hours.

Although the most direct way of describing the decay of a radioactive element would be to give the value of the decay constant λ, this is not commonly done. It is more usual to describe it by giving the time required for the activity to fall to half its initial value. This "half-life" is the quantity usually given in tables of reference. Its relation to the decay constant is easily seen from equation 4. If we put the value of A as $A_0/2$ when the time is t_H, we get $\ln 2 = \lambda t_H$, or $t_H = \ln 2/\lambda$ or $0.693/\lambda$.

To obtain the half-life from a logarithmic plot as in Fig. 2, we do not need to calculate the decay constant, but merely find the time elapsed for the logarithm of the activity to fall by $\log_{10} 2$, or 0.301. Perhaps there is no harm in pointing out that it is quite immaterial where we choose the initial time; no matter how many atoms have decayed, the decay constant is the same for the remainder.

Energy of the Products of Radioactive Decay. The second feature of radioactivity which needs treating in detail is the energy of the products emitted. We have so far indicated that the process of radioactivity is the passage from an unstable to a stable nucleus, and we have said that this takes place by the conversion of a neutron into a proton. It can easily happen that the unstable nucleus attains stability by the conversion of a proton into a neutron; this often happens, and there is no essentially new feature about this method of adaptation except that the proton becomes a neutron and a positron. The emitted particle is then a positron and differs only from an electron in charge and in the fact that its production requires the using up of 1 Mev merely to create the positron. This need for an initial 1-Mev "starter" has interesting consequences which will be discussed later in the chapter. Whichever method of decay is found to take place it is still of interest to consider the energy of the emitted electron or positron.

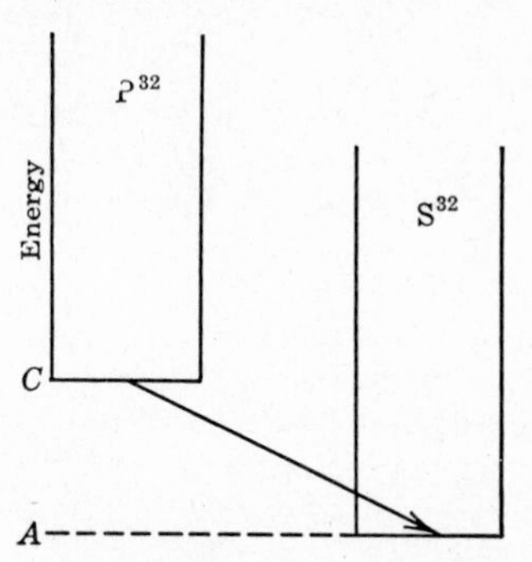

FIG. 3. Potential-energy wells for P^{32} and S^{32} with the ground states of each represented by the bottom of the well. The energy difference represented by AC is the energy available as kinetic energy for the electron, the neutrino, and the recoil atom.

A good way to see the process from the viewpoint of energy is to consider two energy-level diagrams for the initial nucleus and the final stable product. In Fig. 3 we have represented the nucleus of P^{32} and the stable nucleus S^{32} next to it. The upper "well" represents the unstable P^{32}, and the lower, the stable S^{32}. When the radioactive change takes place there is a release of energy represented on the diagram by the height AC. This energy when released causes motion; the distribution of the speeds of the particles concerned (which we at present suppose to be the daughter atom S^{32}, and the emitted electron) will be determined by the conservation of momentum. Since the mass of the atom of S^{32} is so much greater than that of the electron we expect the speed of the electron to be greatly in excess of that of the "recoil atom," and this means that virtually all the energy set free is given to the electron. The picture we have drawn leads us to predict that the radioactive decay of P^{32} will take place with the emission of electrons of one energy, that energy being a little less than the energy available from the difference in mass between P^{32} and S^{32}. Actually this is not so. *It is found that electrons having all energies up to a maximum value are emitted.* The maximum value is that which we would have expected to appertain to all the electrons, but it alone gives the necessary balance of energy.

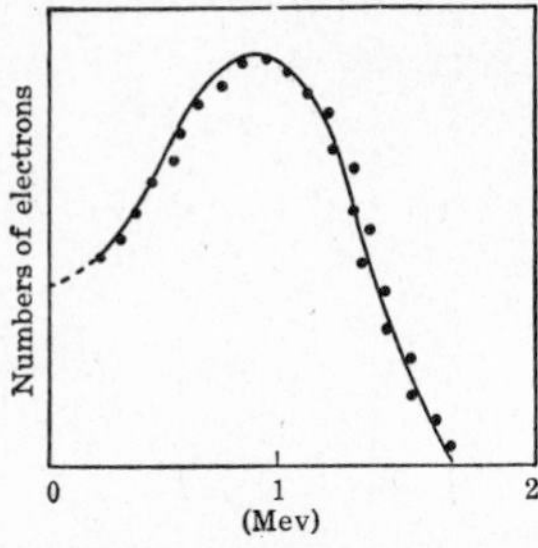

FIG. 4. Experimental distribution curve obtained by Lawson for the electrons from P^{32}. A roughly symmetrical curve is found, which agrees with the Fermi theory, indicating that the electron and neutrino, on the average, share the energy equally. The upper limit of 1.69 Mev corresponds to the difference in mass between P^{32} and stable S^{32}.

The explanation of this rather disconcerting fact has been given by Fermi, following a suggestion by Pauli. Fermi proposed that in addition to the electron a new particle, the "neutrino," having properties rather like a very light neutron, is emitted. This neutrino is hard to detect as it does not produce any effect on our measuring apparatus, but at the same time it is capable of carrying off energy. According to the Fermi theory the total disintegration energy, the energy equivalent to the mass difference between parent and daughter elements, is given as kinetic energy to the recoil atom, the electron, and the neutrino. Since the mass of the last two is so small relative to the first, they absorb virtually all the energy. Then if the electron takes all the energy and the neutrino none, the measured energy of the electron will be the disintegration energy. This fits the experimental observations. On the other hand it is also possible that the neutrino take all the energy, in which event the electron would not even be detectable. The emission of very low-energy electrons is actually found. It is clear that the chance of either of these extremes is rather small and that, somewhere in between, where there is rough equality of energy the chance will be much greater.

It is of practical importance to have some idea of the relative numbers of electrons with energies at various values short of the maximum. This information is given accurately by the Fermi theory, but as this involves relativistic quantum theory it is hard to give a simple explanation here. The result, when obtained, is rather complex, and it is not easy to compile a set of simple tables which will enable the distribution to be calculated in a given case. It is true, however, that the simple assumption that the electron and neutrino share energy on roughly equal terms is correct, and a glance at the distribution curve yielded by the Fermi theory shows that the most probable energy is about half the maximum energy, with a reasonably symmetrical distribution about that figure. The best experiments verify the theory quite accurately.

The distribution curve for the electrons from P^{32} is shown in Fig. 4. A distribution curve is one in which the number of electrons having energies between two limits is plotted against the average energy of the limits. If such a curve is plotted by observing the curvature of the electron tracks in a cloud chamber placed in a magnetic field, the observer will measure the curvature of, say, a thousand tracks, express the curvatures in terms of energy, and then lay out a dozen groups or so, with energies perhaps 200,000 electron volts apart. He then counts up the number of tracks in each interval and plots the values against the average energy appropriate, so producing a distribution curve. The best curves are usually obtained with a so-called beta-ray spectrometer, in which the beta rays are bent through a slit system by a magnetic field and then detected by a counter.* In the pioneer stages of the study of these distribution curves the cloud chamber placed in a magnetic field has the advantage that all the tracks can be seen and individually considered to be sure that they have the assigned energy; after the ground has been broken the spectrometer is more accurate as it allows the measurement of a much larger number of particle energies.

* We do not intend to explain the precise method of determining distribution curves, but, as the reader may consult original work for his own purposes, we feel that a word of explanation of the rather confusing terminology is in place. It is usual to describe the energy of the electron in terms of its curvature in a magnetic field. If we consider a slow electron, of velocity v, then this is equivalent to a current element idl of value ev, and in a magnetic field there will be exerted a force Hev perpendicular to the direction of motion of the electron, where H is the magnetic field intensity. This produces an acceleration perpendicular to the direction of motion and so causes the electron to follow a circular path of radius ρ, such that the applied force equals the mass times the acceleration due to the circular motion. In symbols this is:

$$Hev = \frac{mv^2}{\rho} \quad \text{or} \quad v = \left(\frac{e}{m}\right)(H\rho)$$

Thus the quantity $H\rho$ is proportional to the velocity of the electron. At high speeds these simple equations do not apply, as the mass of the electron is greater, but the quantity $H\rho$ still measures the momentum of the electron. It is therefore not an inconvenient way of describing the momentum, especially for experimenters in this field. A conversion formula to Mev is:

$$H\rho = \frac{10^4}{3}\left\{E(E + 1.02)\right\}^{1/2}$$

where H is in gauss, ρ in centimeters, and E in Mev.

We have mentioned this fact as it is so for almost all applications of the cloud chamber. It yields sure data but not a very large sampling. To return to the distribution curve itself. For experimental reasons the curve is incomplete near the region of zero energy, but the remainder shows a reasonably symmetrical distribution about a mean value of 0.85 Mev, and the maximum energy has the value 1.69 Mev, almost exactly double. It is of importance to notice that there is considerable loss if for any reason a counter or electroscope detects only high-energy electrons, for the numbers fall off rapidly once one has passed 80 per cent of the maximum. This matter of the detection of electrons will be treated fully later.

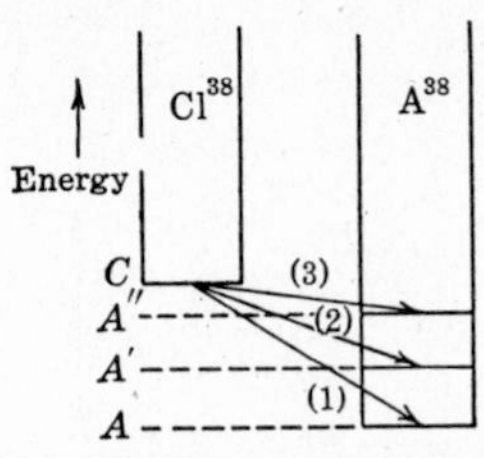

FIG. 5. Energy levels of unstable Cl^{38} and stable A^{38}. Cl^{38} decays into A^{38} by emitting an electron and a neutrino. If the transition is to the ground state as in (1) then the electron and neutrino have the full energy corresponding to the difference AC. If the transition is to the first excited state, the electron and neutrino take the energy $A'C$ and the excitation energy $A'A$ is emitted as gamma radiation. A transition to the second excited state will mean a third group of electrons and the subsequent emission of the excitation energy $A''A$ as one or two quanta.

If we now agree that the bell-shaped distribution curve is the expected type for a simple example where there is only one possible energy release, we have to inquire into the nature of the distribution which holds where the unstable nucleus can change into one or more excited states of the product nucleus. In Fig. 5 we show the "wells" for Cl^{38} and stable A^{38}. It happens that A^{38} has two excited states to which Cl^{38} could go. Referring to the figure we see that in addition to the transition marked (1), or ground state to ground state, there are two other possible transitions marked (2) and (3), or ground state to first and second excited states. It is found that each of these transitions has its own bell-shaped distribution curve, and the complete curve is the composite of the three. The total numbers in the separate bell-shaped curves are not easily predictable, but it often happens that the numbers occurring in the curves of less energy are greater. It is not impossible that in actual fact there are many cases of composite curves which have not yet been adequately analyzed, so that this rule must be taken as not finally established.

In Fig. 6 we show the experimentally obtained distribution curve for Cl^{38}, taken in this instance by the cloud-chamber method and plotted as a histogram. It can be seen that the general shape is different from that of P^{32} and that, though the data do not permit of a final analysis, it is not too great a stretch of the imagination to draw in the three curves as indicated and to regard the actual histogram as due to the superposition of the three. The three curves have maximum energies at 4.8, 2.8, and 1.1 Mev, respectively, and these figures mean that the energy available in each transition is one of three discrete values; these values correspond to the transitions given in Fig. 3. We can therefore deduce that the first excited state of A^{38} is 4.8 − 2.8 Mev above ground level. That is 2.0 Mev. The next state of excitation is 4.8 − 1.1 Mev, or 3.7 Mev above ground.

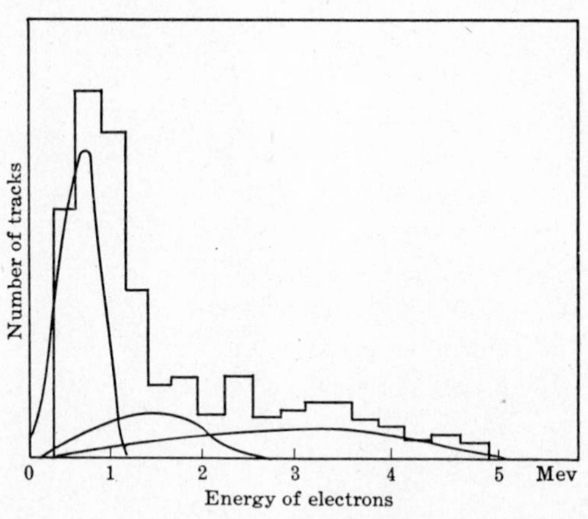

FIG. 6. Distribution histogram for the electrons from Cl^{38} which decays to A^{38} in both the ground state and two excited states. The histogram is the superposition of three symmetrical curves with maximum energies at 4.8, 2.8, and 1.1 Mev, approximately. Each maximum energy corresponds to a particular transition. Such a complex electron emission is always accompanied by gamma radiation.

Now, if this interpretation is right, the fact that the residual A^{38} is often left in an excited state must mean that at some later stage it will emit a gamma ray and return to ground level. This actually occurs, and as it is impossible for a nucleus to remain excited for longer than about 10^{-19} second (unless the degree of excitation is very small, or some great change of spin is involved), the gamma ray is emitted virtually simultaneously with the beta ray. This fact has led to some interesting work in which this coincidence in time between the gamma ray and the electron has been tested by a coincidence method of counting as described in the third chapter. The coincidence is verified, but the unexpected result is found that frequently there is also coincidence between an electron which apparently has the energy of a transition to the ground state, and a gamma ray. This means that the numbers in the true group of electrons which correspond to the ground-state transition are so small as to escape detection and lends support to the suggestion that the lower-energy groups are favored. In concluding this paragraph it should be pointed out that where the beta rays corresponding to such groups as these are considered, where one level of the parent atom decays to various levels of the product, all the beta rays decay with the same period.

Relation between Disintegration Energy and Half-Life: Influence of Structure. We have described the salient features of radioactive decay and particle emission; it now remains to discuss the relation between the rate of decay and the disintegration energy available in the transition. If we take the empirical approach to this subject and tabulate the maximum electron energies against the corresponding half-lives we see at once that there is a strong correlation between great maximum energy and short half-life. If we follow the procedure first used by Sargent and plot the logarithm of half-life against the logarithm of maximum energy we obtain clear indications that several groupings of radioactive elements exist and that within each group there is a relatively simple relation between maximum energy and half-life. In fact, if we set $t_H E^5 = K$, where t_H is the half-life, E the maximum energy, and K a quantity which is dependent on the atomic number and the particular grouping to which the radioactive element belongs, we obtain a very good description of the relation.

This empirical study is illuminated by viewing it in the light of the theory of beta-ray decay. On this theory we consider the parent nucleus and the daughter nucleus and inquire as to the probability of the passage from one to the other. The theory must include three considerations as follows: first, the actual process of change from neutron to proton, or vice versa; second, the energy available in the radioactive change; third, the structures of the original and final nuclei. We have already said that the theory indicates a bell-shaped distribution curve, which is verified by experiment. The complete expression given by the theory is complicated, but it is possible to give a simplified expression which is valid for many cases, namely, those in which the electron energy is greatly in excess of 0.5 Mev. This is

$$W_E^{E+dE} = (A)(G)^2 E^2 (E_m - E)^2 dE \qquad [5]$$

Here W_E^{E+dE} represents the probability that an electron having energy between E and $E + dE$ will be emitted in 1 second, A is a term which contains constants and a function describing the passage of the neutron into the proton, G is a term depending on the structures of the two nuclei concerned, and the remainder concerns the energy. E_m represents the maximum available energy.

We can obtain much valuable information from equation 5. In the first place we can see the reason for the relation between half-life and maximum energy. If we consider the *total* probability that an electron be emitted in 1 second no matter what its energy, we are considering the quantity λ of equation 1. This total probability can be obtained by integrating equation 5 from 0 to E_m, and since

$$\int_0^{E_m} \{E^2(E_m - E)^2\} dE = \frac{E_m{}^5}{30}$$

we obtain

$$\lambda = K_1 E^5$$

where K_1 is a constant, or because $t_H = \ln 2/\lambda$

$$t_H E^5 = K \qquad [6]$$

where K is again a constant. This is the relation found empirically.

It is now of interest to study the nature of K. This can be seen from equation 5 to involve A, the term describing the transition from neutron to proton, a term which will presumably be the same for all such radioactive changes; and $(G)^2$, the term which we said involved the structure of the initial and final nuclei. Now the term "structure" applied to the atom requires care. It is one of the tenets of quantum mechanics that the actual detailed appearance of the atom cannot be ascertained, so that, although the atom clearly has structure, it is useless to attempt to describe it, as it were, photographically. Theory has shown that the quantities most concerned with structure are angular momentum and "spin," and it is in terms of these that we must discuss the effect of structure in nuclei. For example, an atom can be in a state in which its energy is so distributed that there is no net angular momentum. The distribution of the function which gives the chance of finding an electron at any place is then spherically symmetrical. Atoms with varying amounts of angular momentum have varying kinds of symmetry ranging from cigar shape to quite complicated shapes. The term $(G)^2$ will thus be concerned with the angular momenta of the initial and final nuclei. It will also depend on the actual size of the nuclei. If these two factors can be considered the term in $(G)^2$ can be useful in predicting nuclear transitions.

We can dismiss the effect of nuclear size fairly shortly. Nuclear size changes relatively little from nucleus to nucleus so that the expected effect of this quantity would be to cause a gradual difference between elements as the atomic weight became greater. This is probably the reason why, even in the same grouping, elements of high and low atomic number do not have the same numerical value for K in equation 6. The effect of shape, or of angular momentum, is much more important. Atomic transitions are profoundly affected by the angular momenta of the two states involved in the transition. A good example of this is given by ortho- and para-hydrogen. The difference between these two forms of hydrogen is in the directions of the "spins" of the two protons forming the nuclei of the molecule. In para-hydrogen the spins of the two are opposite so that their contribution to the total angular momentum is zero; in ortho-hydrogen the two are in the same direction so that the total nuclear angular momentum is (in conventional units) unity. This apparently small difference is sufficient to render the transition from one to the other completely forbidden; the transition can take place only if a third body is present to introduce some perturbation which renders the change possible.

It is therefore easy to see that a radioactive change which required the passage from one nucleus to another with very different angular momentum would be "forbidden" and that therefore $(G)^2$ would be abnormally small. The calculation of such transition probabilities is very difficult, but numerous experimental cases bear out the truth of this analysis. One example can be given. It has been known for a long time that potassium is radioactive. It has been shown that the isotope responsible is K^{40}, and that the electron energy has the maximum value of 0.7 Mev. We can compare this with Si^{31} having a maximum energy of 1.8 Mev and a half-life of 2.8 hours. Applying equation 6 we expect K^{40} to have a half-life of about 300 hours. This short time would preclude its existence as a nearly stable isotope, which fact requires a half-life of 10^9 years. The transition from K^{40} to Ca^{40} thus is highly "forbidden," and this means that a great difference of angular momentum between the two nuclei must exist. Theory suggests that such a difference as three or four conventional units would be needed to explain the relative stability of K^{40}. Recently Zacharias has shown that the angular momentum of K^{40} is 4, while that of Ca^{40} was known to be zero. The theory is thus nicely verified. The explanation of the various groupings is thus that transitions are either "allowed," with no change of angular momentum, or "forbidden," with a change of one or more units. Within each grouping equation 6 holds.

In the table below we give some sample elements and the values for $t_H E^5$. For positron emission the observed upper limit is increased by 1 Mev to allow the formation of the positron. The figures are given in Mev to the fifth power times minutes.

ELEMENT	$t_H E^5$	GROUPING
C^{10}	240	1
C^{11}	590	"
N^{13}	505	"
B^{12}	91	"
O^{15}	290	"
F^{20}	630	"
Na^{24}	4,750	2
SI^{31}	3,200	"
P^{32}	285,000	3
Cl^{38}	117,000	"
V^{52}	142	1
Mn^{56}	37,000	3
As^{78}	350	1
Br^{78}	2,500	2
Ag^{110}	33	1
Ag^{108}	395	2 or 1
93^{239}	770	2

The groupings can be seen reasonably clearly, although at the same time there is no exact constancy or well-marked trend. It can be seen that the product tends to become less as the atomic number increases, as would be expected from the influence of the increase in nuclear size, which tends to increase the transition probability.

The utility of this rule is more apparent when it is applied to predict maximum energies. Thus, for example, Ne^{23}, which has a half-life of 40 seconds, can be assumed to be in the first grouping with a value of K close to that of F^{20}, say 600. The value of E^5 is then 600/0.66 or 900, and E should be 3.9 Mev. Actually it is 4.1 Mev as found by absorption. The same reasoning predicts a value of 3.3 Mev for the positrons from Na^{21}, whose maximum energy had not been measured at the time of writing. It is possible that by the time of publication this will have been accomplished and the reader may be able to judge the value of the rule for himself.

Nuclear Isomerism. While we are considering energy relationships it is in place to describe the phenomenon of *nuclear isomerism.* This was mentioned in Chapter 5 in discussing the (γn) type of reaction, and it was described as the case where a single radioactive isotope could have more than one decay period and yet decay to the same element. A little earlier in this chapter we said that a nucleus would not "hold" excitation energy if it could release it as radiation; the time of excitation is of the order of 10^{-19} second. We also, however, mentioned the possibility of exceptions to this rule. The exceptional cases were those in which the amount of excitation energy is small and also where the change to the ground state would involve a considerable change of angular momentum. Now if we consider a *parent* nucleus which is formed in an excited state of such a sort, it might remain in a state of excitation long enough for it to decay before it lost its excitation energy, in which event the excess energy would be added to the energy normally available for the beta ray and an abnormally fast electron would emerge. This idea can be seen more easily from Fig. 7, in which an energy-level diagram similar to Fig. 3 is shown for two hypothetical elements X and Y. The element X has an excited state C' a little above the ground state C; this level is metastable, probably on account of a great difference of angular momentum between it and the ground state. Now, if it takes a long time for the transition from C' to C to occur, there will be time for the element X to decay while still in the excited state and the energy of excitation CC' will be given to the resulting beta ray. Now the decay by method (1) of the diagram, by first passage to the ground state and then the final transition, depends on the time it takes for the passage to the ground state, and this is not connected with the ordinary beta decay period. We thus expect that there will be two rates of decay: the one the ordinary beta decay, as indicated in the diagram by (2); the other the double transition by route (1). It can be seen that this phenomenon of nuclear isomerism, many examples of which are now known, is likely to be complicated also by the transition in either case to excited states. The process of sorting complex beta-ray spectra is still going on. One example of nuclear isomerism which is of interest in applied radioactivity is Br^{80}, which decays to Kr^{80} with two half-value periods: 18 minutes, by direct beta decay as in route (2) of the diagram; and 4.4 hours, by the double transition of route (1). A question has arisen whether the excited nucleus in state C' would modify the chemical reactions of the atom itself. This is an important question to answer as it affects the whole validity of the tracer method.

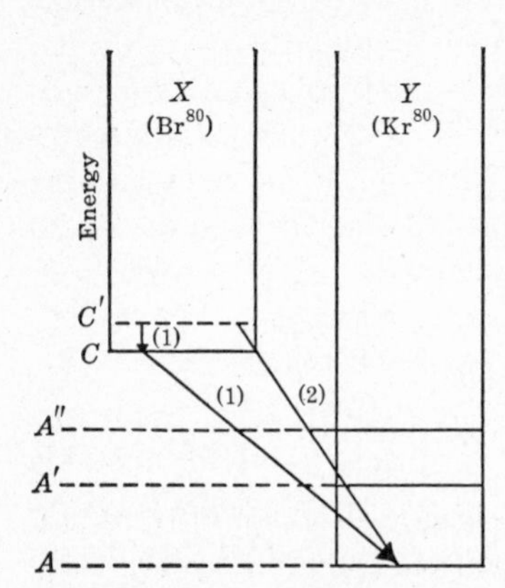

FIG. 7. Nuclear isomerism. An unstable element X has, in addition to the ground state C, a metastable state C' whose angular momentum differs greatly from that of C so that the transition C' to C takes place about as rapidly as the direct decay from C' to A. Then the element X partly decays from C' as in (2) and partly by the double change, first to C and then to A as in (1).

Emission of Gamma Radiation. Although the emission of gamma radiation has been mentioned as a natural consequence of the possibility of decay to an excited state of the product nucleus, a little elaboration will do no harm. If one looks through the list of radioactive elements and their properties given in the Appendix, it can be seen that about a third of the elements are simple, in the sense that they emit only beta rays; the remainder emit gamma rays in addition. This emission of gamma rays is a great help in many counting experiments as their presence permits the detection of the radioactive material through great thicknesses of material. The amount of gamma radiation emitted depends on the relative numbers of transitions to excited states. Thus no general rule can be stated as to which elements will give intense gamma radiations, and it is necessary to consult tables to obtain information on this point.

Positron Emission and *K*-Electron Capture. We have made the point that the process of radioactivity, the passage from an unstable nucleus to a more stable, does not imply that the adaptation always requires the change of a neutron into a proton, electron, and a neutrino; the reverse process of the transition of a proton into a neutron, a positron, and a neutrino can also take place. If this occurs the detected charged particle is now a positron, and, as one or two features of positron emission differ from electron emission, they should now be considered. The first difference has already been mentioned: the fact that a positron is really a "hole" in the states of negative kinetic energy requires that at least 1 Mev of energy be supplied to eject an electron from a place in these states of negative kinetic energy and so create a positron. If there is less than 1 Mev of available energy due to the difference of mass between the initial atom and the daughter atom, the emission of a positron cannot take place, and in any event, the kinetic energy possessed by the positron for a given amount of disintegration energy is always less than that of an electron by this amount of 1 Mev. Thus N^{13} emits positrons with a maximum energy of 1.20 Mev, while the difference in mass between N^{13} and the product C^{13} is 2.22 Mev.

The reader will have natural curiosity as to the events expected if two atoms are found in which the difference of mass is less than 1 Mev, and such that the more stable requires the emission of a positron from the less. Such atoms do occur, and the passage to stability is effected by the absorption of an electron from the outer atom—one of the rare cases in which we become conscious of the existence of the ordinary electronic structure. In any atom the innermost shell of electrons, the *K* shell, possesses no angular momentum, and therefore the function which describes the probability of finding one of these electrons has a definite value inside the nucleus. One is not surprised that this fact makes it possible for an unstable nucleus to have a tendency to absorb this electron permanently and so gain stability. This process, known as "*K*-electron capture," has several interesting features.

They can be understood from a definite example. The nucleus V^{47} has been shown by Walke, Williams, and Evans to be of this type; it is radioactive by *K*-electron capture to form Ti^{47}. The half-life is 600 days. There is not sufficient energy to cause positron emission, and so an electron of the *K*-shell is absorbed by the nucleus. This now produces Ti^{47}, *with an electron missing in the K-shell*, which missing electron must be replaced to render the atom neutral. The filling of this shell causes the emission of the x-rays characteristic of the *K*-shell of *titanium*, not vanadium, and by the presence of this x-radiation the process of *K*-electron capture can be detected; by showing the radiation to be characteristic of titanium and not vanadium the explanation of the process is shown to be correct. Notice that to detect *K*-electron capture we need counting technique which will respond to rather soft x-radiation. It may happen that enough energy is available to cause the absorption of the *K*-shell electron and the emission of gamma radiation also, as in Be^7, which goes to Li^7 with the absorption of an electron and also the emission of a 0.45-Mev gamma ray. Notice that the energy of the gamma ray is always rather small, generally below 1 Mev. Where this gamma radiation is also emitted the detection is easier as ordinary counters are satisfactory.

Positron emission is always accompanied by a by-product in the form of annihilation radiation. The positrons have a transient existence, and, especially in the presence of absorbing material of high atomic number such as lead, there is a considerable production of 0.5-Mev gamma radiation due to the "annihilation" of the positron, or rather the filling of the "hole" in the states of negative kinetic energy, which appears to be a positive particle. This was explained more fully in Chapter 2. The result is that there is always the appearance of gamma radiation from positron emitters, but great care must be taken if the radioactivity is detected by means of this radiation, as the amount varies with the nature of the material around the apparatus, thus giving erratic readings. The annihilation radiation is not generated in the primary radioactive substance, but as a secondary product in absorbing material near by.

"Parent" and "Daughter" Elements. We have so far described the fact of radioactivity as the process of reversion to type. Only a limited number of processes is available for this readjustment, and it is therefore not surprising if the final adjustment does not take place in one radioactive change. Many such atoms are known, as for example the decay of Co^{55} into Fe^{55} by the emission of a positron, followed by the change of Fe^{55} into Mn^{55} by *K*-capture. The Mn^{55} is finally stable. The second radioactive element is called the "daughter" of the first "parent" element. The discovery of the growth of one element from another is often of the greatest value as a means of identification.

Alpha-Particle Emission. The great change that has been introduced into the subject of radioactivity by the discovery of artificial radioactivity can be judged by the fact that we have delayed until now the mention of alpha-particle emission. From being one of the more important methods of radioactive decay, this has shifted to become a rather freakish phenomenon, virtually confined to a few heavy elements. It is of comparatively little importance in tracer work, but at the same time it offers further information about the nature of radioactivity and so should be discussed. It has been stressed that radioactivity is the passage from an unstable to a stable nucleus. In the foregoing it has been assumed that the adaptation is by the change of a neutron into a proton, or vice versa, but there is no real reason why this should be the only method of adaptation. Any method which permits stability to be reached will be expected to take place, but not all such methods will give rise to radioactivity, which is a process which occupies time. Now it can perfectly easily happen that a nucleus is formed which could adapt itself to stability by the emission of a proton or a neutron, but such adaptation would take place at once. In fact, such nuclei are the "intermediate nuclei" of transmutation experiments, discussed in the previous chapter, whose times of existence are so short as hitherto to have been unmeasurable. There is, however, one way in which the lifetime of such nuclei could be longer than instantaneous; if the potential barrier were very high and the excitation energy very small, the probability of passage through the barrier would be so small that the charged particle would make many transits of the inside of the potential well before actually appearing outside. This would be true especially of the excitation of an alpha particle, which, being doubly charged and having a high mass, is subject to confinement by a barrier of low penetrability. In addition the alpha particle can be emitted cheaply, on account of its low mass excess (4.0039 compared with 1.0081 for a proton), and this acts to favor alpha-particle emission, as less energy is required to make the balance of mass and kinetic energy. We wish to make the point that any form of adaptation to produce stability can be thought of in a general way as radioactivity; alpha-particle emission is more favorable for long-lived processes of adaptation.

The details of the process are usually explained by the type of diagram in Fig. 8. This is similar to the diagrams of transmutation processes shown in the previous chapter. The alpha particle is thought of as moving under the influence of the rest of the nucleus, which will be the daughter nucleus after the separation has taken place. It is supposed to have enough energy of excitation so that it could escape, a fact represented on the diagram by a positive value for the line *EF* which denotes the level occupied by the alpha particle. The existence of the potential barrier, which is due to the superposition of the coulomb repulsion on the attractive nuclear field, renders the escape of the alpha particle possible, but subject to being hampered by the necessity of penetrating the barrier: in more accurate language, the alpha particle has, at each collision it makes with the walls at *E* or *F*, a finite chance of penetration. The greater this chance, the fewer transits of the distance *EF* will be necessary before the alpha particle escapes. This chance depends markedly on the height and thickness of the barrier to be penetrated, and these in turn depend on the distances *EG* and *ED* or finally on the degree of excitation of the alpha particle if the shape of the barrier is, in general, the same for different cases. We therefore predict that, if fast alpha particles are observed, the half-life of the emitting element will be short, and if the alpha particles are slow the half-life will be very much longer. This explains the rule found empirically by Geiger and Nuttall, that the logarithm of the half-life is proportional to the logarithm of the energy of emission of the alpha particles. It is not exact, and this deviation from exactness is laid to the variation in the potential barriers from one radioactive element to another. Alpha-particle emission is thus observed virtually only among very heavy elements where the potential barriers are high and also the increased importance of the coulomb forces in the nuclei renders elements unstable with respect to alpha-particle emission.

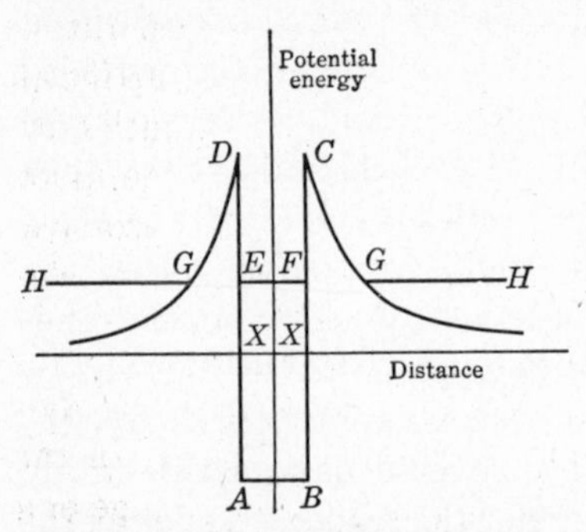

FIG. 8. Alpha-particle emission. The alpha particle has enough excess energy *EX* to escape, but is held back by the potential barrier. It therefore continues to move from *E* to *F* inside the well, but as the barrier has a finite thickness, the particle has a finite time to escape at each collision with *E* or *F*. In time it will do so, its half-life being less, the greater the available energy *EX*.

Radioactive Series. A final consequence of heavy-element decay is that it makes possible the existence of long chains of decaying elements.

Thus, when an element adapts itself by converting a neutron into a proton, for example, it will, in general, have completed the adjustment. However, this is not true for alpha-particle emission. In the region of the elements where alpha-particle decay takes place, there is a great excess of neutrons over protons. The emission of an alpha particle, which takes out two protons with only two neutrons attached to them, tends to increase this excess, and it may well happen that the excess is too great for stability, which accordingly gives rise to ordinary electron emission. This means that the alpha-particle emission is accompanied by beta-ray emission from the daughter element, and we have a chain of radioactive decay. Three such chains have been known for a long time: the thorium, uranium, and actinium series. The feature of these series is the approximate alternation of alpha-particle emission with beta-ray emission. They may be explained roughly as due to the tendency for the highly charged nuclei to eject alpha particles, followed by a tendency to diminish the resulting neutron excess by beta decay.

The subject of natural radioactivity is covered quite satisfactorily in several standard works, to which we refer the reader. As far as the use of naturally radioactive elements in tracer work and other applications is concerned, they may be treated as being the same as artificial products.

To summarize this chapter we may repeat that radioactivity is the passage from an unstable nucleus to a more stable, the change generally being accompanied by the emission of a charged particle which has enough energy to ionize. The commonest process of adaptation is the change of a neutron into a proton, electron, and neutrino; or a proton into a neutron, positron, and neutrino; the rate of the change depends on the available energy according to the relation $E^5 \times$ (half-life) is roughly constant. The energy is divided *on the average* equally between the electron or positron and the neutrino, resulting in a bell-shaped distribution curve, whose maximum value is the "disintegration energy." The rate of decay is proportional to the number of atoms ready to decay, giving a logarithmic decay curve. The existence of excited states in the daughter nucleus can give rise to the emission of gamma radiation, which modifies the distribution curve to a superposition of several curves and favors the emission of electrons of less energy. If a metastable state exists in the parent element, two decay periods are possible for the same radioactive change—the phenomenon of nuclear isomerism. Positron emission differs from electron emission in requiring the extra energy of 1 Mev to create the positron and also in the accompaniment of "annihilation radiation." When there is insufficient energy to effect the creation of a positron, an electron is captured instead, a process known as K-electron capture. Alpha-particle emission occurs among the heavier elements where there are high potential barriers and considerable coulomb forces; it is generally accompanied by subsequent beta emission giving rise to a radioactive series.

We have now covered the necessary account of the nature of nuclear physics sufficiently to make its applications intelligible; in the next chapter we shall consider the manufacture and counting of radioactive elements in some detail.

REFERENCES

HEVESEY and PANETH, *A Manual of Radioactivity*, Oxford University Press, 1938. An excellent and readable account of classical radioactivity with sufficient modern material to make the book most valuable to one who wishes to go more deeply into radioactivity as a subject of study.

J. CHADWICK, *Radioactivity and Radioactive Substances*, Pitman and Sons, 1932. An amazingly compact account of classical radioactivity. Possibly the most perfect short technical "handbook" ever written.

GLENN T. SEABORG, "Artificial Radioactivity," *Chemical Reviews*, **27**, 199, 1940. An invaluable review article, with excellent tables.

CHAPTER 7

TECHNIQUE IN ARTIFICIAL RADIOACTIVITY

This chapter will frankly be written for the individual who is interested in making actual measurements which involve artificial radioactivity. If we were considerate we would advise the general reader to pass on to more rewarding chapters, but as he has taken the trouble to obtain this book we do not see why we should not make the claim that the material in this chapter is as interesting as the remainder and let him prove us to be in the wrong after perusal. The physicist is often accused of being rather aloof, of regarding the applications of his subject as beneath his consideration once he has mastered it; and it may seem to some of our readers that we have in a sense been "holding out" on them until now, for we have not faced any practical problems as yet, and the question may be arising whether we ever intend to do so. This chapter is the answer.

We may begin with the problem of observation of various elements since it is usually this problem that the actual worker has to solve while he is waiting for the physicist to manufacture the sources for his experiments. The question to be answered will always appertain to a particular problem and cannot be answered without thought applied to that problem itself. For example, one might be interested in a problem requiring radioactive sulphur, and a glance at some tables would show that S^{35} has a half-life of 88 days and emits a beta ray. This is a sufficiently long half-life to make it plausible that S^{35} could be used in experiments in animals and followed during their lifetime by counters outside the animal. Actually the beta ray has a maximum energy of only 0.1 Mev; no gamma ray is emitted; and the sulphur would be undetectable through even the skin of the animal. The experiment would therefore fail.

General Considerations in Counting. With this example it may appear that the problem of determining whether a piece of research is to be attempted is one for the expert alone to decide. This is only partly true. A great deal of the problem of counting is related to the question whether the radiation from the radioactive substance can enter the counting mechanism or not. This means that *absorption* is of prime importance in deciding the feasibility of an experiment. Now in the second chapter we described the various types of radiation, and in the third the various types of counting technique. It generally happens that the detection is by means of the effects of beta radiation, and therefore it is in place to consider the absorption of beta radiation first. We made the point in the second chapter that, while a beta ray of a definite energy had a certain maximum range, its path through matter was devious and one could not be sure that the thickness of absorber which would stop the radiation from reaching a counter would represent the thickness corresponding to the energy of the particular electron. This is a real limitation in making measurements of beta-ray energies by absorption, but it is not particularly annoying if one is merely interested in making sure that counting methods will work in a given experiment. In practice one can allot to a beta ray of a given energy a definite thickness of material which it can penetrate. One must be ready to find that this is an average value, not accurately followed every time, but a perfectly good guide. The thickness of material depends on the substance used to act as absorber, but not markedly so if one expresses the absorption in terms *weight per square centimeter* instead of actual thickness.

By and large the absorption depends on the numbers of electrons passed in the material, and in a square centimeter of any material having the same weight there are about the same number of electrons; thus the thickness of gold which will just stop a 1-Mev electron is roughly 0.5 gram per sq cm, while the same electron would have been stopped by 0.4 gram per sq cm thickness of aluminum. In point of fact the thickness (mass per square centimeter) of any material which will stop an electron of given energy depends on the ratio of the nuclear mass to the nuclear charge; the greater this ratio the less effective the material is, and therefore the greater the thickness which must be interposed to be correspondingly effective.

It may happen that the idea of measuring the thickness of an absorber in mass per unit area is unfamiliar to the reader. If this is so we might mention that it is common practice in all kinds of nuclear absorption work to use this way of expression, partly because very thin films can be measured more accurately this way, and partly because it comes close to measuring the really effective quantity; if one measured the number of electrons per unit area it would be still better, but this is rather too far from ordinary practical measurement. To take a definite example, we could consider a thickness of 1 mm of aluminum, which is a very average absorption thickness for beta-ray experiments. This would have a volume of 0.1 cc for every square centimeter of its area; and, as its density is 2.6, the mass per unit area would be 0.26 gram.

We can thus see from the figure quoted above that to stop a 1-Mev electron would require 1.52 mm thickness of aluminum. The same reasoning leads to a thickness of 0.26 mm for gold. As a very rough guide we can give the rule: $t \times d = 0.54E_m - 0.16$. Here t is the *thickness measured in centimeters*, d is the density in grams per cubic centimeters, and E_m is the maximum energy of the electron in Mev. This rule must be considered a rough guide only, but with that proviso it applies to any substance used as absorber. We shall refer to it as the *rough beta-ray formula*.

We can now try out the rule for one or two examples and see what else we need to know. Let us suppose that we wish to count radiophosphorus, P^{32}, with its maximum energy of 1.7 Mev. Suppose also that we have available a counter with a glass wall 1 mm thick and a copper electrode 0.25 mm thick. How effective will this be, and is much to be gained by an elaborately constructed thin-walled counter or electroscope? The density of glass is 2.5 gram per cc; of copper, 8.9 gram per cc; using the rough beta-ray formula we find that this counter will stop all electrons of less energy than 1.2 Mev. In obtaining this result we add the separate products of thickness and density to get the left-hand side of the rough beta-ray equation. A glance at tables will show that P^{32} does not emit any gamma radiation, and we can therefore plot a rough distribution curve for the emitted electrons by drawing a bell-shaped curve with the maximum at the half-limiting energy of 0.85 Mev: this shows roughly that one-quarter the area under the curve or one-quarter the total number of electrons emitted has energy greater than the value of 1.2 Mev corresponding to the least energy which will suffice to enter the counter. Thus, though there is no doubt that the counter will readily detect the electrons from P^{32}, it will be rather inefficient. It would have been better to use thinner glass and thinner copper; the rough beta-ray formula shows that halving the thicknesses of both would permit electrons of 0.75 Mev to register, and this would count 60 per cent of the total electrons emitted.

All further improvements are not very rewarding as it gets increasingly difficult to diminish thickness and the counter is already sensitive to the majority of the electrons emitted. To save the reader a little trouble we might say here that an ordinary counter, constructed without special precautions, will permit beta rays of energies between 0.6 and 0.9 Mev to register. Thin-walled counters can be made which will count as low as 0.1 Mev; below this it is necessary to use electroscopes or actually put the material in the counter itself.

Before we consider these more elaborate techniques we might apply the rough formula above to another substance, Ca^{45}, the 180-day calcium isotope. This has a maximum energy of 0.7 Mev, but at the same time emits gamma rays of two energies, 0.9 Mev and 0.2 Mev, which are useful in the respect that they ensure the detection of the radioelement through large thicknesses of material, but rather annoying in that they greatly diminish the number of electrons associated with high energies. As the Ca^{45} must be prepared from a rare isotope of calcium, and has a long half-life, it is difficult to prepare in large amounts, and so its detection is likely to be a borderline matter and not readily achieved by the relatively inefficient method of observing the secondary electrons ejected by gamma radiation. The counter should therefore be of the thin-walled variety, say one-third the thickness of the example above, and then a great advantage will be gained over the use of an ordinary counter. In the Appendix we present a discussion of the absorption of beta rays which will enable the appropriate counting technique to be decided. In self-defense we should say here that we do not claim that all the figures given are accurate; they are intended to serve as a guide, not as a reference for research in nuclear physics.

The reader who may be intending to ask for a grant to buy apparatus may like to know why sometimes counters are used and sometimes electroscopes. Both have their advocates; a well-equipped institution should own both. The electroscope is probably the more universally useful, and a determined experimenter can adapt an electroscope to fulfill any function that can be satisfied by a counter except the registering of coincidences. For this reason the counter is used most commonly in cosmic-ray work where whole trays of counters working together are commonplace. The Geiger counter is, on the surface, the most sensitive detecting agent since it unquestionably detects a single fast particle, and no more can be asked of it; this fact, however, is not all, as a counter also has inevitably a background count, of the order of 2 per minute per square centimeter of surface of the electrode, and so it is not really practicable to detect less than half the background. This is a serious limitation on an apparently perfect detector, as it requires a source capable of producing about 10 impulses per minute to detect. The electroscope, supposing that the insulation is perfect and that it is shielded carefully, can have a very slow rate of leak; for example, a Lauritsen electroscope has a rate of leak of about 5 divisions per hour, while a source capable of producing 10 pulses per minute in a Geiger counter will add 2 more divisions per hour. The source that can be readily detected by a Geiger counter can thus also be detected by a Lauritsen electroscope. The main difference is that it would take two hours to determine the rate of leak of the electroscope, while the Geiger counter would have yielded complete information in a few minutes.

For rapid work with weak sources the Geiger counter is to be preferred. For ordinary, run-of-the-mill counting of easy elements there is not much choice. The electroscope comes into its own when *slow electrons* have to be counted.

The way in which an electron ionizes as its speed is reduced is of great interest. We give below a short table relating the number of ions produced in a 1-cm path in air by electrons of various energies. Notice that the less the speed the greater the ionization; in fact, a simple relation holds between the *velocity* of the fast electron and the ionization per centimeter. If this ionization is called I, then Iv^2 is a constant, v being the velocity of the electron. This relation is a little troublesome to use as the velocity of an electron of given energy must be calculated by allowing for the change of mass with velocity, and the table is a more convenient way of seeing what happens.

TABLE 1

Energy of Electron in Mev	Ionization Produced in 1 cm of Air (Ion Pairs)
0.05	250
0.10	175
0.20	96
0.30	76
0.50	60
1.00	53

The difference between a counter and an electroscope is that the counter is a "trigger-action" instrument, which records large and small ionization in its sensitive volume equally well, whereas the electroscope records the ionization, giving large readings for large ionization. In the usual Lauritsen electroscope there is a path length of about 7 cm; and an electron of 0.1 Mev, which will just traverse the air in the ionization chamber, will produce 1400 ion pairs, while a fast electron of, say, 1 Mev will produce only 350 ion pairs. It is clear that the electroscope is operating more favorably in detecting slow electrons than fast, and this coupled with the fact that there is no need for a thick case to hold a vacuum as in a Geiger counter which would prevent the entry of slow electrons, makes the electroscope very suitable for detecting low-energy electrons.

Before we consider the counting of gamma radiation it is of interest to consider one or two consequences of the ionization relation given above. It may be desired to employ electroscope technique to count fast electrons which produce relatively little ionization. The sensitivity can then be greatly increased by using an ionization chamber at several atmospheres' pressure. In many respects this is the best way of detecting electrons. The use of high pressure increases the number of atoms of air in the path of the fast electrons on their way through the ionization chamber, and so increases the number of ions formed.

To give an example: it would be possible to obtain the same number, 1400, of ions, with the same ionization chamber traversed by 1-Mev electrons as was formed by slow electrons; this would be achieved by filling the ionization chamber to 4 atmospheres. This type of ionization chamber has the advantage that it can be made to be recording and is not subject to variations in sensitivity if the pressure is kept the same. It is also common practice to fill the ionization chamber with some heavy vapor such as SO_2 or methyl iodide, which fulfills the same purpose.

The question of constant sensitivity is important. An electroscope is generally well protected from mechanical disturbance and will always have the same properties. This is also true of a Geiger counter if it is carefully sealed and is constructed to have a good "plateau" so that extraordinary precautions to ensure constancy of the voltage supply are not required. Nevertheless, the recording equipment is more elaborate, and unless the operator is sure of his business it is quite possible that some factor (e.g., the bias on the thyratron recorder) will vary and this will introduce a varying sensitivity. Therefore it is easier to secure foolproof constancy of operation with an electroscope than with a counter, and it is especially preferable to follow electroscope technique for work where long-lived elements are concerned and comparison has to be made between readings taken several days apart. With these considerations in mind the reader can decide for himself which method of observation to adopt.

Gamma-Ray Counting. The counting of gamma radiation is the next matter to consider. Gamma rays are not counted directly; it is the secondary electrons that they produce that cause the ionization necessary to be detected. This fact should be considered carefully. The radiation has various methods of interacting with electrons (or any charged particle), and these produce various effects. For instance the photoelectric effect means that the whole energy of the gamma-ray quantum is given to an electron in one occurrence; the formation of a pair of electrons also uses up the whole gamma-ray energy; on the other hand the process of Compton recoil imparts only a fraction to the electron. As far as counting the gamma ray is concerned we need mostly to note that the radiation produces secondary electrons which have somewhere near the energy of the incident gamma radiation, and that it is these electrons which must be detected.

It is still true that absorption plays a fundamental part in the design of a detecting apparatus, but in a rather different way because the absorber has two effects: the first is the usual stopping of the electrons; the second is the actual formation of the fast secondaries. The second effect introduces important differences. Electromagnetic radiation will interact only with charged particles, so that unless some charged particles are encountered there will be no effect on the gamma radiation. As soon as material containing electrons is placed in its path the radiation has a chance of interacting with the electrons and losing energy to them; this means that initially the number of secondary electrons increases as the thickness of material interposed increases. What happens as the amount of material is still further increased depends on the energy of the gamma radiation, for, if it is great, the electrons produced will not be absorbed until a considerable thickness of matter is interposed, whereas if it is small the secondary electrons will have rather low energy and will be absorbed by a small thickness of matter. There is thus an increase in the yield of secondary electrons as matter is interposed in the way of the radiation up to a thickness at which the electrons begin to be absorbed. Therefore counters with thick walls are better for gamma-ray counting than thin-walled counters; in fact, there is also an improvement if a heavy element such as gold is used as the electrode of the Geiger counter.

Absorption of Gamma Radiation. A word here on the absorption of gamma radiation in general will be useful. The three processes of interaction of radiation with matter—photoelectric effect, pair formation, and Compton recoil—all contribute to the absorption. All three are different in nature. There is, however, the similarity among all three that the moment of interaction cannot be predicted, only a probability of interaction. This means that gamma radiation is never completely absorbed by any finite thickness of material, for if we have a source emitting many gamma-ray quanta there is always a chance that one of them will not interact with an electron until it has passed the absorption screens interposed, no matter how thick they are.

Notice that any *one* gamma-ray quantum is often completely absorbed; it is a large number from a source that cannot be absorbed *for sure*. We can express this fact that there is a probability of an interaction by saying that in any thickness dx of material a number dN of quanta interact with electrons. We can suppose for simplicity that each interaction removes the quantum concerned, a supposition true for the first two methods of interaction but only partly true for the third (although the difference introduces no change in the form of the relation we are about to derive); then with this assumption dN represents the number of gamma rays absorbed in the thickness dx. We can then represent the statement that the chance of interaction in a thickness dx is a constant by the relation:

$$\frac{dN}{N} = -kdx$$

(where "k" is a constant), which leads to the result:

$$N = N_0 e^{-kx}$$

or putting it in a more convenient form

$$\log N_0 - \log N = k_1 x$$

where k_1 is a different constant clearly related to k.

This form of relationship for the absorption of radiation was stated in the second chapter; we have now shown the assumptions on which it is based. The constant k is referred to as the absorption coefficient. With different materials, different absorption coefficients must be used, a fact which is rather confusing and which has led to the practice of writing the absorption coefficient *per electron*, which gives values that can be more readily compared from one material to another. Thus if we consider lead as the absorber and write the absorption coefficient appropriate for dx in centimeters, we may take account of the fact that 1 cc of lead contains 27×10^{23} electrons and replace the absorption coefficient k by k_e if we set $k = k_e \times 27 \times 10^{23}$. Then k_e is referred to as the absorption coefficient per electron.

Of the three processes we have mentioned as causing the absorption of gamma radiation, the first two depend markedly on the nature of the element used as the absorber, while the third and most important (in general) is independent of the material but depends only on the number of electrons present for a given energy of the gamma ray. If we write the absorption coefficient per electron as the sum of three coefficients with self-explanatory symbols, $k_e = k_{ph} + k_{pa} + k_{cr}$, we can discuss each process separately. To take the photoelectric absorption k_{ph} first. This process requires the transfer of the energy of the "photon" (the gamma-ray quantum) to an electron bound in the atom by a process already familiar in atomic physics. The chance of such an event is great if the energy of the photon is close to the energy of the electron in its orbit, and, as for light elements this never exceeds a few thousand electron volts, the high-energy gamma quantum is unlikely to give up its energy; for heavy elements the energy of an electron in a deep level is of the order of 100,000 electron volts and the chance is much greater. The absorption coefficient for the photoelectric effect

k_{ph} is then greatest for heavy elements and relatively low-energy gamma radiation. The coefficient for pair formation k_{pa} will be zero unless the radiation has an energy exceeding 1 Mev for all elements, as pairs cannot be formed unless the energy equivalent to the mass of the pair is available. The theory of pair formation shows that the chance of such an event is greater in the proximity of a heavy element and also greater for energetic radiation; the coefficient therefore increases for increasing atomic weight of the absorber and with the energy of the incident radiation. Finally the third coefficient, k_{cr}, depends only on the energy of the radiation, increasing smoothly with energy.

The reader will see that if an absorption coefficient is measured in lead there is a chance that it correspond to two energies of radiation: one of high energy which is being absorbed mostly by pair formation, and one of low energy which is being absorbed by the photoelectric effect more than any other way. This fact discourages the use of lead as absorbers in experiments to determine the energy of the radiation and leads to the use of aluminum, for which the only effect which is important is the process of Compton recoil, and which leads to a unique value for the deduced energy.

It is not likely that detailed knowledge of gamma-ray absorption will be needed by many readers, but it may happen that a quick determination of the energy of a photon may be required for the purpose of checking the absence of an impurity, or some other reason, so we give here a table of absorption coefficients per electron for the Compton effect alone. If absorbers of light elements such as aluminum are used, these values will be accurate for energies up to 3.5 Mev, which covers most radioactive elements.

Energy of Gamma Ray (Mev)	Absorption Coefficient per Electron	Half-Value Thickness in Aluminum (Cm)
0.5	2.7×10^{-25}	3.1
0.8	2.3	3.8
1.0	2.0	4.2
1.2	1.7	4.5
1.5	1.6	5.0
2.0	1.3	5.8
2.5	1.2	6.5
3.0	1.1	7.1
4.0	0.8	8.2

To save a little time in calculation we include also figures for the half-value thickness in aluminum; this thickness is the thickness which will absorb half the radiation on the assumption that only one energy of gamma ray is present. If several energies are involved, as is frequent, the curve for the logarithm of the ionization versus thickness must be decomposed in a manner similar to that about to be described for the logarithmic decay curves found when several radioelements are present simultaneously; to each single line so obtained there will correspond a half-value thickness characteristic of the particular gamma quantum involved.

With this information and the understanding of the general features of detecting electrons, the reader can decide for himself whether any given counting arrangement is satisfactory for measuring gamma rays. It will be noticed that the yield of secondary electrons obtainable is not greatly dependent on the energy of the radiation, for the greater the energy, the thicker the material which will evolve secondaries before they are absorbed.

Complex Decay Curves. In the last chapter we described the features of a simple decay curve, and in the above section we have explained that a single gamma energy gives an exponential absorption curve. Both these cease to be simple exponentials when more than one radioactive substance is present in the plotting of decay curves or when more than one gamma quantum energy is present in the plotting of absorption curves. What can be done to sort out the complications which result in such cases? Let us consider the first case of superposed exponentials, namely, decay when several elements having different periods are present. Suppose that we have a target fresh from the cyclotron, for example radiophosphorus. This is supposed to have a half-life of 14 days, and if we put the target in front of a Lauritsen electroscope and observe the decay of the activity, we would expect that it would remain constant during the first day at any rate. Actually it is almost certain that the rate of decay would show a marked fall within the first 10 minutes and that even after a day or two there would be a deviation from the simple logarithmic diminution. The reason for this deviation is the presence of impurities, of which the two most likely are N^{13}, of half-life 10 minutes, and Na^{24}, of half-life 15 hours. The first is due to the presence of carbon, an almost universal contaminant, the second to sodium, the two reactions being $C^{12}(dn)N^{13}$ and $Na^{23}(dp)Na^{24}$. The target thus contains three radioelements in place of one, and each of them decays with its own characteristic half-life. If necessary, the three could be shown separately experimentally very easily. Thus N^{13} emits positrons, and by using a magnetic field to bend out the electrons the activity of N^{13} alone could be detected; also Na^{24} emits hard gamma rays, and by interposing several centimeters of lead as absorber the activity of Na^{24} alone could be followed; the activity of the phosphorus would then be the difference between the separate effects of the sodium and the nitrogen and that of the total (a little correcting would have to be done for the different sensitivity of detection of gamma radiation and beta radiation).

We can then see that the simple decay curve obtained without any such experimental sorting out would be the sum of three curves, each of which is a simple exponential, following a definite manner of decay. In fact, we could write the equation of the complex curve as

$$N = N_1 + N_2 + N_3 = N_n e^{-k_1 t} + N_{na} e^{-k_2 t} + N_p e^{-k_3 t}$$

where N is the total number of radioactive atoms present at any time; N_1, N_2, and N_3 are the numbers of atoms of nitrogen, sodium, and phosphorus present at any time; N_n, N_{na}, and N_p are the initial numbers of nitrogen, sodium, and phosphorus produced by the bombardment; and k_1, k_2, and k_3 are the three decay constants for the three elements. A similar relation holds for the activities. If we write the above relation in terms of logarithms we get

$$\ln N = \ln (N_c e^{-k_1 t} + N_{na} e^{-k_2 t} + N_p e^{-k_3 t})$$

This will not give a straight-line graph for the logarithm of the activity against time. However, if we wait several days we find that a graph so plotted actually straightens out and obeys the relation for the simple decay of radiophosphorus. Looking at the equation above we see that the two first terms on the right-hand side approach zero in a few days; the first, indeed, does so in a few hours. Then the equation becomes

$$\ln N = \ln (N_p e^{-k_3 t}) = \ln N_p - k_3 t$$

We can therefore use this simple relation to calculate the number of phosphorus atoms at any time or, more directly, the activity due to phosphorus at any time. This can then be deducted from both sides of the composite equation above, leaving an equation involving the activity due to nitrogen and sodium only. In turn the logarithmic plot of this activity straightens out after a few hours and enables the activity due to sodium alone to be deducted. This finally leaves the nitrogen alone.

This kind of "peeling off" is made very easy by plotting on semilogarithmic graph paper. Such paper can be improvised by laying off the units for the ordinates from a slide rule. With such a graph, as indicated in Fig. 1, the line found at long times can be extrapolated back to zero time and the corresponding activity read off directly.

This can then be deducted from the composite activity very easily, and a new curve drawn giving only the sodium and nitrogen. The same treatment can now be applied to this curve, the sodium deducted, leaving only the nitrogen. The decomposition of a complicated curve in this manner is only a matter of minutes. The various lines are shown in Fig. 1. Notice that, if each straight line is carried back to the time corresponding to the conclusion of the bombardment, the yield is given by the value at that point; and also that if the analysis has been carried out carefully there will be agreement between the slopes of the lines and the accepted decay constants. It is of interest that this procedure could be applied as a method of analysis for small traces of elements. So far this has not been done. The curves of Fig. 1 correspond to an actual sample; notice that only about half the initial activity is the required phosphorus.

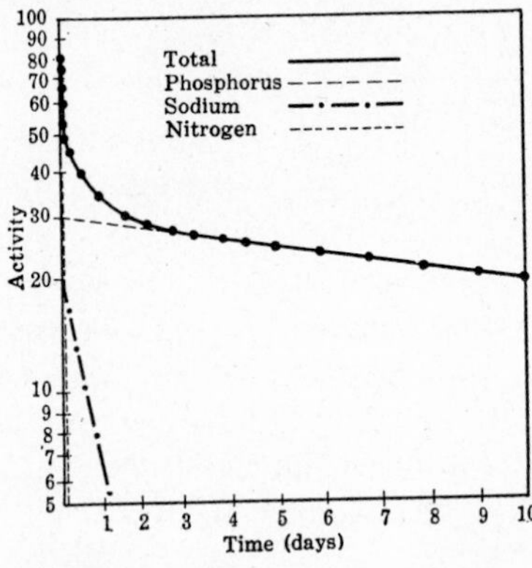

FIG. 1. Decay curve for several elements present at once, plotted semi-logarithmically. After a long time all the activity is due to the long-lived element, and by drawing the straight line back, the part of the activity at short times due to this element can be deducted. This gives a second activity curve, from which the activity due to the element of intermediate half-life can be deducted. The result is three separate straight lines corresponding to the three elements present. The background activity must first be deducted as it does not obey a logarithmic decay law.

The same type of analysis can be applied to absorption curves for gamma rays; the logarithm of the activity is then plotted against the thickness of the absorber.

It may happen that the various periods are rather close in value, in which event the peeling-off process is less accurate. (It is at its best when the half-lives are quite different.) There one is up against the sort of problem faced by an analytical chemist and must seek what aids one can. A very useful technique is to follow the decay of several sections of the sample, using a magnetic field to bend out positrons for one, or a layer of lead for the other, in the hope that the various elements will have different properties and so will be detected alone by one of the detecting apparatus. Each target prepared should be analyzed by plotting a decay curve with an electroscope and a rough absorption curve in aluminum before it is decided that the sample is satisfactory for the intended purpose.

It will be realized from what follows that the manner of preparation may greatly influence the nature of the product formed, and it must be repeated that each mode of bombarding should be tested as described to make sure that the later experiments are not nullified by the presence of an impurity. To make this point clear consider numerical work with the sample of phosphorus of Fig. 1. If it were measured quickly in the cyclotron laboratory and handed over as having the full value at short times, then put into an animal and various sections of the animal brought back to the same laboratory at the end of a week, it would have appeared that much of the phosphorus had disappeared somewhere, and startling theories would be advanced to account for the loss. By taking both decay and absorption curves and looking up the values obtained in reference tables, it is easy to avoid such errors. The use of the decay curve has been illustrated above; it might be worth pointing to an example of the use of absorption. If a sample of K^{42} were needed, it might well be that Na^{24} might be present with a half-life very near that of the K^{42}. However, K^{42} emits a beta ray of 3.5 Mev and no gamma ray, while Na^{24} emits relatively low-energy (1.4-Mev) electrons and rich gamma radiations. If the absorption curve shows practically no gamma radiation but energetic beta radiation, it is safe to conclude that there is no appreciable sodium contamination.

Growth of Sources under Bombardment. Most of the readers who have assimilated the material on the decay of sources will be able to foresee the nature of the yield obtained for various times of bombardment. There will be a steady increase in the yield of atoms available to decay until the rate of production is equal to the rate of decay, after which there is no change. The exact nature of this increase in the yield can easily be seen. We remember that there are two rates of change of the number of radioactive atoms present, one an increase at a rate depending on the beam current, and the other the decrease due to decay, a decrease proportional to the number of radioactive atoms present. With the simplifying assumption that the beam current is steady, we can represent the sum of these two rates of change as follows:

$$\frac{dN}{dt} = k - \lambda N$$

where N is the number of radioactive atoms present, k represents the constant rate of production of radioactive atoms due to the beam, and λ is the familiar decay constant. This equation leads to the conclusion that

$$N = \frac{k}{\lambda}(1 - e^{-\lambda t})$$

The reader will see the similarity to the growth of the current in a circuit containing inductance and resistance when the source of electromotive force is applied. It will be noticed that it requires infinite time for the final value of N to be reached but that there is 50 per cent completion after a bombardment time equal to the half-life. If we put N_∞ for the total possible number of radioactive atoms obtainable with a given beam, then $N_\infty = k/\lambda$, and the equation above becomes

$$N = N_\infty(1 - e^{-\lambda t})$$

and substitution of the value of $0.69/\lambda$ for t as explained in the previous chapter gives the figure of 50 per cent N_∞ mentioned above. If bombardment for two half-lives is carried out, the percentage of the greatest possible yield is 75.

It is of interest to apply this equation to an actual example. Let us suppose that we are interested in preparing both radioactive iron and radioactive phosphorus by bombarding a target of iron phosphide, which we will call Fe_3P_2. The iron we wish to prepare has a half-life of 47 days; the phosphorus has a half-life of 14 days. These two are to be made by bombardment by 5-Mev deuterons on a probe where the current is steadily maintained at 100 microamperes. If we suppose the layer of target to be thick enough to absorb the deuterons completely, then it is not a bad estimate to say that a pure phosphorus target would be converted at the rate of one changed atom per 10^4 deuterons falling on the target; and if it were pure iron this rate would be one changed iron atom per 10^5 deuterons incident, the difference being due to the greater height of the potential barrier of iron. Now if the proportion is two atoms of phosphorus to three of iron and if we make the simple assumption that these are the only two radioactive periods concerned, then we can calculate the numbers of iron and phosphorus atoms formed. In the case of iron we must remember that the 47-day activity is formed from an isotope which is only present to 0.3 per cent of the total so that only 0.3 per cent of the changed iron atoms will be due to the formation of Fe^{59}, the required isotope. We have then, for phosphorus, the value $2/5 \times 1/10^4 \times n$ for the rate of production of radioactive atoms, the quantity n being the number of deuterons incident per second. This is 6×10^{14}, as 1 microampere means 6×10^{12} deuterons per second. The rate of production of phosphorus atoms is thus 2.4×10^{10} per second and is represented by k in the previous equations. For Fe^{59} the corresponding quantity is $0.003 \times 3/5 \times 1/10^5 \times 6 \times 10^{14}$, or 1.3×10^7 atoms per second. Notice that the rarity of the needed isotope, Fe^{58}, introduces the factor 0.003 which greatly diminishes the yield per second. To find the maximum possible yields we need to know the decay constants, which are given by the relation $\lambda = 0.69/t_H$, where t_H is the half-life, and for P^{32} this gives 5.6×10^{-7} sec^{-1} while for iron it is 1.7×10^{-7} sec^{-1}. The two maximum yields are then: $2.4 \times 10^{10}/5.6 \times 10^{-7}$, or 4.3×10^{16} atoms of radiophosphorus; and $1.3 \times 10^{7}/1.7 \times 10^{-7}$, or 7.6×10^{13} atoms of radioiron. Both these are large numbers, but they are still only of the order of a microgram, so that weighable amounts of radioactive materials can hardly be said to have yet been prepared.

The figures given above are for infinitely long bombardment. Actually the physicist in charge of a cyclotron or other form of "atom smasher" prefers to bombard for a few hours, say an afternoon, or three hours. This makes a considerable difference in the number of radioactive atoms of each element produced. If we take the formula for the production of a radioactive substance we find that after three hours the two amounts formed are: 3.8×10^{14} of phosphorus and 1.7×10^{11} of iron. It is noteworthy that the activity observed after cessation of bombardment depends also on the rate of decay. From the same number of active atoms more will change per second for an element of short half-life. It is for this reason that impurities of elements having both short half-lives and low potential barriers are to be watched; good examples are N^{13} from C^{12} and Na^{24} from Na^{23}.

The Curie. Once the numbers formed are known, these, together with the decay constants, tell us the amount of initial activity by the simple relation $dN/dt = -\lambda N$. It is common to measure this activity in terms of the curie, and a word of discussion on this method of meas urement is advisable here. The "curie," named in honor of the discoverers of radium, refers to the amount of radon in equilibrium with 1 gram of radium element; a "millicurie" is one-thousandth of this amount. The convenient fact that radium can be detected without taking it out of its container led to the practice of comparing amounts of radium by their effect on an electroscope which was so shielded as to detect only the gamma radiation; provided that the comparison was always between radium sources the measurements had definite meaning. However, the convenience of the method of comparison has brought with it a tendency to compare sources of different elements with one another by the same means, which has reduced the term "millicurie" to something less precise than its true meaning. Thus it is common to speak of a millicurie of radiophosphorus, which is neither radium nor a gamma-ray emitter. If one looks at the fundamental quantity one seeks to describe about a radioactive source it is not so much the ionization which will be produced in an electroscope, because this will depend greatly on the nature of the particular radioelement.

of which some three hundred are now known, but rather the number of atoms decaying per second. This quantity can be measured accurately, and it is fair to compare two elements on this basis even if one is a beta-ray emitter and the other decays by K-electron capture which produces almost no ionization at all. Even if we accept this as the measure of activity it is still possible to use radium as the standard, for radium decays by alpha-particle emission and the number of atoms decaying per second can rather easily be determined by counting the number of alpha particles emitted per second by a known amount of radium, and so we can adopt a new definition of "millicurie." This new definition is: *a source which decays such that* 3.7×10^7 *atoms change per second is of 1-millicurie strength.* With this definition it can be seen that the bombardment of iron phosphide for three hours gave 5.7 millicuries of phosphorus and 7.8×10^{-4} millicurie of iron. A useful figure to remember in appraising the merits of a cyclotron is that the total theoretically possible yield in millicuries is the rate of formation of a radioelement (in numbers of atoms per second) divided by 3.7×10^7, or, more definitely, if the beam is given in microamperes and it be assumed that one deuteron in 10^5 produces a radioactive atom, the yield in millicuries *after long bombardment* will be approximately *two per microampere.* For short bombardments of long-period elements this must be diminished in the ratio of the bombardment time to the half-life. For bombardments of intermediate length the formula given before must be used. This relation, of course, is only a rough guide; the true yield actually depends on the energy of the beam very definitely, but for a quick estimate this approximation is not bad.

Preparation of Radioelements. The physicist who is in charge of an installation for producing radioelements naturally hopes that all possible elements will find a use in applied physics, but in fact the useful elements are quite limited in number. As time progresses there will no doubt be an increase in the variety of elements actually usable in tracer work, so that here we can cover only the preparation of the more commonly used elements and indicate the general methods available.

Before we describe in detail the preparation of radioactive elements one point of importance must be made concerning the compound in which the radioactive atom will be found after bombardment. It generally happens in biological work that the tracer element is required to be in some special compound, perhaps an organic compound. Thus one might wish to study the mode of action of sulfanilamide containing "hot" sulphur, in which event it would be unfortunate if the sulphur registered on an electroscope but was not contained in the sulfanilamide. Now the process of bombardment involves very large transfers of momentum to individual atoms, and it is safe to say that every transmuted atom is dislodged from its original combination. If this form of combination is very strong, as in an ionic compound, the dislodged, and now radioactive, atom will return to its original mode of combination (unless some better form is also available); if the combination is very weak the radioactive atom will change its location in favor of some more stably linked compound.

To illustrate this we can cite the bombardment of sodium chloride by deuterons, in which both the sodium and the chlorine formed remain as sodium chloride; and the bombardment of an organic dye containing sodium by deuterons, in which dialysis of the resulting mixture showed almost complete separation of the sodium into the part which passed through the dialyzer, indicating that almost all the "hot" sodium was in the form of NaOH. This result of the large momentum transfer is a mixed blessing and disaster; it is of great help in concentrating radioactive materials on the one hand, and on the other it necessitates elaborate syntheses of any organic compounds to be used experimentally. It is really necessary for considerable research to be done in suitable syntheses before many of the radioactive elements which could apparently be used can actually be put to best use.

The commonest elements used in applied nuclear physics are:

Prepared by Deuteron Bombardment	Prepared by Neutron Bombardment
Sodium	Bromine
Phosphorus	Iodine
Sulphur	Silver
Chlorine	Gold
Potassium	
Manganese	
Iron	
Copper	
Arsenic	
Iodine	

They have been arranged in two columns to indicate the method of preparation. Those on the left are made by bombardment by deuterons; the remainder, by neutron bombardment. Many elements have been omitted, but the account of the preparation of those mentioned here will show the general features of the manufacture of radioelements, and consultation of the tables in the Appendix will probably be all that is needed to fill in the required knowledge. We can link together Na^{24}, P^{32}, Cl^{38}, K^{42}, Mn^{56}, Cu^{64}, and As^{76}. All these are made by the bombardment of their inert isotopes by deuterons for a relatively short time, say a few hours. The deuterons should have an energy exceeding 4 Mev for moderate yields to be obtainable, and if this is the fact the production of all these elements is quite simple.

The only difficulty is in finding a target of the element concerned which will stand up to the heating produced by the beam; and, of course, it is always necessary to cool the target by mounting it on a metal support which is oil or water cooled. If a target is at all volatile, then, even if it is excellently cooled, it is essential to cover it by a thin foil which will stop the volatile part from interfering with the vacuum chamber but will not stop the beam from hitting the target. Foils of gold, platinum, or even aluminum are suitable for this purpose. We list below targets which have been found to be reasonably satisfactory, with the emphatic statement that this list should be no deterrent to the individual concerned with manufacture as far as his own ingenuity is concerned. A good cooperative chemist around the cyclotron does a power of good when it comes to devising targets.

Sodium:	NaOH (well cooled); NaCl (if allowed to age).
Phosphorus:	Red P (covered by a foil); soluble iron phosphide.
Chlorine:	LiCl (not pleasant, but free from other complications).
	KCl (if there is time to extract the chlorine).
Potassium:	K_2CO_3 (anhydrous).
Manganese:	The metal.
Copper:	The metal.
Arsenic:	The metal (well cooled and covered by a foil).
Iodine:	Eight-day variety, bombard tellurium; (*dn*) reaction.

Sulphur and iron are both in the category of long-lived elements which derive from rare isotopes. Their production in anything like large quantities requires long bombardment by large beams of some compound which will stand prolonged heating. Iron is best bombarded as the phosphide (one of the forms which is soluble in acids), which gives both iron and phosphorus and is suitable for the probe technique of bombardment where the target is left partially in the beam for a long time while other work is done in the bombardment chamber. The probe does not intercept all the beam and leaves sufficient for many purposes to pass on into the bombardment chamber. Sulphur can be bombarded in the same way as iron pyrites.

All four elements which we have listed as prepared by neutron bombardment fall into the category of slow neutron reactions. At first sight this is an excellent method of preparing a radioactive source since neutrons are so efficient in producing transmutations and also are inevitably present around an atom smasher using high-speed deuterons and therefore can be employed as a by-product without interfering with other research. This is true, but with a few difficulties. To obtain large sources the neutrons must be induced to do their transmuting within the sample required, and this means that very large volumes must be used or only a small fraction of the neutrons will be effective; the product is therefore distributed throughout a large volume, and, if this is objectionable, as it nearly always is, the radioactive material must be concentrated in some way. Where a successful method of concentration can be devised the method of neutron bombardment is quite satisfactory and can, for example, be substituted for direct deuteron bombardment in the preparation of chlorine and arsenic with great success.

The material bombarded should be about a liter in volume and be surrounded with about 8 cm of paraffin, water, or other hydrogen-containing material. Doubtless large amounts of radioactive materials could be obtained by using the water tanks which normally surround a cyclotron as containers for some material to be enriched in radioactive isotope; in fact, the efficient use of a cyclotron permits much ingenuity along these lines. After bombardment for the available time, the material is then radioactive, but the radioactivity is distributed throughout the whole volume and the concentration must then be attempted. Silver is generally used as a means of neutron detection, and there is no need for concentration, especially as the half-life is very short.

Concentration of Radioactive Preparations. There is much room for research in concentration techniques. The most successful is that due to Szilard and Chalmers, and it bears their names. It depends on the two facts that the total number of radioactive atoms is small compared with a small amount of inert isotope and that the momentum transfer in the process of becoming radioactive by neutron bombardment is enough to knock the active atom out of combination. Now, if the bombarded atom was originally in combination in an organic compound and is knocked out of combination, it becomes, for the moment, free. Later it, *or some other atom like it*, must return, unless there is some more stable compound it can form. The trick employed by Szilard and Chalmers is to add a little of the free element to the substance bombarded, a little, but still far in excess of the amount of radioactive substance produced. The atoms of this free element are just as good as the ejected radioactive atom when the time comes to return into the original compound, and as they are in excess of the radioactive atoms the chance that a stable atom will return is very much greater than that a radioactive atom will do so; there is therefore a tendency for the radioactive atoms to accumulate in the atoms of the free element, and by extracting this after the bombardment, as much as 40 per cent of the active element can be concentrated in a small volume.

A concrete example will aid in understanding this method. If ethyl bromide, to which just enough free bromine to make a reasonable coloration has been added, is bombarded, and then the free bromine extracted by shaking up with water, the bromine is found to contain a large proportion of the activity. The bombardment ejected the active bromine from the ethyl bromide, and these active atoms mixed with the chemically inseparable inactive atoms; after a short while the ethyl group recombined with a bromine atom by a chance encounter, and as the chance of an encounter with an inactive atom was so much greater than with an active atom, the active atom remained among the free atoms to await separation later. This method is perhaps the most successful of those yet suggested. It is still not reduced to a definite technique, for, though any reasonably stable organic compound will serve, the degree of recovery varies considerably among different compounds; for instance, of the three compounds $CHBr_3$, CH_2Br_2, CH_3Br, the dibromide is definitely a better choice than the other two. The Szilard-Chalmers process can be applied very effectively to the halogens and to arsenic using organic halides or arsenic compounds.

A rather ingenious extension of the availability of this process has been devised by Steigman. The essential feature of this method of concentration is the firm binding of the element to be irradiated, firm in the sense that individual atoms stay where they are unless dislodged by the transmutation. It is very hard to recognize such binding, but Steigman has pointed out that if one chooses to bombard one of the "Werner complex" compounds there is a good chance that the metal will be bound as desired. If it is not so bound then a separate test exists, namely, whether it has been found that one of these compounds racemizes after having been made in an optically active form. If it does, then there is good evidence that the atoms wander; if not, that they remain in place until dislodged by the arrival of a neutron. Since such compounds exist for a variety of metals and considerable literature is extant for them it should be possible to devise suitable methods of concentration for many metallic elements previously not approachable by this method. Steigman has shown experimentally that factors in excess of 40 can be obtained for rhodium, iridium, and platinum concentrated by this technique.

Other methods which have been employed involve the same idea, of getting hold of the active atom after it has been driven out of combination by the bombardment; for instance, active charcoal will adsorb the active halogen atoms from alkyl halides after they have been split off by the bombardment. Colloidal gold in an alkaline gold chloride solution acts as a condensing agent for the active gold and keeps it in the metallic form. Many further forms of concentration still remain to be discovered.

It is feasible, of course, to concentrate a radioactive substance chemically if it differs from the target substance. This method can often be applied when the bombardment is by a direct beam; for example, the 33-minute positron emitting Cl^{34} could easily be separated from the target element sulphur by chemical means. These methods are not of much use for production purposes with neutron bombardment, for they require that the neutrons change the chemical nature of the element, which in turn means the ejection of a charged particle, a relatively inefficient process, as was explained in the fifth chapter. It has, however, been applied to the extraction of S^{35} from chlorine bombarded by neutrons, the reaction being $Cl^{35}(np)S^{35}$; long neutron bombardment is here able to compete with deuteron bombardment of a rare isotope of sulphur (S^{34}).

More Difficult Elements. In concluding this chapter a few words should be said about the harder elements. Among them is the much-sought-after long-lived carbon. This element is C^{14}, which has a half-life plenty long enough for all purposes, a half-life in the hundreds of years. We can attempt the preparation of this element in three ways, by bombarding the rare stable isotope of carbon with deuterons according to $C^{13}(dp)C^{14}$; by neutron bombardment of nitrogen according to $N^{14}(np)C^{14}$; or by alpha-particle bombardment of boron according to $B^{11}(\alpha p)C^{14}$.

The first would appear to be the best, but the yield is rather low and the amounts so produced are rather small. The same is true of the third method. It is significant, however, that a super cyclotron is not needed to prepare C^{14}; a moderate apparatus which would be prepared to bombard a probe of carbon would be able after a year or so to deliver a fair sample of long-lived carbon. Also, as there is generally some carbon deposit on the walls of the dees in a cyclotron, it would pay a chemist to extract the cleanings of a cyclotron that had been in operation for a year or more.

Ruben and Kamen have recently studied the method of production of C^{14} by the slow neutron reaction $N^{14}(np)C^{14}$. They bombarded 10 gallons of a saturated solution of ammonium nitrate by the neutrons from the Crocker Laboratory cyclotron and found that after six months it was possible to obtain sources of C^{14} giving 10^5 counts per minute. The active carbon is evolved as volatile material and can be pumped off and oxidized to CO_2. Since this reaction does not require the cyclotron for a specific bombardment, but uses neutrons, which are virtually always present as a by-product, it means that any laboratory with a moderate-sized cyclotron and the desire to utilize it efficiently can turn out a certain amount of C^{14}.

Carbon will never be too plentiful, but it should be not uncommon in a year or so. In passing it should be noted that the 22-minute C^{11} can be prepared abundantly by deuteron bombardment of B^{10}, or the proton bombardment of boron, and, as it is possible to follow an intense source for twelve half-lives (more when extremely large sources have been prepared), experiments lasting several hours can be carried out.

A second element of great interest but hard to prepare is calcium. An isotope of half-life 180 days and emitting detectable beta radiation is known but is prepared from a 2 per cent isotope of calcium by the reaction $Ca^{44}(dp)Ca^{45}$. This is not so difficult a proposition as C^{14}, but still it is not easy. It calls for a special plan by an institution to bombard a target for a long time. Sources in the millicuries should be available if such a procedure is adopted.

Summary. To summarize this chapter: We have considered the types of nuclear radiation and the detection problems arising, pointing out that beta rays are absorbed by the rough rule $t \times d = 0.54E_m - 0.16$, and giving an account of the absorption of gamma radiation; we have also appraised counters and electrometers, indicating their strong and weak points. The problem of dealing with a mixture of decay periods (or absorption coefficients) has been considered and the method of procedure outlined, after which the way in which a source grows under bombardment was explained and actual examples considered. A "millicurie" was defined as a source which decayed at the rate of 3.7×10^7 atoms per second, and the methods of preparation of about a dozen of the more common radioelements were outlined, with special mention of the hard but important elements C^{14} and Ca^{45}. The methods of concentration of radioelements after neutron bombardment, especially the Szilard-Chalmers process, were described.

The chapter might, in mathematical language, be described as "necessary but not sufficient." There has been a sense of completeness in the authors' minds as the previous chapters were written, but here that sense is lacking. It is certain that many new methods of concentration will be developed, that many more radioactive elements will find application, and that better bombardment techniques will soon be forthcoming. However, this book does not aim at being a complete reference source; it is intended to make available many known facts in nuclear physics to the people who are advancing the subject of applied nuclear physics, and to make others appreciate their work. This little postscript leads very nicely into the following chapter, where we move right up to the frontier; and while we attempt to describe some of the experiences on that frontier we have some of the troubles of frontier days in that all the news of discovery does not get away from its locale fast enough and the account we give of actual experiments will be rather like the tales that filtered back to the east from travelers in the west a hundred years ago—interesting, but not a complete story. It should be read in that spirit.

REFERENCES

Glenn T. Seaborg, "Artificial Radioactivity," *Chemical Reviews*, **27**, 199, 1940.

Joseph Steigman, "A Concentration Method for Certain Radioactive Metals," *Phys. Rev.*, **59**, 498, 1941.

F. N. D. Kurie, "Technique of High Intensity Bombardment with Fast Particles," *Rev. Sci. Instruments*, **10**, 199, 1939.

CHAPTER 8

ARTIFICIAL RADIOACTIVITY IN PRACTICE

A space whose every cubit
Seems to cry out · · ·

The study of the nucleus of the atom is one of the newest and most rapidly advancing in the whole subject of modern physics. Yet in writing thus far we have had a feeling of relative stability; a feeling that we have not omitted a great deal of the content that a reasonably satisfactory account of the nucleus should have. This feeling is totally lacking as we begin this chapter. Instead we have the feeling that we are here starting an account which cannot but be incomplete, that we are putting a heading on a single chapter which in ten years' time will require several volumes to describe. This being so, we wish to make it clear that this chapter is intended only as a collection of illustrative experiments which may make it easier for some specialist in a field of work to devise his own experiments and to add his quota to the volumes of important literature to be accumulated in the next decade.

We can make a rough division of this chapter into tracer work and other, and begin by considering the problems involved in the former.

Tracer Experiments in General. There is only one feature common to all types of tracer experiments and that is the obvious one of preparing the radioactive form of the element to be used. This is the problem that has to be solved by the nuclear physicist, and we can here suppose that it has been solved. This means that the biologist or the chemist or other worker is presented with an unsavory-looking substance which has been removed from a water-cooled target which has been exposed to the beam. The chemist will be wise if he retains all his suspicions of the purity of any material which the physicist handles and first satisfies himself that the impurities which are bound to be present do not matter.

His next problem is to get the radioactive material in the right form for introducing into the system he wishes to study. This stage is one of the severest "bottlenecks" in the progress of tracer experiments and should be considered most seriously immediately after the idea of using radioactive materials has occurred to the experimenter. It may happen to be relatively easy; for example, if one wishes to use sodium or potassium in water solution, all one has to do is to assure oneself that the physicist in charge of the cyclotron has not included a large amount of copper along with the sodium, for example, and then dissolve the sodium salt in water and go ahead. On the other hand the biochemist may have great curiosity about the way in which a hormone produces growth: where does the original carbon of the hormone go after the growth has progressed? The answer to this question could be obtained by using radioactive carbon, but it would mean the synthesis of an extremely complicated organic molecule from carbon monoxide, which is how the radioactive carbon is generally formed.

The reader can well understand our feeling that this section is incomplete, for in the long run it will include the account of many new syntheses which as yet either are undiscovered or lie buried in the literature. We can mention here, as an example of the ingenuity forthcoming, the use of micro-organisms to synthesize, among other compounds, acetic acid, propionic acid, methane, and carbohydrates from carbon dioxide, a technique introduced by Ruben and others at California.

A method having been devised for introducing the radioactive element in the correct form into the experimental system, the next question that arises is, what is the dilution that will occur? Thus if a straightforward chemical extraction is to be carried out the amount of the original material in the final volume which is placed near the detection apparatus will generally be somewhere around a tenth of the original material, while if a cocktail of some radioactive material is given to a human being the amount detectable is likely to be in the proportion of the volume of the cocktail to that of the individual, and that is of the order of 1 part in 10,000. These figures are intended only to illustrate; they emphatically do not give even a rough guide, for the amount of material at the end depends markedly on the chemical and physiological behavior of the element under the conditions of working. Often the dilution factor can be determined only after trial and error, but it is clearly wise to start biological work with mice rather than cattle. The need of a large dilution factor should not discourage the attempting of an experiment. The ordinary yield of an element from a cyclotron is 10^9 counts per minute, and it is not so difficult to determine 10 counts per minute with a Geiger counter, so that a dilution factor of 10^8 can be handled. The physicist running the cyclotron should, however, be aware of the fact if great dilutions are to be used, since he can be of great aid both in making a large source and in devising sensitive means for its detection.

With these preliminaries the actual experiment can be carried out and the events studied by counting the pulses from the tagged element. Any carefully chosen method of operation which takes account of the decay of the source, the variation of sensitivity of detection, and the reduction of counts due to absorption should be satisfactory. It is wise to duplicate all the conditions in observing the radioactivity, so that counting at the start and at the end will make a true comparison. Thus, if work were being done with C^{14}, great care would have to be taken to ensure that in each sample counted the same percentage of the beta rays, which are so easily absorbed, were being detected. It is an excellent idea to spend some little time carrying out trivial experiments, like simple dilution, to make sure that consistent numerical results are obtained with the equipment used for counting, before the actual experiment is made. On the surface, radioactivity offers speedy results—in fact, that is one of its main attractions; but, unless the experimenter takes care to become familiar with the features of the new technique of observation, it has its pitfalls.

We can mention here some of the experimental conditions to watch. First, the position of the test substance with respect to the detection instrument must be the same. Second, all samples must be prepared in the same way and must have the same thickness and material composition. If this is not possible, careful calibration with known amounts of material must first be undertaken. The consistent operation of the counter or electroscope must be tested during the experiment from time to time with a standard radioactive substance such as uranium glass or a clock face. In this connection it must be remembered that no electroscope has a truly linear scale, and that a Geiger counter may not be consistent at high rates of counting, particularly just before the rate at which the mechanical counter "blocks off." All these difficulties can be overcome by sufficiently familiarizing oneself with the counting apparatus before use.

Illustrative Experiments: Carbon. With this introduction we can proceed to describe some illustrative experiments. The first we choose is the use of radioactive carbon in the study of photosynthesis, carried out by Ruben, Hassid, and Kamen. The carbon used was the positron-emitting C^{11}, which has the relatively short decay period of 21 minutes. It was prepared by bombarding boron with deuterons according to the reaction

$$B^{10} + H^2 \rightarrow C^{11} + n$$

The boron was bombarded in a gas-filled chamber and the gas was swept through a tube containing heated cupric oxide to convert the CO to CO_2. In addition the target itself was placed in the combustion tube and strongly heated in a current of air. In this way the activity was initially up to 10^8 times the counter background.

The active carbon dioxide, which we shall indicate by the asterisk as C^*O_2, was admitted into large Pyrex desiccators containing barley plants. A 500-watt floodlight was placed directly above the desiccators. After various times of exposure to the active carbon dioxide, the plants were cut into small pieces and placed in boiling 80 per cent ethanol for five minutes to extract the water-soluble carbohydrates. The solid material was removed by filtration and the alcohol boiled off, leaving the carbohydrates in water solution. To test the radioactivity of the solution, a small volume (1 or 2 cc) was pipetted off, absorbed in a small piece of blotting paper, partially dried, and covered with cellophane. It was then wrapped around a small aluminum Geiger counter having 0.1-mm. wall thickness, and the activity was measured. This was the total activity. The activity in the carbohydrates was determined by precipitation with phenyl hydrazine both directly and after hydrolysis with HCl for three minutes. The osazone precipitates were washed, dried, covered with cellophane, and wrapped around the Geiger counter, and the resulting activity was measured.

The table below, a shortened version of that published by Ruben, Hassid, and Kamen, shows the percentage of carbon fixed as water-soluble carbohydrate for various previous treatments and exposures to C^*O_2.

Experiment	Previous Treatment	Exposed to C^*O_2	C^*O_2 Content of Gas Phase, per cent	Percentage of C Fixed as Water-Soluble Carbohydrate
1	Light 1 hr	15 min light	1	18
2	Light 1 hr	30 min light	1	21
3	Light 1 hr	50 min light	1	23
4	Light 1 hr	70 min light	1	25
5	Dark 20 hr	40 min light	1	11
6	Light 1 hr	60 min light	3	5
7	Light 1 hr	15 min dark	3	0.7
8	Light 1 hr	30 min dark	3	0.4
9	Dark 3 hr	15 min dark	3	0

It can be seen that, unless the plant is kept in the dark for some time before and also during the exposure, a percentage of the radioactive carbon is fixed as water-soluble carbohydrate. This percentage is small if the exposure is made in the dark, and much larger if it is made in the light. In order to verify the conclusion that the carbon is also fixed as chlorophyll, three isolations of chlorophyll derivatives were also made, which showed that in the absence of light during exposure no carbon was fixed in this form.

We do not wish to pose as critics of a piece of work such as this. Our chemistry just extends to knowledge of the method of precipitation of osazones, so that we could nod our heads sagely if we heard the paper given. We would, however, like to point out one or two features of this work which we think of note. The first is the ability to use a relatively short half-lived element in work requiring considerable manipulation and also exposure time. The second is the scatter in the data. The third is the fact that the experiment still leaves undecided the fate of a large fraction of the radioactive carbon. The experiment thus has clear signs of being pioneer work; almost certainly more knowledge of more features of the experiment can be obtained. It is not simply a quick settling of a point, leaving no further interest, but encourages more study on lines that were not thought of when the experiment was first attempted.*

Phosphorus. As a second illustration we choose the work of Ballard and Dean, who applied radioactive phosphorus to soil studies. Phos-

* This criticism, which was written at an early stage of preparation of the manuscript of this book, has proved to be almost prophetic in view of the later work of these three experimenters. During the course of following the labeled carbon they found that in the dark a certain amount of activity was traced to compounds of the type RCOOH. The amount of this activity increased at first but *attained an equilibrium*, indicating that a reversible reaction of the type

$$RH + CO_2 \leftrightarrows RCOOH$$

was taking place. When the exposure to tagged CO_2 was made in the presence of light the results of the table already given were observed, results which indicate a *steady increase* of the activity in the carbohydrate part. This is not a reversible reaction, and the three collaborators suggest that a photo-sensitive reaction then takes place, of the type

$$RCOOH + H_2O + h\nu \rightarrow RCH_2OH + O_2$$

The new molecule RCH_2OH can act as though it were (RCHOH)H and react with CO_2 by the first reversible reaction process, so paving the way for the photosynthesis of a more complicated sugar. This interpretation means that the formation of sugars is a step-by-step process, at variance with the classical theory of the formation of formaldehyde by the reaction

$$H_2O + CO_2 + h\nu \rightarrow HCHO + O_2$$

and subsequent polymerization.

No better illustration of the use of tagged atoms could be found than this series of researches, because it must be remembered that the plant is "breathing" all the time and is evolving carbon dioxide as well as fixing it as described above. *Only* by following certain definite atoms can the individual process be separated from the whole complex aggregate of reactions taking place at the same time.

phorus is one of the several elements essential to plant growth, and information about the best method of applying phosphorus, and where it goes in the plant, is of great importance. Ordinary methods of studying these matters suffer from the need of many analyses, since it is never certain that the actual phosphorus administered is being measured in the analysis. The use of radioactive material, however, permits easy study of the motion of phosphorus in a plant, and also permits the study of a particular sample of it. The phosphorus measured is that which was administered.

The experiments of Ballard and Dean are pioneer in that they mainly describe the technique of observation and the results of a limited series of observations. The results they obtain are nevertheless very significant, and each experiment is suggestive of further study, which should be attempted. They employed a Lauritsen electroscope to detect the phosphorus, taking care to have arrangements such that they could duplicate exactly the conditions of detection each time. They studied first the effect of increasing the depth of radioactively impregnated soil in a dish placed under the Lauritsen electroscope and found that the radioactivity measured rapidly increased with the depth for the first 2 mm but soon flattened off, attaining a constant value at 6-mm thickness. This behavior is to be expected because P^{32} emits electrons only, with a maximum energy of 1.7 Mev; no gamma rays are present. This being so, the electrons can be completely absorbed in a relatively small thickness of material, actually much less than the observed 6 mm, which is greater than would be expected on account of the rather loose packing of soil.

After these studies, they measured the activity of different dilutions of radioactive substance and found that the ratio of the observed activity to the dilution factor remained constant to 1 per cent for dilutions up to one-eighth. After these preliminary experiments were completed they proceeded to apply their detection equipment to experimental studies. For one study they very wisely verified the decay period of the phosphorus with that found in the literature.

Next they studied the sorption of phosphorus by soils, ingeniously using the fact that 1.7-Mev electrons are completely absorbed to determine the amount of P^{32} removed from the solution by a layer of soil which had first been shaken up with the solution and then allowed to settle. The activity of the solution above was determined, and the amount absorbed appeared as the difference between the original activity and the final activity after shaking up with the soil. The activity removed by the soil could not affect the electroscope as the intervening solution absorbed completely the beta rays it emitted.

They found in this manner that a low fixing soil would only sorb 20 per cent of the P^{32}, whereas a high fixing soil would sorb 95 per cent. The testing was carried out quite rapidly.

They then studied the effect of placing the phosphorus near the roots in different ways. Here they used surface, mixed, and bottom placements of the P^{32}. The radioactive substance was added to pots containing high fixing soil and tomato plants. After these plants were allowed to grow for various periods the radiation from the pot was shielded off by means of lead shields, and the activity of the leaves determined by placing them near the electroscope. The surface treatments were found to introduce relatively little active phosphorus into the plant, but the bottom treatment was much more successful. The rather rough method of measuring the activity by direct observation on the leaves was checked by ashing all the green matter at the end to see that the same conclusion was borne out by the ashed matter. They made the interesting discovery that in the bottom exposure the plant did not absorb much phosphorus in the leaves until a week had passed.

In comment on this experiment we can mention the intelligent use of the ready absorbability of the radiation from the phosphorus, and the simple effectiveness of the method of detection.

It seems likely that, until more C^{14} is manufactured, the results obtained with radiophosphorus as tracer element will be of greater biological interest than those with any other element. The ready availability of this element and its very convenient half-life combine to make its use most attractive, and already almost half the literature on tracer work is concerned with phosphorus. For example, it has been easy to trace the distribution of labeled phosphorus throughout the various organs of rats at varied intervals after administration. It is found that four hours after administration the greatest percentage of labeled phosphorus is present in the blood and liver, but after a long interval the vast majority of the phosphorus is in the bones. This means that only the bones appreciably retain a sample of phosphorus. The passage of labeled phosphorus into the teeth is found to be quite rapid, appearing almost at once in small amounts and reaching large concentrations in a few days. By placing a section of an animal on a photographic plate it is possible to record the distribution of P^{32} in a shallow layer near the plate. In this way it is found that P^{32} tends to concentrate near the joints.

This technique of making "radio-autographs" is illustrated by a remarkable picture taken by Dr. Hamilton. It is shown in Plate II. The leaves of a tomato plant which had been fed on radioactive phosphate were placed on a photographic plate, and the resulting activity was observed. It is clearly visible in the photograph, showing heavy accumulation in the stem with definite accumulation in sections of the leaves.

We may mention here, as an example of the way in which research in artificial radioactivity can be made to bear on actual treatment of disease, the experiments of J. H. Lawrence and his associates on the treatment of leukemia. Leukemia is an unpleasant disease in which the number of white blood corpuscles becomes abnormally high. It can be alleviated by irradiation of the patient with penetrating x-rays, and in mild cases this treatment is of great help in keeping the individual reasonably normal. Such treatment, however, has many disadvantages because the radiation does not act selectively on the white cells but on the whole body, and the individual may soon suffer more from the x-rays than from the leukemia. If it were possible to use some artificially radioactive material which emitted absorbable beta rays, and to choose one which would concentrate itself in the leukemic cells, then the degree of radiation could be stepped up several times, for it would be localized and the damage done by the beta rays would be largely confined to the region where damage was desirable.

PLATE II. Radio-autograph, taken by Dr. J. G. Hamilton, of the distribution of radiophosphorus in the leaves of the tomato plant. The accumulation of phosphorus is shown by the light areas.

Lawrence was impressed by the fact that phosphorus shows definite tendencies to concentrate, for example, in the bone, and with Erf and Tuttle he has studied the absorption of phosphorus by cells, first of yeast in various media, and second in leukemic mice. The experiments indicate that the phosphorus tends to concentrate in leukemic cells and that therefore it appears to be a good element to use for selective irradiation. When tried in practice on a moderate sampling of cases the treatment is reasonably successful; a cocktail every few weeks keeps the patient well and free from the reactions from heavy x-rays. When one remembers that the study of treatments on such a disease as this necessarily takes time, the progress is at least significant.

Sodium. We can now pass on to some studies made with sodium. It soon becomes apparent, once the physicist has prepared an element in suitable radioactive form, that the type of result to be found depends on the outer electronic structure of the element, a factor which the nuclear physicist generally ignores most cheerfully. Sodium is an illustration of this point. By far the majority of inorganic sodium compounds are ionic, which means that in solution the sodium is found in ionized form. In this form it is clear that there is a free-for-all among the sodium atoms when it comes to a re-formation of a solid salt, and there is no guarantee that the original state of combination of the sodium will be recovered; in fact, the reverse is true. Then if one studies the movement of radiosodium through the body, for example, and finds it to be rapid, it does not mean that some specific rapid chemical action is taking place, but only the exchange of the radioactive sodium for sodium atoms already in combination.

This feature of virtually instantaneous exchange of atoms of the same element, though normally not much considered in chemistry, as it is not directly detectable unless "tagged" atoms are used, is of great importance in evaluating studies made with radioactive elements as tracers, since the exchange of the tracer atoms may effectively prevent their use as tracers. For this reason, although radiosodium is so easily prepared, the fact that one is almost certainly dealing with rapid exchange processes has meant that relatively little work has been done with this element. We can, however, mention the work of Hamilton, who measured the radioactivity in the hand of a subject who had been fed some radioactive sodium chloride containing Na^{24}. The interesting result was observed that the activity began to show itself almost immediately—within five minutes, in fact—and had reached equilibrium value in three hours. Similar results were found to hold for chlorine and phosphorus, but not for potassium, where the rate of absorption was found to be much slower.

This work has been attacked from a different angle by Smith, Winkler, Eisenman, and Ott, who have studied the exchange between radioactive potassium, sodium, phosphorus, and chlorine in the blood serum and the cells. By adding the radioactive elements to the blood, allowing time to elapse for absorption, and then separating the cells from the serum, they found that potassium, chlorine, and sodium passed freely from serum to cells in a few hours' time; phosphorus passed through freely at body temperature but not at a few degrees above freezing point. This shows that the passage of the phosphorus through the cell walls is not by physical diffusion, for then the rate of diffusion would depend on the square root of the absolute temperature, so that the rate would hardly change in going from body temperature to 40° F.

Iodine. Studies with sodium are limited by its ready exchange, but iodine is more available as it forms a number of organic compounds which do not ionize and are found to remain in the same individual state of combination and not merely so on the average. One of the first questions that arises about iodine is the possibility of finding out more about the absorption of iodine by the thyroid, and a considerable amount of work on this subject has already been done. The first experiments were made with the 26-minute half-life I^{128}. Hertz, Roberts, and Evans injected radioactive iodine into rabbits and then studied the relative concentration of the activity in the various parts of the animal. They found that, with the exception of the blood, where the iodine was originally introduced, there was no significant activity other than in the urine and the thyroid. The activity in the thyroid increased sharply for iodine-deficient rabbits, but after the first administration the rate of uptake was much less, indicating that the maximum benefit in treatments with iodine is contained in the first dose, and that unless considerable time elapses there is not much benefit to be obtained from steady repetition of the administration of the iodine.

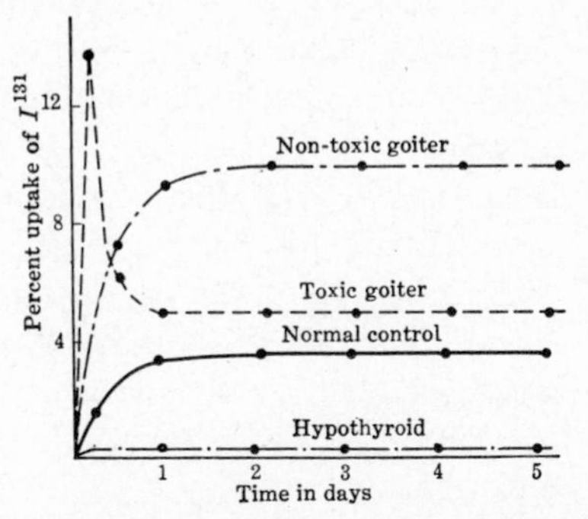

FIG. 1. Four graphs showing the uptake of radioiodine by normal human subjects and patients with three types of thyroid disorders. The non-toxic goiter and the normal control follow the same type of curve, indicating that dietary deficiencies had caused the development of an oversize but normal thyroid. The toxic goiter, or hyperthyroid case, shows *both* an extremely rapid uptake *and* a rapid discharge. The hypothyroid case is characterized by the almost total inability to absorb iodine.

In Fig. 1 we reproduce four curves taken by Hamilton and Soley, which tell a most interesting story about the three commonly known thyroid aberrations. These are hypothyroidism, in which the metabolism of the individual is too low; hyperthyroidism, in which the thyroid is too active and metabolism too high; and non-toxic goiter, which is due to faulty diet. The experiments were made by feeding various individuals I^{131} and observing, by means of an external Geiger counter, the activity in the thyroid after various intervals, amounting to several days in all. The fourth curve is a control taken with normal subjects. The normal uptake rises smoothly to a steady value attained after two days. A curve of the same sort is found for the uptake by persons with non-toxic goiter, except that the amount taken up is far greater. This is because the individual has adapted to the deficient diet by developing an oversize thyroid gland, which, *functioning normally*, naturally absorbs more than one of ordinary size. The curve for hypothyroidism is also clear; almost no iodine is absorbed, hence little thyroxine is produced. As this thyroxine controls metabolism, the rate of metabolism is low. Most interesting of all is toxic goiter, or hyperthyroidism. Here the thyroid absorbs extremely rapidly, far more so than normally, and subsequently loses iodine much too rapidly also. This shows that the abnormal thyroid cells are defective both in *rapid uptake* and also in *ability to hold* the iodine in combination. Hamilton points out that this characteristic rise might be useful in diagnosis.

Experiments of this kind are most significant but do not tell all that can be learned by means of tagged atoms. The thyroid gland is a complex piece of matter, and it would be of interest to discover the *exact* location of the iodine therein. The tracer technique offers the way to obtain this information if the proper method of detection is employed. Unfortunately the counter method gives composite information unless the specimen is cut into different parts and each separately counted, a tedious process.

The photographic technique, first introduced for natural radioactivity by Lacassagne and Lattes in 1924, here comes into its own. It gives the story of detailed distribution, taking place simultaneously, in a very direct way, with relatively little trouble—at least, very little trouble that is not already overcome by known techniques. Such photographic "autographs" have been taken by Hamilton and Soley of the iodine distribution in various kinds of thyroids; the results are of the greatest interest.

These autographs are made as follows. The subject is given radioiodine, which is allowed two days to "settle," and the thyroid is then removed. It is immersed in formaldehyde for twenty-four hours and then embedded in paraffin to permit the cutting of thin sections with a microtone. The thin sections are placed on slides, the paraffin is removed with xylene, and the sections are protected by dipping in collodion solution. These sections are then placed in contact with photographic plates, exposed, and developed. The developed film shows dark in the regions bombarded most by beta rays, in other words, in the region in contact with great density of deposited iodine. The film can then be compared with the appearance of the stained section under the microscope, and conclusions can be drawn about the fate of the iodine *in detail.*

Four such radio-autographs are shown in Plate III. The first shows the accumulation of iodine in a normal thyroid. The characteristic

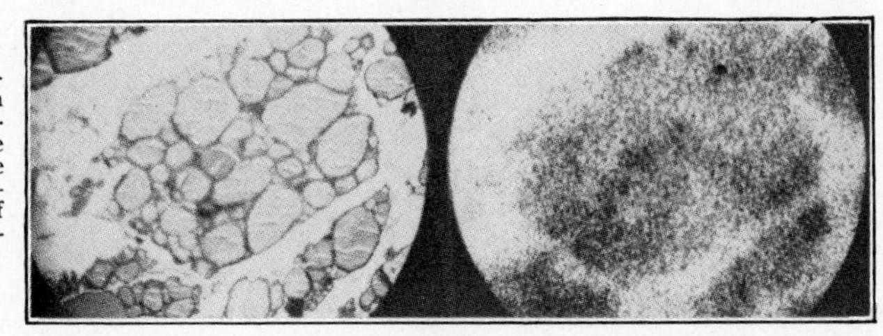

Normal thyroid tissue. Photomicrograph on left, radio-autograph on right. The darkened areas in the radio-autograph represent the regions of greatest accumulation of radioiodine.

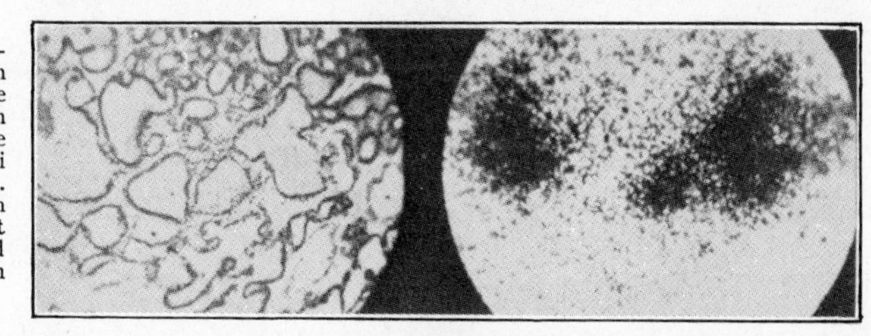

Hyperplastic thyroid. The section on the left shows large grayish areas which contain colloid, while the remaining acini are devoid of colloid. The radio-autograph indicates that most of the accumulated iodine was stored in the colloid.

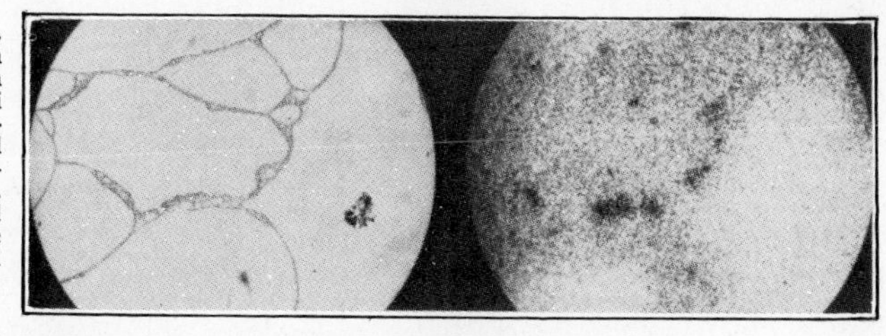

Non-toxic goiter. Photomicrograph on left, radio-autograph on right. The acini are enlarged and distended with colloid which has accumulated very little iodine. The cells and small acini surrounding the colloid deposits stored much more iodine.

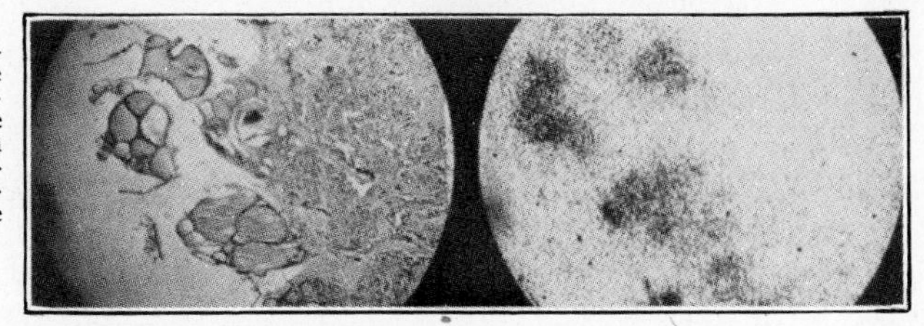

Cancer of the thyroid. There are three small islands of uninvaded thyroid tissue which can be seen from the radio-autograph to have accumulated most of the radioiodine.

PLATE III. These photographs were made by Dr. J. G. Hamilton, and the legends are virtually those given by him in his article in the *Journal of Applied Physics.*

structure of the thyroid is visible in the photomicrograph on the left; it is made up of cells which enclose non-cellular material. The cells are called "acini"; the non-cellular material, "colloid." In the normal thyroid there is roughly uniform distribution of the iodine throughout the whole structure, as can be seen by comparing the autograph on the right with the actual photomicrograph. The second pair shows a thyroid which is hyperplastic as the result of the destruction of most of the gland by cancer. The large gray areas in the picture on the left are the areas of undamaged colloid, and the uptake of iodine in these areas is clearly spectacular. In hyperplasia the iodine therefore *rapidly transfers to the colloid* and thence to the blood. The third pair show a non-toxic goiter thyroid. The enlarged cells are clearly visible, but the autograph shows that the colloid gets relatively little of the iodine, which goes preferentially into the cell walls. If the colloid were smaller in amount the density distribution per cell would be normal, a state of affairs which could not be attained in hyperplasia. The fourth pair shows an area which is partially destroyed by cancer. No deposit appears in the area changed by the malignant growth.

The same two workers have also studied the effect of giving element 85, which is called "eka-iodine" and fits a position in the periodic table which indicates that it is a halogen, to a patient, and also to two guinea pigs. The eka-iodine is concentrated in the thyroid much as normal iodine would be, which is most interesting and significant. The result is all the more interesting when the chemical properties of eka-iodine are considered. It is found that eka-iodine behaves very much as a metal, and is almost entirely devoid of properties characteristic of a halogen; for example, it is deposited on the cathode in electrolysis. Yet it is concentrated in the thyroid. The significance of this discovery is not yet clear, but it gives us a powerful method of studying the chemistry of the iodine-absorbing part of the thyroid.

In addition to this biological type of study, radioactive iodine has been used in a considerable number of experiments designed to test the degree of exchange between an organic iodine compound and an inorganic compound. For example, McKay finds that there is no exchange between CH_3I^* and I_2 at room temperature in alcohol, but at 100° C there is exchange in 15 minutes. There appears to be exchange between CH_3I^* and NaI under all circumstances.

Zinc. Very little work has so far been described using zinc. However, we show in Plate IV a reproduction of radio-autographs made from slices of tomato fruit which had been given radioactive zinc chloride in the nutrient solution. The autograph, made by Dr. Perry

Stout of the University of California, shows clearly the concentration of the radioactive zinc in the seeds.

Iron. We may conclude this series of illustrative experiments with a reference to work with iron. Fe^{59} has a half-life of 47 days, which is nearly perfect for most purposes, and, in spite of the relative difficulty of making it, several interesting series of experiments have been carried

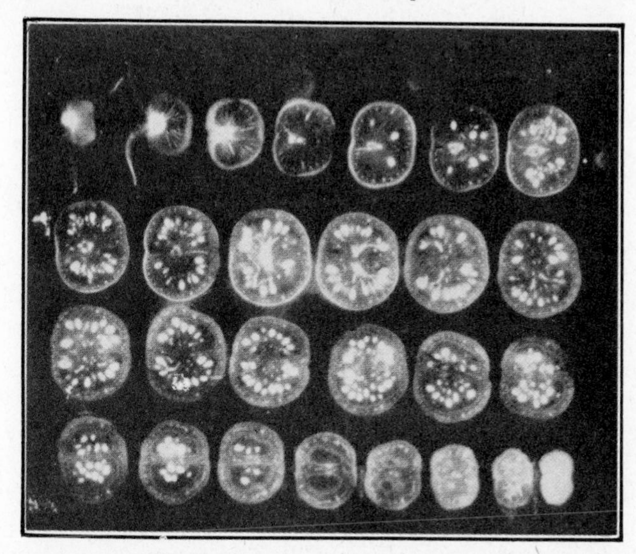

PLATE IV. Radio-autograph made by Dr. Perry Stout of the Department of Plant Nutrition of the University of California showing the distribution of radioactive zinc in the fruit of a tomato plant which had been fed radioactive zinc chloride. The slices of the fruit were placed on a photographic plate and the beta rays from the zinc caused action in regions where zinc was concentrated. It can be seen that the zinc concentrated in the seeds.

out. Hahn, Bale, Lawrence, and Whipple found that a non-anemic dog absorbed only small amounts of iron, whereas anemic dogs absorbed considerable amounts. Anemic dogs showed a strong tendency to absorb the iron into the red blood cells; the non-anemic animals did not do so. A most interesting experiment is described by Hahn and Whipple, in which a normal dog which absorbed only 1.3 per cent of a dose of iron was rendered anemic by removing two-thirds of its blood. In that condition iron was given to it, but practically no absorption took place. In due course the amount of circulating hemoglobin returned to about normal and the animal was then fed radioactive iron. The absorption was now about 10 per cent, a high figure. This experiment shows that it is not simply the state of anemia which conditions the readiness to absorb iron, but rather the amount of iron in the tissue. The great interest which attaches to the work with radioactive iron shows that here, at least, the tracer method has already proved its value.

New Elements. Before we conclude this section on tracer elements the interesting subject of new, artificially made elements should be mentioned. It is fairly well known that of the 92 elements four are still to be discovered. All four of these have probably been found by observation of radioactive forms of the elements. For example, if molybdenum is bombarded by deuterons a large number of activities is found which can be ascribed to "element 43." The chemistry of this element will no doubt be fully worked out in time simply by following the progress of the appropriate activity through the various chemical procedures.

A more interesting new element has been announced by Corson, MacKenzie, and Segrè, namely element 85. This is made by the bombardment of bismuth with 34-Mev alpha particles from the Crocker Laboratory cyclotron, and its chemical properties prove to be of the greatest interest, for the metallic characteristics prevail over the halogen ones to the extent that the attempts to isolate it as made in the past (on the basis of a supposed similarity to iodine) could not possibly have succeeded. The information obtained by studying the radiochemistry of the element indicate that it is still a question whether its natural occurrence will one day be observed or not. For example, element 85 is precipitated as sulphide by H_2S, but when in solution in dilute nitric acid it does not follow iodine when silver nitrate is added. The metal is volatile below 275° C. All these properties and others have been observed by studying the progress of the radioactivity of an unweighable amount of material during chemical reactions.

Biological Effects of Nuclear Radiations and Neutrons. We can now pass on to the rather different subject of the biological effects of nuclear radiations and some of the possible applications of these effects. It is well, at first, to look at the progress of nuclear radiation through, for example, tissue from the physicist's point of view and then see whether he is able to simplify the actual findings. Let us therefore remind the reader that the two radiations most effective in producing useful biological reactions, hard electromagnetic radiation and neutrons, do not, themselves, produce any effects at all—their action is entirely by virtue of the action of charged particles which they produce as secondary products. *There can therefore be no action of nuclear radiations on living material other than that which would be produced by fast charged particles.* The essential difference between neutrons and gamma radiation is that the neutrons produce *heavy* charged particles as secondaries, whereas gamma radiation produces electrons as secondaries. The action of a charged particle in passing through matter was described in the second chapter; we can remind the reader that the particle acts as a field of electrical force to attract or repel electrons out of their normal positions in atoms and so produces *ionization* and *excitation with subsequent emission of light.* The heavy charged particles knocked forward by neutrons produce dense local ionization (called columnar ionization); the light electrons secondary to x- or gamma radiation cause ionization which is far less dense and covers a much greater volume.

If the material traversed by the charged particle is in a state of chemical combination, then the moving field of electrical force, in acting on the charged parts of the atoms in the molecule, may produce disruption of the molecule. In addition the effect of ionization may make it possible for unusual reactions to take place after the primary ionizing particle has passed by. The reader can see that the most definite action of the swift charged particle is the disruption of the established order. The consequences of this disruption will depend greatly on the tissue concerned in the bombardment, but the first process will nearly always be destructive. It is for this reason that it is hard to be too optimistic about the future of radiation as a method of treatment; it appears to be too crude. However, it has certainly proved to be of value in many respects, and so the best thing to do at the present time is to devise methods of making the use of radiation as effective as possible.

Many studies of the effects of x-rays and gamma rays on tissue have been made, with results that bear out roughly the supposition that the effect produced by the radiation is proportional to the ionization it produces in the part affected. There is not always perfect agreement, which shows that the actual changes observed are the consequences of complex chemical reactions, if not chains of reactions, and that the simple primary ionization is greatly complicated by what the tissue does about it afterwards.

One great result of significance about the effects of radiation on tissue is the fact that tumor tissue is destroyed more rapidly by the action of fast charged particles than healthy tissue; and that this affords a method of treatment of cancer is well known. The question arises whether it would be better to bombard the tumor by means of densely ionizing particles, such as would be produced as secondaries by fast neutrons, rather than by the secondary electrons of gamma radiation; and also whether the harmful effects of neutrons on the healthy organs are less than those of gamma or x-rays.

The answer to these questions is being sought in the Crocker Laboratory, where it has already been shown that neutrons produce regression of tumors by doses that do not permanently harm normal tissues. Whether the method of neutron treatment will ever be a practical alternative to x-ray treatment is not yet known, nor will it be known for some years, but clearly the fact that the nature of the bombardment is different from that due to x-rays, in that heavy charged particles, with short intense paths of ionization, are doing the bombarding of the tissue, makes it desirable to give neutron therapy a thorough trial.

A rather ingenious suggestion due to Kruger may make it possible to apply selective irradiation by neutrons in such a way that the neutrons themselves produce only feeble effects except at the desired location. The method utilizes the fact that two very prolific slow neutron reactions which cause the emission of charged particles are known. These are $B^{10}(n\alpha)Li^7$ and $Li^6(n\alpha)H^3$. If it were possible to saturate the tumor with boron or lithium in some form and then bombard the patient with *slow* neutrons the neutrons would produce negligible effect on the body as a whole but very intense effect on the region containing one or other of these two elements. Thus if boron had been introduced, the slow neutrons would release more than two million electron volts of energy in a space less than a millimeter from the boron, while themselves producing almost no effect elsewhere.

In order to test the effectiveness of this method of irradiating tumors Kruger subjected sarcoma, mammary carcinoma, and lymphoma immersed in boric acid solution to varying degrees of slow neutron bombardment and then studied the number of takes when the tumors were implanted in mice. He found that the bombardment of all three types of tumor was effective, less so for mammary carcinoma, but greatly so for the other two. Control experiments in which the same amount of cyclotron irradiation was given but the slow neutrons were shielded out by means of boron screens showed much less effect, and specimens containing boron but not irradiated showed no effect at all. The method of treatment is therefore likely to succeed if the problem of introducing boron or lithium into the tumor can be solved. A study of the treatment *in vivo* has been made by Zahl, Cooper, and Dunning with definite evidence that mice having tumors which had been injected with, for example, boric acid in sesame oil showed definite regressions of the tumors.

The problem of irradiating with slow neutrons *alone* as a practical matter also presents itself. Zahl, Cooper, and Dunning estimate that, though the injected tumors in their experiments received about 1000 roentgens, the animal as a whole received less than half this.

Zahl and Cooper have also made an interesting step in the direction of selectively depositing lithium in a tumor. It is known that certain diazo dyes have the property of passing through damaged or tumor tissue, and that if these dyes are injected into the veins they will not pass through the walls unless there is some damage or its equivalent, the presence of a tumor. In this way a dye containing lithium could be favorably located in the tumor and so the preferential irradiation could be carried out. This kind of idea indicates that the problem of selective irradiation by means of slow neutrons is not so out of the question, and as it combines both of the advantages of neutron irradiation, namely heavy particle bombardment of the tumor and absence of deleterious effects on the denser parts of the body, there may be a future for it as a method of treatment.

Genetic Changes. A second important effect of radiation is concerned with *genetic changes*. Whatever a gene may be, it is at least something like a large organic molecule with a binding energy between any two of its atoms of not more than an electron volt or so. If any one of the secondary ionizing particles happens to pass right in the midst of a gene, or even close enough for an effect by the strong electric field of the flying particle, there will be a local liberation of energy of at least a hundred electron volts. The gene therefore ceases to be a gene, or at any rate changes its nature abruptly. This is a small matter from the point of view of the change of a complex organic molecule, but devastating when the molecule controls a whole consequent biological development. The observation of the genetic effects of x-rays was made in 1937 by Muller and bears out the above general explanation. Indeed the effect is so great as to raise the question whether the observed number of mutations is not entirely due to radiation—cosmic radiation or radioactive—but this apparently is not so unless a small dose of radiation is about ten times as effective, relatively, as a large one. The majority of these mutations are lethal; most of them also are recessive. As far as can be judged the number of mutations is proportional to the radiation over a wide range of dose, and there is *no threshold dose.* The tendency is for such mutated genes to divide less rapidly than normal, and so they lose out in competition with ordinary genes. This tendency to recover from the effects of radiation has been verified by experiment.

Other Effects of Radiation. Of the various known effects of radiation we can choose two more for mention. The first is "sunburn" or skin erythema. The points of interest about this are the great dependence on the nature of the radiation (greater for long wavelength in the x-ray and gamma-ray region), and the small amount of energy needed to produce erythema in comparison with that needed to keep the body working. This latter energy is normally 1.25×10^{11} ergs per gram of tissue per day, while 100 roentgens or 8270 ergs per gram per day, produced a definite erythema. The ratio is about fifteen million.

The second effect is that on the blood count. This is chosen for mention as it affords some means of keeping track of the health of a cyclotron worker. Radiation tends to diminish the number of white cells and also the relative proportion of polymorphonuclear cells among them. Counts should be taken every month or so, and any drop in the white-cell count, or in the proportion of polymorphonuclear white cells, should be watched. So also should other conditions (such as long hours of work) which also reduce these; and the correct remedy should be applied.

Dosage Measurement of Neutrons: the *n*. To return to the more straightforward effects of neutrons on living material. We have mentioned that the fundamental processes produced by neutrons do not differ from those produced by x-rays, and that it is only in the difference between intense heavy ionization due to heavy particles and electron ionization that their effects may be distinguished from one another. The study of these differences is up to the biologist collaborating with an atom smasher, and it will take time. There is one problem the physicist has to settle before the biologist can begin, however, namely, the measuring of the dosage of neutrons. It is useless to compare x-rays with neutrons unless the amounts of both can be measured.

The present practice in describing doses of neutrons is founded on an extension of the method of describing doses of x-rays. These are measured in terms of the *roentgen*, a unit describing a total amount of ionization; a roentgen is the amount of radiation which will produce 1 electrostatic unit of ions in a volume of 1 cc. Notice that it is a cumulative unit; it does not define a rate. Now it is possible to measure the dose of neutrons in this way, but the measurement is rather indefinite as the ionization depends more on the nuclei of the material traversed and less on the number of electrons. Thus we pointed out that the absorption of gamma radiation was, by and large, the same if we expressed the thickness of material in terms of number of electrons per square centimeter (more roughly the mass per square centimeter). This is far from true for neutrons, which are absorbed relatively greatly by hydrogen, less so by helium, and far less by other materials even if the thickness is expressed in terms of the mass per square centimeter. It would give more even absorption coefficients if the number of nuclei per square centimeter divided by the atomic weight were used.

This fact that absorption and with it ionization in different materials varies so much for neutrons leads to the question whether there is a more fundamental property which could be used as the basis of neutron and also x-ray measurement. This property is the energy liberated in 1 cc of ordinary tissue. If we take as the unit of energy liberation the amount of energy liberated in 1 cc by 1 roentgen, which is 82.7 ergs, then we can call this amount of energy release the subsidiary unit, the *e*. It is customary to define a neutron dosage unit, the *n*, as equal to 2*e*. The factor 2 is purely arbitrary; it has arisen because the dosage of neutrons was originally measured with an x-ray meter (Victoreen), and under the conditions of the measurement this dose of neutrons was equivalent in its action on the meter to 1 roentgen of x-rays.

If the definition of *1 n as 165.4 ergs per cubic centimeter of tissue* is made standard, it is hardly beautiful as a unit, but at least it will not matter, once familiarity with it is acquired. It is rather to be regretted that the actual number of neutrons which have passed a square centimeter of tissue is not used as a dose, for it is a direct measure of the quantity to be considered, and if conversion factors must be introduced one might as well use them to multiply a unit that has absolute significance. So much time has been spent in comparing the effectiveness of neutrons and x-rays that a unit which seems to cover them both has been attempted. Actually such a unit is extremely hard to devise, for radiations of both kinds differ among themselves, let alone in comparison. The physicist would prefer to speak of the number of x-ray quanta and the number of neutrons, both of which are definite quantities, and to relate the observed performance of a given number of either to their energies, rather than to attempt to take care of the variation of ionizing power by means of a single instrument. With this remark we can proceed to describe work on the biological effectiveness of various doses of neutrons and x-rays.

Relative Biological Effectiveness of Neutrons and X-Rays. A simple method of obtaining a rough comparison between the so-called biological effectiveness of 1 *n* and a roentgen is the observation of the threshold irradiation which will produce a skin reaction. A definite reaction can be produced by 1000 roentgens of x-rays while the same approximate degree of reaction is produced by 200 *n* of neutrons. This indicates that, for some purposes, at least, the *n* is a more potent dose than the "r," roughly five times as great. Then, if it is considered a safe dose to suffer exposure to $\frac{1}{10}$ roentgen per day, the same safety will obtain for $\frac{1}{50}$ *n* per day. Such other measurements as are available bear out this conclusion. On the other hand, gamma rays seem to be rather less potent than x-rays, about a factor of 10 less. The ability to produce genetic changes has not yet been thoroughly studied, but experiments have been made which indicate that neutrons can be as much as sixteen times as effective as x-rays in producing mutations.

Protection of Workers in Radiation Laboratories. The general interest in the protection of workers in the field of nuclear physics from the radiations which they are liable to absorb is great enough to warrant a short discussion of the matter here. Before treating the more subtle influences of neutrons and gamma radiation, for example, a word on electrical shock is not amiss. Even though it may be boasted that an installation for nuclear research has no exposed high voltage, it is as well to remember that the nuclear physicist has a rather specialized idea of the meaning of "high" voltage and is prone to discount voltages of the order of a thousand or two as not worth considering. The ordinary Geiger counter, working at about 800 volts, packs considerable "wallop" and should be understood by all who are using it. Such matters as the accelerating voltage on the filament emission of a cyclotron are often forgotten by the physicist who put in the installation, and yet they may be capable of great, if not final, damage. The fatalities among workers with high-voltage equipment are not many, but they are not zero, and death due to relatively low voltage has occurred. This point about the relative importance of the accident hazard has been well brought out in a paper by Aebersold on the subject of protection for cyclotron workers, and we wish to add our weight to his remarks.

The effect of radiations is rather more sinister and for that reason is discussed much more than straight accident. The horrible suffering of early workers with x-rays, who unthinkingly took large doses in quite trivial ways—for example, in showing the "shadow" of the bones of their hand at a demonstration—has made the pioneers in work with neutrons rather more careful, and there is no real reason to repeat any such "martyrdom to science." It is accepted among radiologists that the maximum safe dose in a normal day's work is $\frac{1}{10}$ roentgen. The safe dose for neutrons on the same basis is $\frac{1}{50}\ n$. The authors take the attitude that these figures represent the safe dose for an individual who does not fear any genetic changes which may be caused by radiation.

Accepting the two "tolerances" given, it is necessary to consider the way in which precautions should be taken. Consider x-rays first. Very roughly, we may say that $\frac{1}{10}$ roentgen will require 10^8 quanta to pass a square centimeter of surface. If this number is all that is given by the machine at a given distance, then it is safe without any protection. If this is not the case, then it is necessary to interpose some kind of absorber which will reduce the number to the safe figure. This is quite easy for soft x-rays produced by electrons of energy less than 10,000 volts but is a much harder matter for the x-rays now being used in many hospitals where the energy of the bombarding electrons is a million electron volts or more. To reduce the primary intensity of such x-rays by a factor of a hundred would require about 3 inches of lead, which means a very expensive protecting wall. It is cheaper to interpose a foot or more of concrete between the target in the x-ray machine and the operator. We do not intend to discuss the details of safety precautions for x-ray workers, as they are best studied in the publications of the Bureau of Standards.

Neutrons and gamma rays are more likely to be encountered under circumstances where the installation is still in the research stage and where protection is not elaborately carried out. A table given by Aebersold is reproduced here to indicate the type of precautions which should be taken for neutron sources of various strengths. The strengths are compared with the intensity given by a radon-beryllium mixture of 1 curie. It will be noticed that, with even a moderate accelerating equipment, the safe distance with no shielding is over 30 meters, and that a large cyclotron would be unsafe over a radius of nearly a mile. It is therefore necessary to cut down the number of neutrons passing through a square centimeter of area by some absorber, and it is common to use water for this purpose.

Curie Equivalent	n in 8 Hours at 10 Meters	Safe Distance No Shields, meters	Thickness of Water for Safety at 10 Meters, centimeters
1	10^{-4}	1	0
10	10^{-3}	3.2	0
10^2	10^{-2}	10	0
10^3	10^{-1}	32	34
10^4	1	100	70
10^5 *	10	320	100
10^6 †	10^2	1000	140
10^7	10^3	3200	180

* 37-inch cyclotron. † 60-inch cyclotron.

The important feature of the water is the hydrogen content, which slows the neutrons down and finally absorbs them. The act of absorption with water involves a simple capture with emission of a gamma radiation so that all that is accomplished is the exchange of a neutron for a gamma quantum. This is a favorable exchange, as a gamma quantum is less effective biologically than a neutron, but it should be remembered that this method of absorption may cause considerable gamma radiation. It can be greatly diminished by adding boric acid to the water, for then the neutrons are absorbed by a reaction which emits a particle and no gamma ray, and the dangerous activity is completely eliminated. The fourth column of the table shows the thickness of water tanks for safety at 10 meters, and it can be seen that tanks 5 feet thick must be installed before there is reasonable protection for a worker who gives most of his time to operating a cyclotron. It should also be remembered that neutrons can be scattered over the top of water tanks and that it is necessary to put tanks over the top of a cyclotron as well as elsewhere.

Actual measurements at Berkeley indicate that with shielding as indicated by the table the control room has less than $\frac{1}{1000}$ n per 1000 microampere-hours of operation but about $\frac{1}{10}$ roentgen of gamma radiation. Notice that the question of the safety of the room is now as much a matter of gamma-ray intensity as of neutron intensity. We conclude this section by quoting Aebersold's recommendations for shielding a 60-inch cyclotron:

1. The emergent ion beam directed away from working quarters.
2. Completely surrounding walls of water at least 5 feet thick.
3. A roof and floor equivalent to at least 3 feet of water.
4. A minimum of openings through the shielding.
5. Additional shielding provided wherever possible between the magnet coils.
6. A concrete walled room over 10 meters away.

As far as gamma rays are concerned they are less effective biologically than x-rays, and the dose of $\frac{1}{10}$ roentgen daily is therefore safe. To produce this would require about $\frac{1}{10}$ curie at a meter distance, the figure being very rough and quite dependent on the nature of the radioactive element. Such a dose is not at all difficult to obtain from *artificial* radioelements, and the danger to the worker is therefore not over when the target has been removed from the cyclotron. The question of protection from gamma rays is also treated in a publication by the Bureau of Standards.

The final word of caution we wish to write concerns genetic changes. The exposure of an individual to radiation automatically renders him liable to suffer a mutation, and there *is no threshold to the radiation dose* which will produce the change. It is just a gamble. There is thus no safe dose that can be prescribed; all one can do is to consider what has been taken safely in the past, and this is not a negligible amount, for at high altitudes cosmic rays produce about $\frac{1}{1000}$ roentgen per day, and this seems to be safe. We therefore suggest that the young nuclear physicist and radiologist limit his daily dose to something nearer to $\frac{1}{100}$ roentgen per day. It appears that the majority of changes are recessive, and so unless both parents are subject to bombardment the danger to subsequent generations is well in the future. There is also a slow recovery as the changed genes have less tendency to divide and are gradually supplanted by normal genes.

We can conclude with a word about beta rays. These are similar in action to the secondary electrons produced by gamma rays except that their action is confined to a rather thin surface layer. It is very intense, about thirty times more so than gamma radiation itself. It is therefore important to avoid even short exposures to primary beta rays, for a minute's exposure to the beta rays from 100 millicuries of P^{32} will produce a definite effect on the skin. This caution is even more significant for alpha rays or, still worse, the direct beam from the cyclotron or other accelerator. A few cases in which the direct beam has been taken by an individual on the hand are known, and in each of these it is fortunate that the exposure has been only a matter of seconds for the burns produced take months to heal. Where remote control is essential, as for a large cyclotron, it is important to ensure that no person can be within range of the beam while the machine is on.

Outlook. We have made a practice of summarizing at the end of the previous chapters. It seems more fitting here to substitute a short section in which we discuss the future for the application of nuclear physics. We are thus for the moment in the role of prophets, and we do not claim that we are necessarily right.

We look to the most significant results from the field of tracer work in biology, botany, and their attendant sciences. Where the tracer work is carried out among chemical compounds which do not freely exchange their elements one with another, clean, accurate results should be found once a few techniques have become standardized. The amount of literature already accumulating testifies to the safety of our prediction. We look to a rich, but rather slower, development of radioactive tracer work in chemistry proper, for accurate quantitative results are important in that field. This means the development of reliable measurement methods and will take time. The chemists are still feeling out the new technique, and obvious applications are not being found so fast. The same is true of metallurgy, although very little actual work has been attempted here.

As far as therapeutic work is concerned it is hard to predict. One field which will take years to develop, namely, the use of tracers in diagnosis, seems attractive, but it is foolish to say that there is a great future for a wholly untried method. It is quite likely that artificial radioelements will take their place beside radium for the kind of treatments given today. Thus the cost of a source of radiophosphorus which would be effective in treating surface cancer is not so very much greater even now than the cost of radon. The future of neutron therapy still awaits further work before we can make any statement.

These last two paragraphs lead up very nicely to the one general field which is certain to be of interest, and that is research in the whole subject. The great pleasure we derive from writing this book stems from the fact that we are able to describe the weapons to be used in an attack on one of the strongholds of nature and are also able to be among those actually engaged in battering at the stronghold. It is a new subject, not one in which the dotting of i's is all that remains. Rich prizes are yet to be won in this domain of science, perhaps without extreme effort, and it is the sense of pioneering and possible rewards which keeps the interest stimulated.

REFERENCES

GLENN T. SEABORG, "Artificial Radioactivity," *Chemical Reviews*, **27**, 199, 1940.

C. ROSENBLUM and JOHN F. FLAGG, "Artificial Radioactive Indicators," *Journal of the Franklin Institute*, **288**, 471 and 623, 1939.

JOSEPH G. HAMILTON, "Applications of Radioactive Tracers to Biology and Medicine," *J. Applied Phys.*, **12**, 440, 1941.

ROBLEY D. EVANS, "Applied Nuclear Physics," *J. Applied Phys.*, **12**, 260, 1941.

DAVID M. GREENBERG, "Mineral Metabolism of Ca, Mg, and P," *Ann. Rev. Biochem.*, **1939**, 269.

G. HEVESEY, "Application of Radioactive Indicators in Biology," *Ann. Rev. Biochem.*, **1940**, 641.

G. FAILLA, "Biological Effects of Ionizing Radiations," *J. Applied Phys.*, **12**, 279, 1941.

"Abstracts from the Conference on Applied Nuclear Physics," *J. Applied Phys.*, **12**, 296, 1941.

CHAPTER 9

STABLE ISOTOPES AND THEIR APPLICATION

Isotopes in General. In the first chapter, and often in subsequent chapters, we have spoken of the building blocks of nature as neutrons, protons, and electrons. The neutrons and protons were the constituents of the atomic nucleus, and the electrons made up the outer atom, their number being just sufficient to render the whole atom neutral. In these chapters we have pointed out many times that it is possible to have nuclei which are off the beaten track, with an unusual number of neutrons relative to the generally found number. It has been implied that such nuclei are radioactive, and as a first step in understanding radioactivity such an implication is fair enough. In actual fact, however, very many atomic nuclei having a certain definite number of protons, which number characterizes the element, can contain several different numbers of neutrons and yet remain stable. The discovery of this fact has been of the utmost importance in nuclear physics. It was first suspected when certain of the naturally radioactive elements which differed greatly from one another in their radioactive properties were found to be chemically inseparable, suggesting that their external structures are identical though their nuclei differ. This early suggestion did not, however, specify anything about the possibility of *stable* elements existing in forms which differed only in the nuclei, and it was not until the celebrated parabola experiment of J. J. Thomson in 1912 that it was shown that neon existed in two forms.

This experiment is worth a little consideration, even though rather different techniques are used today, because it shows rather well the fundamental problems of detecting isotopes. The main object of the experiment is to associate a charge with a nucleus and to subject it, in this charged condition, to the action of electric and magnetic fields in such a way that they cause deflections of the moving charged nuclei which depend on the mass of the nuclei. If nuclei were normally supplied with no attendant electrons the problem of associating a charge with them would clearly not arise as the nucleus is already charged.

In actual fact the only available form in which nuclei can be obtained is as part of a neutral atom, and it is therefore necessary to ionize the atom in order to produce the associated charge. This can be done quite easily by several methods, that chosen by J. J. Thomson being the discharge. A discharge was produced in a large glass discharge tube, using rather high potentials; and by boring a hole in the cathode it was possible to obtain a fine jet of positive ions. These ions were traveling at high speeds, and owing to their manner of formation their range of speeds was considerable. The ions were then made to pass into a space in which they could be subjected to the influence of parallel electric and magnetic fields.

In Fig. 1 the apparatus is represented schematically, and the poles *NS* of the magnet, and the two electrodes + and −, were composed of

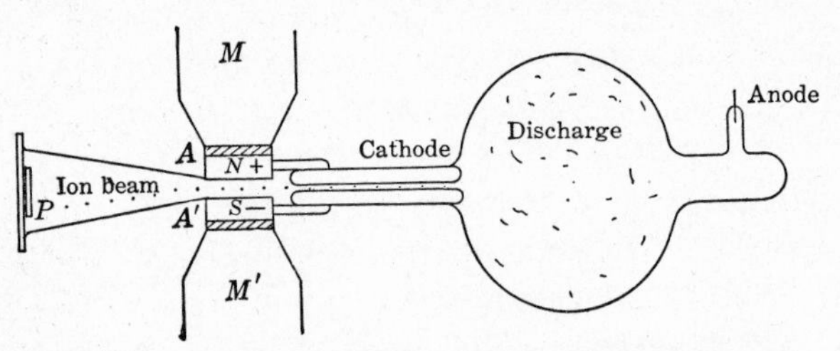

FIG. 1. Essentials of J. J. Thomson's parabola method of studying positive ions. The ions are formed in the discharge tube. A few of them pass through the hole in the cathode and into a space (N, S; +, −) where they are subjected to parallel magnetic and electric fields. These produce deflections at right angles to one another, and traces in parabolic form are found on the photographic plate. Ions having different charge-to-mass ratios produce different parabolas, so that two parabolas from one element constitute evidence for the existence of isotopes.

the same two pieces of iron, insulated from the remainder of the magnet MM' as shown. The charged ions are subject to two different forces in this space AA', forces which act perpendicularly to the motion of the ions and also mutually perpendicularly. The magnetic field alone causes a force to act which is equal to $\frac{Hev}{c}$, where H is the magnetic field intensity, e the electrostatic charge carried by the ion, and v the velocity of the ion. This force acts perpendicularly to the path of the ion and so produces an acceleration of constant magnitude perpendicular to the motion. This means that the motion is circular with a radius of curvature r such that the mass m times the acceleration v^2/r is equal to the force causing the acceleration. That is,

$$\frac{Hev}{c} = \frac{mv^2}{r}$$

or

$$r = \frac{mvc}{He}$$

Now a little simple geometry will show that the deflection from the original path taken by a neutral ion will be inversely proportional to the radius of curvature, at least to the first approximation, and so we have for the magnetic deflection d_H, where

$$d_H = A\frac{He}{mvc}$$

A being a constant. The ions will be spread out into a streak, the streakiness being due to the non-uniformity of v. All such streaks will be superposed no matter whether m varies or not. However, if the electric field is now turned on, these streaks will be pulled out to one side. If the manner of deflection were just the same it would not help, for it would simply turn the streaks around. But the manner of deflection is different, for the force does not depend on the speed of the particle, but only on its charge and the intensity of the electric field, which we can denote by X. The force is then Xe, and this produces an acceleration a given by

$$Xe = ma$$

The ion then "falls" in this field in the manner of a projectile, while between the electrodes, and so is deflected a distance s, where

$$s = \tfrac{1}{2}at^2$$

t being the time spent between the electrodes. This time, however, is the length of the electrodes l divided by the velocity v, so that

$$s = \frac{\frac{1}{2}al^2}{v^2}$$

or

$$s = \frac{\frac{1}{2}Xel^2}{mv^2}$$

where we have substituted Xe/m for a. Again by simple geometric reasoning it can be shown that the deflection d_X due to the electric field is a constant B times this, or

$$d_x = B\frac{\frac{1}{2}Xel^2}{mv^2}$$

Now, if the values of H and X do not change, each ion having a definite value of e, m, and v will have a definite place on the photographic plate and if there is a continuous spread in the values of v those ions having the same e/m will lie along a definite trace and those having a different

e/m will have a *trace separated from the other.* This is easily seen in terms of the equations by eliminating v from the two expressions for the deflections and then getting

$$d_x = \frac{Xl^2Bc^2}{2A^2H^2} \cdot \frac{m}{e} \cdot d_H{}^2$$

which shows that the traces are parabolas but different parabolas for particles with different m/e.

Thomson's experiment showed many parabolas which could easily be explained as due to molecular ions or multiply charged ions, but in neon, where no molecules are formed and the gas is light, two traces were always found close together, and no matter how the discharge was run the relative intensities of the two were always the same. No explanation could be found for this fact other than the existence of two forms of the one element neon, the difference being only in the mass of the nucleus of the atom, as the chemical properties (and hence electronic structure) were the same. In terms of our present-day knowledge of the constituents of nuclei we say at once that the nucleus of the light form has ten protons and ten neutrons while the heavy form has ten protons and twelve neutrons. The name *isotopes* was given to such nearly identical atoms.

We propose to return to the point later, but we wish to point out here that the experiment showed that the ratio of the intensities of the two isotopes remained the same under all conditions; this is an essential feature of all normally occurring material, the ratio of the concentrations of the various isotopes is always the same.

This discovery of the existence of stable isotopes was followed by the steady uniformly directed work of Aston, who showed the generality of the phenomenon and in the years 1919 to 1925 discovered new isotopes in an almost continual flow. For his experiments the fundamental idea of the parabola method, to subject positive ions to electric and magnetic fields, was retained, but the method of subjecting the ions to these fields was changed to give better resolution among different isotopes. The main defect of the parabola method is that it does not tend to focus the ion beam. Aston directed his attention to a method by which ions which had different velocities but the same e/m would arrive at the same point on the photographic plate *even though they started their paths at different angles.* This is achieved by separating the electric and magnetic fields so that the electric deflection is applied first and the magnetic afterward. The two deflections are also arranged to be in the same plane as the plane of the beam; that is, the electric and magnetic fields are perpendicular to one another. Now the reader can see from the equations for the parabola method that the electric deflection of a fast ion is small, depending on $1/v^2$, whereas the magnetic deflection depends on $1/v$. By letting the ions travel a long way after the influence of the electric field and only a short way after the influence of the magnetic field, and by choosing a suitable inclination for the detecting plate, it is possible to obtain a beam of ions, focused at one point on the plate for variable velocity and angle of origin, but the *same* e/m. This property of focusing mass is similar to the action of the spectrograph in focusing light of various wavelengths, hence the term "mass spectrograph" or "mass spectrometer."

From the point of view of nuclear physics some of the most interesting results have been obtained with mass spectrographs of very high resolution; but, as such work is highly specialized and the apparatus elaborate, we prefer here to describe only mass spectrometers which are suitable for analysis of elements into their constituent isotopes, and hence of interest in the application of isotopes to organic chemistry and biology.

Mass Spectrographs. The problem which dominated the early experiments on isotopes—devising an apparatus which would focus a beam of ions having widely different velocities—is now no longer the major difficulty. One very simple method was suggested and put into practice by Dempster between 1918 and 1922. This method utilizes the fact that particles bent in a semicircle will be focused at the end of their path and so may be detected with accuracy. The best way of seeing this is to construct circles of the same radius but with centers a little above one another. It will be seen that though the circles can be far apart above the centers they lie quite close together near the horizontal diameter. This focusing action is often made use of in nuclear physics, for example in beta-ray spectrometers. In Dempster's experiments the positive ions were produced by bombarding atoms of an element evaporated from a hot surface, by electrons accelerated after leaving a hot tungsten wire. Such ions are formed with very little energy other than their energy of ionization, and if they are then made to fall through a definite potential difference of about a thousand volts they will each have virtually the same energy. After this they are made to pass through a slit system in a magnetic field and enter a chamber where they are collected on an insulated plate and their number measured as a current on an electrometer. The magnetic field will not be of the right value to bend (and hence focus through the slit system) the ions into semicircles unless it is specially adjusted, and each isotope will have its own particular value of the field. By plotting the detector current against magnetic field the various isotopes appear as peaks of current, and their abundance may be compared by comparing the heights of the peaks.

A second method of obtaining a definite velocity for the ions is that used by Bainbridge. Bainbridge subjected the ions to a preliminary passage through a region in which electric and magnetic fields applied opposing forces. If the forces are equal the ions can pass through the slit system, and as this equality requires that

$$\frac{Hev}{c} = Xe$$

the velocity v is determined by the ratio of the electric and magnetic fields. These ions that have passed through the "velocity selector" are then bent into semicircles and detected on a photographic plate. Since the velocity is fixed the various semicircles can correspond only to definite values of e/m.

The design of mass spectrometers for routine work with separated isotopes has not yet been standardized. At the time of writing there is not available on the market a mass spectrometer, although it should be possible to construct and sell such an instrument for about $2000. Two designs have found favor in laboratories where separated isotopes are being used, the designs of Nier and Bleakney. As Nier's design is more recent and quite simple it will be described first.

The apparatus does not look particularly like Dempster's arrangement, yet it differs in principle only in the focusing arrangements. The ions are produced by bombarding by electrons the gas or vapor to be studied. These ions are accelerated by a potential drop of about a thousand volts, and the beam of ions so produced passes into a magnetic field in which they suffer a deflection of 60°, rather than 180° as in Dempster's method. This deflection permits the use of a very simple magnet and succeeds in focusing the ions owing to a fact first pointed out by Barber, that, if a magnet having pole pieces in a wedge shape is used to deflect ions and the ions enter and leave the pole pieces perpendicularly to them, then the source slit, the apex of the wedge, and the focus lie on a straight line.

The experimental arrangement is as indicated in Fig. 2. The ions are formed by electron bombardment from the filament F, in the space indicated by the dotted lines. C is a wire attached to the collecting electrode used to measure the bombarding current. The ions are accelerated to the slit in the plate P by a variable potential of around a thousand volts and proceed down the tube to M the magnetic field. Here they are deflected and then are focused on the slits S_2, S_3. The second slit S_3 is needed to apply a repelling field to keep electrons produced in the first slit S_2 by positive-ion bombardment from registering in the recording equipment. These secondary electrons depend on a number of factors, and although at any given time the number of secondary electrons is proportional to the positive ions their number may vary as the bombarding energy is changed and so interfere with accurate abundance figures. The very small current of ions at the collector is measured by an electrometer tube arrangement as described in

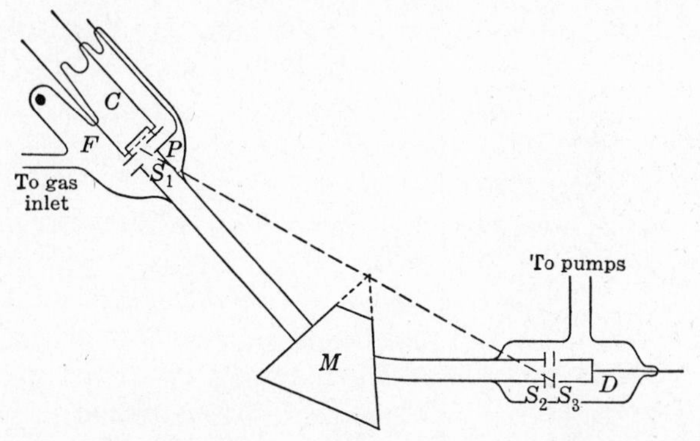

FIG. 2. Nier's mass spectrometer. The ions are formed by bombardment of electrons in the space indicated by dotted lines. They are accelerated by a variable voltage to the slit S_1, pass down the tube to the magnetic field M, and are focused by it on the slits S_2, S_3. The slit S_3 is used to apply a repelling potential to any secondary electrons formed at S_2. The ion beam is detected by an electrometer tube.

Chapter 3. The slits are so arranged that the peaks have flat tops, which greatly helps in making abundance measurements.

To focus different isotopes at the collector the accelerating potential is varied. The relation which governs the curvature of the ion paths is the familiar relation

$$Hev = \frac{mv^2}{r}$$

and the velocity of the ions is given by

$$\tfrac{1}{2}mv^2 = Ve$$

where V and e are in electrostatic units in the second equation and H and e in electromagnetic units in the first. If V is expressed in electron volts, H in gauss, m/e in atomic mass units divided by electronic charge, the formula which applies is

$$\frac{m}{e} = 4.82 \times 10^{-5} \frac{r^2H^2}{V}$$

Then, if the value of V is changed, with H fixed, the various values of m/e will fit the focusing conditions and register on the meter. According to Nier a current of 5×10^{-11} ampere is readily detectable without much difficulty, and it is possible to carry out an analysis with 1 cc of gas at 1-cm mercury pressure, which is about 1 microgram of material. The cost of the whole equipment, if it is built and set working by the laboratory, is about $1100.

Bleakney's mass spectrograph is also commonly used. It is of the conventional Dempster design, the most important feature being that the whole evacuated space in which the ions move is of glass, which makes it extremely simple to bake out and so remove occluded gas from the solid parts. The magnetic field is produced by air-cored coils and is rather expensive to construct.

A few technical points are of interest. First is the ability to heat the whole apparatus to remove trapped vapors, the process known as "baking out." This is achieved in Nier's apparatus by rolling the magnet out of the way and replacing it by a furnace which heats the copper pipe while the pumps are running. A second point is the presence of "natural" impurities. Both carbon monoxide and water vapor can be expected to show up every time and must be allowed for. Nier suggests that by varying the speed of the electron bombardment in the space where the ions are formed it would be possible to diminish the proportional effect of impurities. Thus OH requires a higher ionization potential than CH_4, and by using a rather low-energy bombardment the OH line might be reduced to a minimum.

Separation of Isotopes. We have so far explained the discovery of isotopes and the method of detecting them. This does not explain their application in other studies. The reason for their usefulness is that nature has arranged matters so that there is almost no deviation from the abundance ratios of various isotopes no matter in what form they are found. Such deviations as are found are of the order of one part in a million, with a few exceptions in which the isotopes may result from radioactive changes. This fact means that a sample of material which has an abnormal ratio of isotopes, though it is chemically identical with ordinary material, is nevertheless detectable by the mass spectrometer. Thus, if carbon dioxide containing 10 per cent C_{13}, in place of the usual 1 per cent, is given to a plant to breathe, any part of the plant which subsequently shows that the proportion of C_{13} is abnormally high must have received that C_{13} from the labeled carbon dioxide. In this way the use of separated isotopes is similar to the use of radioactive isotopes, the only difference in principle being that the mass spectrograph acts as a "counter" which will detect non-radioactive material. This being so, the problem of the biologist or organic chemist who expects to use isotopes as tracers is to obtain elements which have been enriched in one or more of their isotopes. This requires consideration of the process of separating isotopes.

Clearly the problem of isotope separation is not simple, except for two freak materials, deuterium and light helium, where unusual methods can be employed. Leaving these two aside for the moment, it can be seen that the very small difference between elements which differ only by a neutron more or less in the nucleus is going to be exceedingly hard to utilize in separation. Nevertheless, if the amount of material required is not large it should be possible to make use of these small differences and secure some kind of separation if one is ready to make an apparatus elaborate enough and have enough patience. Many such elaborate arrangements have been tried, but at the present time only two are of much use in practice, the method of thermal diffusion and the method of chemical exchange.

Before describing these methods more fully a word about isotope separation in general is in place. In ordinary material we have a mixture of components which we seek to separate one from the other to give us material with enriched isotopes. This is not unlike the problem of obtaining energetic and "cool" molecules from a mixture of the two at ordinary temperatures, a problem which, as is well known, requires the use of some external agent doing work to produce the required result. In thermodynamic terms we are seeking to reduce the entropy of the substance, and we can do this only by the expenditure of the appropriate amount of energy. The hope that some extremely ingenious inexpensive method of separating isotopes is about to be devised is therefore doomed. We should rather expect that all the various possible ways of isotope separation would tend, when efficiently used, to be of about equal value.

With this preliminary word let us consider first the method of thermal diffusion, which can be discussed more generally than chemical exchange. The explanation of this method in easy terms seems to be difficult. In brief, it is the combination of two factors: the first, the factor of thermal diffusion which in many gases causes a concentration of a lighter component near the hotter of two surfaces; and the second, the factor of convection which can be used to "cascade" the separation produced by the process of thermal diffusion. Thermal-diffusion equipment therefore consists of long tubes, cooled on the outside, with a hot wire, or cylinder, along the inner axis. The gas is allowed to remain in these tubes for some time until the two processes result in a separation of the heavy component at the bottom of the columns and the light at the top. The separation factor depends on many variables, mainly on the length of the column, the temperature difference between the hot wire and the cooled outer wall, and the nature of the gas—the more noble the better.

This rather brief account can be amplified by considering the two parts of Fig. 3. In *A* is an attempt to explain the existence of thermal

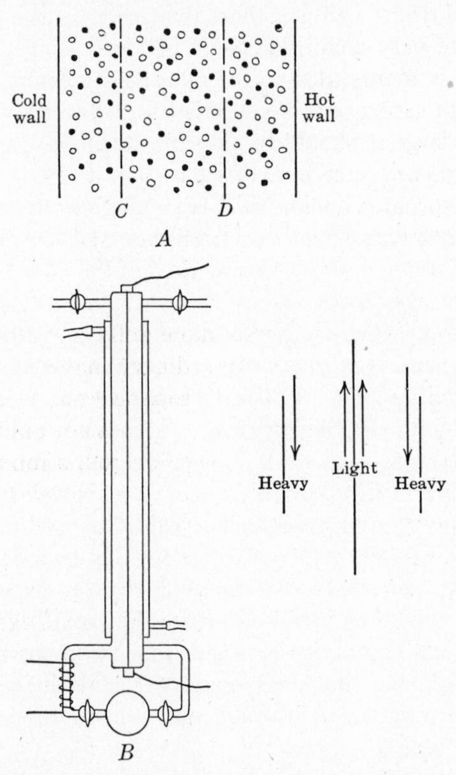

FIG. 3. Schematic representation of the thermal-diffusion method of isotope separation. *A* illustrates the phenomenon of thermal diffusion; *B* is a diagram of a single-column apparatus.

diffusion. The space between the dotted lines, the average part of the gas, can be looked on as separating the regions near the hot and cold walls. Now these regions are still very thick as far as numbers of collisions are concerned, and a faster molecule, after leaving the hot wall, will still have to share its momentum with the molecules in the space near the hot wall before it, or one it has struck, reaches the center. The molecules which arrive at the region *CD* with greatest speeds, and thus with the greatest tendency to diffuse through the layer *CD*, will be those which have received the greatest amount of momentum from the other molecules in the region near the hot wall. The key to the phenomenon of thermal diffusion is therefore to be sought in the transfer of momentum from one molecule to another, and this will not be an easy matter to predict. In this respect the phenomenon of thermal diffusion brings out clearly the essential complexity of a complete theory of a gas, for the interaction between molecules, which is often dismissed as "elastic," for example, here plays the most important part. It is far from obvious, but it turns out that the transfer of momentum is predominantly from light to heavy for interactions that are very rapidly varying with distance—the so-called "hard-spheres" case—and for an inverse fifth-power law of force disappears entirely. Gases which approximate to hard spheres are therefore easy to separate, while those in which the force varies more slowly are difficult. In the first category fall the noble gases; in the second, gases like hydrochloric acid.

Granted, then, that a thermal-diffusion coefficient exists, it will cause a concentration gradient in the gas which will increase until it is balanced by the ordinary diffusion process tending to make the concentration uniform. A single arrangement like *A* in Fig. 3 will thus produce only a very small separation factor, and it is necessary to repeat the process many times to obtain useful separations. The beauty of the thermal-diffusion process is the great ease with which this repetition can be achieved, as can be seen in part *B* of Fig. 3. Here a schematic arrangement of a single column is illustrated. The central hot wire is heated electrically, while the outer part is cooled by a steady flow of water. The thermal diffusion causes the concentration of light isotope near the hot wire and then the ordinary process of convection carries the light isotope upward. This means that as time goes by there will be a concentration gradient not only across the tube but also up the wire, since the gas near the wire is continually being replaced by the convectively carried light component. The result is that the gas at the top of the column is light and that at the bottom heavy. The heavy component can easily be removed by continuing the convective circulation through the flask by means of a heating coil around one of the glass tubes, and after a suitable time the stopcocks can be closed and the flask removed. The light component can be removed similarly.

When the gas to be separated is suitable the method is very powerful. For example, Watson found that a single 2-meter column operated on neon for a few days gave a separation factor * of 8, which meant that

* The separation factor is the ratio of ratios of the two isotopes. If N_A/N_B is the normal ratio of *A* to *B* and S_A/S_B the separated ratio, the separation factor is $\frac{S_A/S_B}{N_A/N_B}$.

one component was for all intents and purposes pure Ne^{20}. On the other hand a several-column apparatus employed by Shrader on HCl gave a separation factor of 3 or so after several weeks of running. This great difference illustrates the large effect of the nature of the interaction between the molecules.

It is quite possible to employ several columns in series, the passage of gas from one to the other being achieved by convection. Both glass and metal columns can be used, and the apparatus lends itself to more or less automatic running; no special attention is needed if the water and power supplies are reliable. For this reason it is likely that thermal-diffusion equipment will become a commonplace in most large experimental institutions.

Considerable success has been attained by the method of chemical exchange as developed by Urey and his associates. Although the primary process is apparently quite different from the method of thermal diffusion there is considerable similarity between the two methods in the use of long columns to cascade the primary process. The method of chemical exchange requires considerable research into the equilibrium of various exchange reactions to find one which is suitable for use. By this is meant that, if, for example, we have a gas and a liquid in which heavy and light isotopes are exchanging, an appreciable difference in concentration of light and heavy will exist in the liquid and gaseous phases. To consider a specific reaction:

$$N^{15}H_3(\text{gas}) + N^{14}H_4^{+}(\text{sulphate}) = N^{14}H_3(\text{gas}) + N^{15}H_4^{+}(\text{sulphate})$$

It is found that when final equilibrium is reached the ratio of the concentration of the light nitrogen isotope as gas to that of the heavy is 1.02, a factor which is appreciable. Now if there can be devised a method of cascading this separation it will not be excessively difficult to obtain from this rather small factor a final very large separation. The method of cascading the process is the familiar method of fractionation. A stream of gas rises up a column to meet a flow of ammonium sulphate down, and in this way there is a continuous tendency for the light isotope to move upward with the gas and the heavy to move downward with the liquid. With enough care and ingenuity very large yields of N^{15} of greater than 50 per cent abundance have been secured, and as nitrogen does not exist in a suitable radioactive form for tracer work this makes feasible experimental work which otherwise would be impossible. The method has also been used for oxygen and carbon with good yields, and there is evidence that sulphur can be separated in this way.

A certain amount of healthy rivalry exists among the various schools of isotope separation, and we hesitate to make any pronouncement as to the merits of these two methods. We feel that thermal diffusion is undoubtedly at its best in separating the noble gases, where it functions beautifully. It is in general more suitable for an installation in a laboratory where isotope separation is to be carried out for other ends and special financial assistance is not available. On the other hand it looks as though a large commercial plant constructed to operate on the principle of chemical exchange would be highly successful. To buy the products of such a plant would be of the utmost usefulness to many research institutions where it is thought inadvisable to set up expensive equipment for separation, and yet where problems arise requiring the use of separated isotopes.

Brief mention should be made of the first large-scale isotope separation by Hertz, using a very large number of diffusion pumps in series. This method may perhaps be more common in the future, but at present it is too expensive to develop on a scale which will give enough material to be of value in tracer experiments. Also the mass spectrograph should be mentioned since it is one of the few methods of producing a virtually complete separation in one stage. It has been applied to the separation of lithium, boron, and uranium in amounts which have been of value in nuclear research but not elsewhere.

One or two "freaks" are also of interest. Deuterium, in which the ratio of masses is so large and the difference of properties so great that, for example, separation by electrolysis is quite easy, is familiar. The other is He^3, which could readily be separated from He^4 by using the extraordinary properties of ordinary helium at very low temperatures. Ordinary helium, when cooled below 2.5 degrees absolute, becomes a super fluid with very abnormal properties—virtually zero viscosity—and almost any process requiring the flow of helium as a liquid would separate He^4 from He^3. The reason for this is the symmetry of ordinary helium which requires that it obey the Einstein-Bose statistics, while He^3, with two protons and a neutron, could not do so. He^3 would thus have the normal viscosity of a liquid, and the separation of the two isotopes should be a simple matter.

Biological Use of Stable Isotopes as Tracers. One of the simplest uses of stable isotopes is concerned with the exploitation of simple mixtures. If we have a mixture of a number of rather similar substances (Rittenberg quotes alpha amino acids, but any mixture which is difficult of separation can be treated in the same way), and desire to know the proportion of one of the constituents present, we may do so without actual analysis as follows. We prepare a small sample of mass w of one of the amino acids containing a percentage *excess* of, say, C^{13}, of P_{13}. This means that if there are in this sample N_{13} *extra* molecules with the heavy isotope, and N_{12} ordinary molecules, the value of P_{13} is given by

$$\frac{P_{13}}{100} = \frac{N_{13}}{N_{13} + N_{12}}$$

Now if the sample is allowed to mix in with the conglomerate and some of the original amino acid is isolated and tested in the mass spectrograph a new value for the percentage excess P'_{13} will be found. If N'_{12} is the number of molecules of this particular amino acid present in the conglomerate we can see that

$$\frac{P'_{13}}{100} = \frac{N_{13}}{N_{13} + N_{12} + N'_{12}}$$

and on dividing the two equations by each other we get

$$\frac{P_{13}}{P'_{13}} = \frac{N_{13} + N_{12} + N'_{12}}{N_{13} + N_{12}}$$

If W is the mass of the amino acid present in the conglomerate, the right-hand side of the above equation is simply $(W + w)/w$, and so we deduce that $W = w(P_{13}/P'_{13} - 1)$. This means that only a small amount of the amino acid under test need be isolated, and as about 20 mg is ample this is not usually difficult. Notice that no exchange must take place, and that P and P' refer to percentage *excesses*.

Rittenberg has used this method to examine the extent of racemization of glutamic acid in tissue. A *d-l* mixture containing excess N^{15} was added, and the two were separated in samples sufficient to permit the determination of the new excess. In this way the amount of either kind of glutamic acid was determined and the racemization shown to be small.

The use of deuterium, carbon, and nitrogen tracers has necessitated the synthesis of organic compounds of the kind occurring in biological organisms. This difficult task has been attacked notably by Schoenheimer. Schoenheimer has made an extensive series of syntheses of compounds containing deuterium and nitrogen. The deuterium is always used in compounds in which it is bound to carbon, and it therefore acts as a tracer for the carbon chain. Nitrogen is used in the form of amino acids. The procedure is first to introduce a small amount of the substance to be studied into an animal, which of necessity is small;

after a short time of exposure the animal is killed and a large number of pure compounds isolated from the animal. The presence of excess of deuterium in any of these samples is determined by measurement of density, and by measurement of nitrogen by mass-spectrograph analysis. The fact that different compounds are found to contain the excess isotope indicates the various chemical changes which have taken place.

Schoenheimer, by introducing fatty acids with excess deuterium content, has shown that although the proportion of various fatty acids in the body remains the same there is actually a continuous interconversion of one into the other. A simultaneous synthesis and breaking-down process was observed in which a series of complex fatty acids was built up from simple compounds while complicated substances were broken down into simple ones. The processes are quite rapid. The same feature of complicated interchange, with some means regulating the actual amounts of each substance, was found among the amino acids of the proteins in living animals. From the fate of N^{15} administered as various amino acids it has been inferred that peptide linkages are continuously opening and closing, and that amino groups can be detached from amino acids while nitrogen can be attached to nitrogen-free substances. The interchange takes place among virtually all the proteins of the animal. A detailed account of Schoenheimer's work is not to be attempted by the authors of this book, as the erroneous description of intricate organic reactions would not add to its value. The fundamental processes taking place in organisms seem to be coming within our comprehension, however, as a result of this type of work.

There is not much difference in principle between experiments in which stable isotopes are used and those using radioelements. The two important elements oxygen and nitrogen do not occur in suitable forms as radioelements, and so they are available only as stable isotopes. In general, if a radioactive isotope is conveniently available, it should be preferred, as the means of detection are so simple. Radioactive isotopes can also be diluted many more times than stable isotopes and so have a rather wider range of application. It is greatly to be desired, however, that several different methods of approach be available to the same problems, for the confirmation one gives to the other is the most certain way to guarantee good experimentation.

REFERENCES

Harold C. Urey, "Separation and Use of Stable Isotopes," *J. Applied Phys.*, **12**, 270, 1941.

F. W. Aston, *Mass Spectra and Isotopes*, Longmans, Green and Company, 1933.

A. O. Nier, "A Mass Spectrometer," *Rev. Sci. Instruments*, **11**, 212, 1940.

W. Bleakney, *Phys. Rev.*, **40**, 496, 1932.

H. S. Brown, J. J. Mitchell, and R. D. Fowler, "The Construction of a Mass Spectrometer for Isotope Analysis," *Rev. Sci. Instruments*, **12**, 435, 1941.

R. Schoenheimer and S. Ratner, "Metabolism of Proteins and Amino Acids," *Ann. Rev. Biochem.*, **1941**, 197.

H. B. Vickery, "End Products of Nitrogen Metabolism in Plants," *Biological Symposia*, Vol. V, Jaques Cattell Press, 1941.

CHAPTER 10

NUCLEAR FISSION

Practically every physics teacher has at some time attempted to catch the imagination of his elementary students by stating that there is sufficient energy in a gallon of gasoline to lift the *Queen Mary* as high as the Empire State building. Or, perhaps he preferred the one which asserts that a lump of coal the size of an egg ought to serve as sufficient fuel for a transatlantic voyage. Although both statements are quite correct, it is doubtful that even the professor took such a statement very seriously prior to January 1939. Even today, the odds are pretty good that none of us will live to see either of the above phenomena a reality, but practically every physicist will admit that it *might* happen. What, then, the reader could well ask, took place in January 1939 to change the attitude of scientists toward subatomic energy from one of skepticism and disbelief to one of optimism? The answer lies in the discovery of uranium fission by Hahn and Strassman. This finding promises to exert a greater influence on the shape of things to come than any other discovery in the past century of scientific miracles. An account of the experiments leading up to this event reads like a modern mystery thriller. None of the elements is missing. We find clues so baffling and misleading that some of the keenest "Charlie Chans" in chemistry and physics guessed wrong on the "killer" as far back as 1934, and for the next five years no one dared to question their conclusions.

The story begins at the University of Rome. The neutron had just been discovered by Chadwick in England, and a young Italian physicist, Enrico Fermi, with characteristic scientific curiosity, exposed practically all the elements which make up the periodic table to these uncharged particles. His efforts were rewarded by the discovery of a large number of new radioactive substances. The usual process involved the capture of a neutron by the nucleus in question. This, in turn, often produced an unstable nucleus possessing too much mass for its charge. This atom then proceeded to return to the stable state by emitting a beta ray. This, of course, resulted in an element one unit higher in atomic number than the parent atom. What, reasoned

Fermi, would happen if uranium were exposed to neutrons? Uranium stands ninety-second and last in the periodic table. If the above mechanism were followed, we should finish with an element of atomic number 93. But, in all nature, no such element is known to exist. This was an experiment to excite the imagination of even a future Nobel laureate. So Fermi and his associates did just that. After an extended exposure to the neutron source, the uranium showed an activity that could be broken down into four half-lives: 10 seconds, 40 seconds, 13 minutes, and 90 minutes, with some indication of still longer ones.

Now there are but three stable isotopes of uranium, so the appearance of four and possibly more half-lives showed that some unusual process was operating. It was reasonable to guess that one of these activities corresponded to an active form of element 93. Element 93 would appear in the periodic table in the same column with Mn, Ma, etc., and presumably have similar chemical properties. Hence, to test this point, a manganese salt was added to a uranium salt solution which had been irradiated by neutrons. The Mn was then precipitated as MnO_2. About one-sixth of the 13-minute and 90-minute period activity was brought down by this procedure. None of the natural uranium activity appeared. This proved that the active bodies were not chemically like uranium or its immediate daughter products, inevitably present in uranium. It was found further that if small amounts of an isotope of radium or actinium were added to the uranium solution neither would be precipitated with MnO_2. This, together with certain other facts, permitted Fermi to conclude that the precipitated activities were not to be associated with any element between atomic numbers 86 and 92 inclusive.

Considering the known nuclear reactions, this was evidence, beyond a reasonable doubt, for believing that at last man had pushed beyond the bounds of nature into the realm of the transuranic elements. Naturally, this announcement created a great deal of interest among physicists and chemists, and several became active in further work on the problem. By the end of 1935 it had been pretty definitely established that the bodies responsible for the two longer periods could not be isotopic with any element from mercury to uranium.

Having convinced themselves that these activities had to belong to transuranic elements, three German scientists, Hahn, Meitner, and Strassman, tackled the job of identifying the elements responsible. After an extensive series of experiments with various times of irradiation, the use of fast and slow neutrons, and numerous chemical tests, they finally proposed a scheme whereby three active uranium isotopes were formed, each of which decayed into successive transuranic elements. By this time, through more careful experiments, the original four half-lives had increased to nine, and elements of atomic number up to 97 had to be called into service to take care of all the findings.

This scheme, though it did seem to cover the experimental results, raised several questions almost as perplexing as the original one of identification. The radioactive yields for each mode of decay required that the prolific isotope U^{238} be responsible for all three active uraniums. How was one to explain the formation of three isomeric uranium nuclei of mass 239, two produced by either thermal or fast neutrons, the other by resonance capture of 25-volt neutrons? How could one justify their subsequent decay through the same transuranic elements, but with greatly differing half-lives at each stage? And why should the addition of one neutron to the practically stable U^{238} set off a chain firecracker that had to belch up five beta rays before returning to normal? It is doubtful that anyone, including the experimenters themselves, relished this solution of the mystery, but no one was prepared to offer a better answer.

To attempt an explanation of these difficulties, several workers stuck doggedly to the problem. In 1938, two of them, Curie and Savitch, struck a hot clue, but unfortunately muffed it. They discovered still a new active body in irradiated uranium, this one with a 3.5-hour half-life. It was precipitated with lanthanum as a carrier, thus suggesting that it might be actinium, since lanthanum and actinium appear in the same column of the periodic table. They actually added some actinium to a solution containing the 3.5-hour activity and by fractional precipitation succeeded in changing the relative activity of the two. We now know that the 3.5-hour period is in reality due to an isotope of lanthanum, and the above result might well have been the key, allowing Curie and Savitch to be the discoverers of fission. But fate ruled otherwise, and, after a further series of experiments, they decided that the active substance differed slightly from lanthanum. This left only the already overpopulated transuranic territory in which to dump the 3.5-hour stepchild. In doing so they stressed the difficulty of finding a place for an element having chemical properties like lanthanum in the region of the periodic table just beyond uranium. This added another complication to the already impossible maze.

About this time Hahn and Strassman reenter the picture. They repeated the experiments of Curie and Savitch and then went on to discover that, with barium as a carrier, certain activities could be precipitated from an exposed uranium solution which grew into other active elements precipitatable with lanthanum. The former they tagged as due to an isomeric radium isotope and the latter to isomeric actinium nuclei. But, again, difficulties confront us. To get from uranium to radium, the nucleus involved must lose four positive charges. The most logical way in which this could happen would be by its emitting two alpha particles. These were searched for, but without success. Again the picture darkened, but, as we shall see, it proved to be the darkness before the dawn.

Realizing that it would be difficult to convince responsible physicists that a U(n, 2α) Ra reaction could take place with slow neutrons, Hahn and Strassman carried out an elaborate series of tests to prove rigorously that the active atoms in question were truly like "radium." Their researches finally reached the point where they could say definitely that radium and barium were the only two elements to which the activities in question could possibly belong. All that remained now was to eliminate barium and they would have proved their point. To do this they took some of the separated "radium" obtained from irradiated uranium, and added a little barium and $MsTh_1$ (an isotope of radium). They now performed fractional precipitations and crystallizations of the kind used for separating radium from barium. They expected that the "radium" atoms would go along with the $MsTh_1$ and concentrate in the usual way, thus eliminating barium from consideration. But the expected did not happen. True, the $MsTh_1$ concentrated as it should have done, but the "radium" remained uniformly distributed among successive samples. The conclusion, though dumbfounding, was inescapable. The "radium" atoms were really barium. A new concept was necessary. For some reason, when a neutron is added to a uranium atom the union can result in a splitting off of a barium atom. Instead of pushing off into the uncharted transuranic seas, workers had for years been blindly paddling in well-known waters, halfway down the periodic table. It was a discovery to thrill the most sophisticated person and yet at the same time fill even the egotist with a sense of humility. So, it was probably with mixed emotions that Hahn and Strassman announced their discovery.

If these so-called radium atoms were truly barium, then the immediate daughter activities should be in reality lanthanum. As a double check on their momentous discovery, they proved that this was so.

The reader may wonder why such far-reaching importance is attached to this discovery. The answer lies in the tremendous energy release which attends the breaking-up of uranium into two or more lighter fragments. A glance at a table of atomic masses shows that the combined masses of any two elements in the middle of the periodic table so chosen as to contain the same number of protons and neutrons as uranium yields a total mass considerably smaller than that of the uranium. According to Einstein's mass-energy equivalence concept, such a breakdown of uranium would cause all this excess mass to appear in the form of kinetic energy. Relatively speaking, this energy release is tremendous, since in converting from mass to equivalent energy one multiplies by the square of the speed of light. As a specific example let us assume that after capture of a neutron the uranium nucleus splits into $_{54}$xenon and $_{38}$strontium ($54 + 38 = 92$). The outcome of this is that more than 200 Mev of energy (0.00032 erg) would be released. The greater part of this energy would be in the form of kinetic energy of motion of the fragments. The remaining fraction would appear as beta and gamma radiation, during the return of the xenon and strontium atoms, overburdened with neutrons, to a stable form. This energy release is astounding when it is recalled that the burning of one molecule of gasoline releases only a few electron volts, not million electron volts, of energy.

The announcement of this discovery by Hahn and Strassman caused a beehive of activity in many places. First word of it in this country was received in a telegram to Professor Niels Bohr, at that time a visiting lecturer at the Institute for Advanced Study, Princeton, New Jersey. On the day that he received the message, Professor Bohr was attending a meeting of the American Philosophical Society in Washington. Upon learning of this exciting discovery, he made an impromptu address, disclosing it to the many scientists in attendance. The announcement almost broke up the meeting. Every nuclear physicist present realized that, if such a splitting of the uranium atom actually took place under neutron bombardment, the energy release could be easily detected by the simplest kind of research apparatus, present in every nuclear laboratory. Consequently, those living in and around Washington rushed home to devise an experiment which would allow them to see for themselves. Others burned up the wires to associates back home, urging them to give it a try. The success of these various efforts is to be found in the "Letters to the Editor" column of the following issue (January 15, 1939) of the *Physical Review*. Six communications concerning fission of uranium appeared, all telling of similarly positive results. Under neutron bombardment uranium *did* split into two lighter fragments. Hahn and Strassman were entirely correct. In three different ways was this shown.

The most obvious arrangement included an ionization chamber lined with a uranium-containing material and having the output of its amplifier connected to an oscilloscope. In the absence of a neutron source the pulses on the oscilloscope screen were those caused by the alpha particles from the natural radioactivity of uranium. The energy of these particles is well known, and the size of the pulses could thus serve as a standard of comparison for those due to fission. Whenever the ionization chamber was placed in the proximity of a source of neutrons,

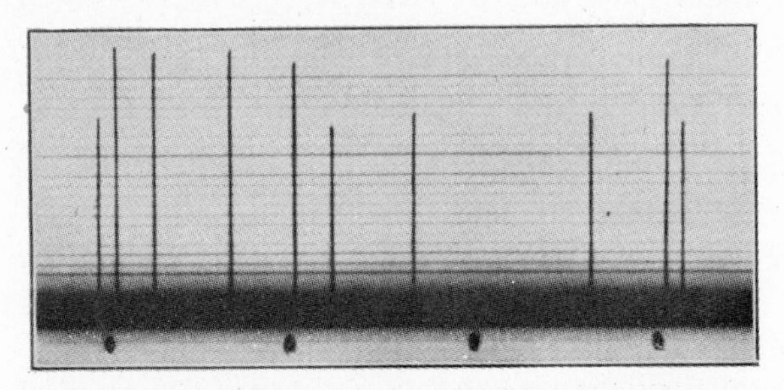

FIG. 1. Photograph, taken by J. R. Dunning, of an oscilloscope screen showing pulses due to ionizing fission fragments.

strange things began to happen on the oscilloscope screen. Huge kicks, judged to represent ionizing particles with energy of 100 Mev or more, appeared. Figure 1 is a representative picture. Indeed, here on display was the greatest man-made nuclear catastrophe yet produced. Stranger than the effect itself is the fact that no one had accidentally stumbled onto the phenomenon years before.

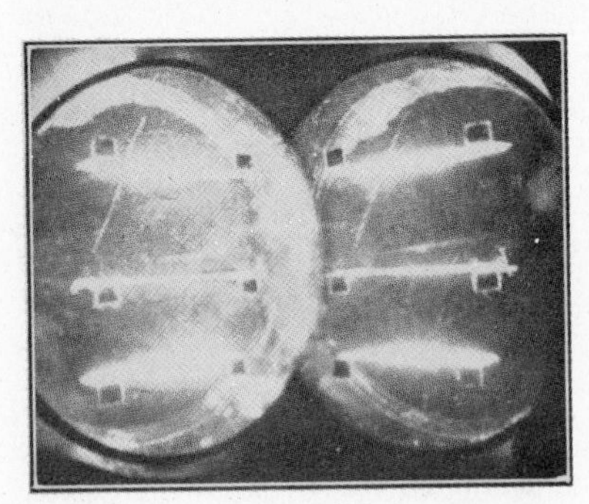

FIG. 2. Cloud chamber photograph, taken by D. Corson, of a uranium fission track.

A second picturesque way of demonstrating fission involved use of a Wilson cloud chamber. A plate containing a layer of uranium oxide was fastened inside the chamber. The chamber was then placed in the neighborhood of a neutron source. Periodic expansions of the chamber were made and photographs taken of each. At first only the thin lines of condensed vapor representing paths of uranium alphas were seen, originating at the surface of the plate. Then it happened. A thick stubbly line of ionization appeared in one picture. It was without doubt one of the heavy fragments from the splitting of a uranium nucleus. Figure 2 is a reproduction of one such cloud-chamber picture. Final proof that the responsible particle is a very heavy one is seen in the short spurs jutting out from the main track. These are due to glancing collisions of the fission particle with nuclei of oxygen or carbon, present in the vapor of the chamber. The proof of the heavy mass of the particle comes from the fact that these collisions do not cause the fragment to deviate noticeably from its straight-line path. In order that the principle of momentum conservation be adhered to, the two parts of the uranium nucleus will fly off in opposing directions when it is a slow neutron which touches off the fireworks.

A third way of verifying the explosive nature of the process is less spectacular than the preceding ones, but nonetheless fully as conclusive. Here one takes a layer of uranium and places close to it, but not in contact, a collector. For the collector Joliot used a cylinder of Bakelite; Meitner and Frisch employed a water surface; McMillan used stacked cigarette papers; Bretscher and Cook used a glass plate. All found what they expected to find; namely, that upon exposure to neutrons the collector became covered with radioactive atoms and that the half-lives agreed with those produced in the uranium itself. The conclusion was inescapable. These atoms had reached the collector by explosive disruptions of uranium nuclei, for mere capture of neutrons and ejection of beta particles would not have given sufficient energy to heavy atoms to eject them from the sample. This was direct evidence indicating that the whole group of radioactive "transuranic" elements must be in reality isotopes of an element of lower atomic number. There is one exception to this. McMillan prepared a thin uranium sample from which practically all fission products could escape. After exposure to neutrons the uranium layer contained a 23-minute activity. This is attributed to U^{239} decaying to a true transuranic element.

These experiments were of an exploratory nature mainly intended as a proof of the existence of the fission phenomenon. Once it had been definitely established that uranium did break up with a gigantic energy release, workers settled down to a systematic study of the reasons for and the results of such a process. Many questions remained to be answered. What was the mechanism whereby a slow neutron was able to set off such an explosion? Did any other elements behave similarly? What isotope or isotopes of uranium were responsible? Did the uranium nucleus always break into just two fragments? If so, were they of equal size and charge? Were any new neutrons released in the process of fission? If so, why was the action not cumulative, i.e., a new neutron causing another fission, and so on? Of course, the fact that large quantities of uranium have lain around for years without blasting this old planet out of existence indicates that something prevents a chain reaction of the type mentioned. Also, uppermost in the minds of physicists was the question whether bombarding particles other than neutrons could induce fission. Finally, both scientist and layman alike pondered the possibility of a uranium bomb and the utilization of subatomic energy.

After several years, most of these questions have been answered, some completely, others only partially. Certain others have as yet evaded the answer. The remainder of the chapter will concern itself with a summary of the major findings relative to this subject.

In presenting a brief chronological development of the fission idea, the authors have preferred to neglect several associated experiments that had bearing on the subject. For example, thorium had been exposed to neutrons and found likewise to yield "transuranic" radioactive elements. It was soon shown that this was also a true fission process. Other heavy elements were investigated for fission but only one other $_{91}Pa^{231}$ has yielded positive results. In the case of uranium both fast and slow neutrons can cause splitting of the nucleus; for thorium and protoactinium only fast neutrons are effective.

The true explanation of what happens when neutrons fall on uranium cleared up the difficulties encountered in explaining the experimental results. For instance, it was no longer necessary to assume $(n\alpha)$ and $(n, 2\alpha)$ processes for such heavy elements, or the formation of long series of transuranic elements. Nor was there any need for a single uranium isotope possessing triple isomery. In a way this whole business was another example of man's calling into being unnecessarily complicated explanations for natural phenomena simply because he failed to understand the actual nature of the processes. Truly, antithesis precedes synthesis. Fission, however, did raise new theoretical problems. The principal one concerns itself with how the moderate activation of the nucleus, resulting from the capture of a neutron (for a thermal neutron, only the binding energy of $\sim$ 5 Mev would be added to the capturing nucleus), can lead to such a complete break-up of the nucleus. The masses of various nuclei show that all massive elements could be broken down into two lighter elements with a release of energy. Why, then, are the heavy elements stable in the first place?

The most reasonable answer to this is found if we assume the nucleus to behave like a drop of water. This nuclear liquid drop concept has been vigorously pushed for several years by Bohr, and it helps admirably to explain the how and why of fission. Just as a drop of water can be split into two drops by being set in vibration, so might a nucleus be split into two smaller nuclei. There are always two competing forces inside a nucleus: the electrostatic repulsive forces exerted by the protons, and the short-range attractive forces of all nuclear particles. These attractive forces are analogous to the cohesive forces in a liquid drop which tend to make it assume a spherical shape, the most stable configuration. But so far as the electrostatic forces in a nucleus are concerned this is the most unstable state. So we would expect the nucleus to be stable as long as the total of the surface energy and electrostatic energy has a minimum for the spherical shape. Because of the short range of the cohesive forces this minimum becomes less pronounced as the nuclear drop becomes large, i.e., contains more and more particles. Wherever this minimum disappears one would expect the drop to break automatically into two smaller drops, which would result in a more stable condition. Meitner and Frisch, who first developed this idea, estimated that this would occur for an element of Z around 100. This is extremely close to 92 and infers the reason for stable nuclei ending with uranium. Thus it seems reasonable to assume that uranium exists in a barely stable form and hence requires only a slight deformation to induce the breaking into two smaller nuclei.

Bohr and Wheeler have made theoretical studies on the critical energies necessary to produce distortions in heavy nuclei sufficient to cause instability and, hence, fission. The table below shows the critical energies for several interesting atoms and the corresponding excitation energy induced when this nucleus is produced by capture of a thermal neutron.

Nucleus	Critical Energy, Mev	Excitation Energy Due to Added Slow Neutron, Mev
U^{234}	5.0	5.4
U^{235}	5.2	6.4
U^{238}	5.9	5.2
Pa^{232}	5.5	5.4
Th^{223}	6.9	5.2

Thus, we see that only U^{234} and U^{235} can produce fission in the presence of thermal neutrons. Fission is not the only process possible when a neutron is captured, however, even when the excitation energy is sufficient. The neutron's energy of excitation will very quickly be distributed among the various particles of the compound nucleus. Any one of three things can then happen: (*a*) reemission of a neutron, (*b*) gamma radiation, (*c*) fission. The relative probabilities of the competing processes will depend on the energy of excitation.

We are now able to understand why slow neutrons fail to produce fission in thorium and protoactinium. In these elements the fission threshold energy is greater than that produced by slow-neutron activation. Considering the resonance capture of 25-volt neutrons by U^{238} to form a 23-minute U^{239} it is difficult to see how even slower neutrons could compete to cause appreciable fission. This caused Bohr to suggest that the fission observed by thermal neutrons should be attributed to U^{235} (present to almost 1 per cent in ordinary uranium) which has a lower fission threshold. This hypothesis has been tested experimentally and found to be true. A small amount of relatively pure U^{235} obtained in a mass spectrograph did exhibit fissions in the presence of thermal neutrons while a U^{238} sample gave negative results.

Previously we raised the question whether secondary neutrons accompanied the fission process. It has been mentioned that any division of a uranium nucleus into two lighter nuclei leaves both of them with a large excess of neutrons. This unbalance can most easily be corrected by the emission of several successive beta rays until stability is attained. But it is quite conceivable that the excited nucleus could just as well gain stability by emitting one or more neutrons or even by a combination of the two methods. Since secondary neutrons must be a reality if a chain reaction is to be at all possible, several workers undertook to find an answer to this question.

The method used by Fermi, by now moved to Columbia University, is representative. He surrounded a radon-beryllium neutron source with a spherical bulb containing uranium and placed the unit in a large tank of water. He next measured the neutron distribution in the water, both with and without the uranium bulb present. A slight increase in neutron density was found with the uranium present, indicating that neutrons did accompany fission. Calculations indicated that an average of two neutrons per fission resulted. Even though this means that a cumulative chain reaction is possible, we can now discern why it will not happen with ordinary uranium. In order to use the neutrons efficiently, they would first have to be reduced in energy by adding some hydrogen-containing material such as water. But on being slowed down a majority of the neutrons will be quickly gobbled up by the more numerous U^{238} atoms present, and from this capture only sedate U^{239} atoms will result. Now, if someone could succeed in isolating a few pounds of U^{235} and the whole were to be submerged in water, very interesting developments would almost certainly follow. The separation of the uranium isotopes in quantity lots is now being attempted in several places. If the reader wakes some morning to read in his newspaper that half the United States was blown into the sea overnight he can rest assured that someone, somewhere, succeeded.

Before leaving the subject of secondary neutrons arising from fission, the presence of delayed neutrons should be mentioned. Roberts, Meyer, and Wang found that neutrons continued to come from irradiated uranium even after the primary neutron bombardment had been discontinued. The intensity fell off exponentially with a half-life of 13 seconds. More recently, delayed neutrons with a 3-second half-life have been reported. It is most likely that these neutrons arise from fission fragments after emitting a beta ray which leaves the residual nucleus in a highly excited state.

So far, we have given very little attention to the products resulting when fission occurs. One of the first experiments bearing on this subject was carried out by the Columbia group. They measured the size of the ionizing pulses from a thin electrolytically deposited layer of uranium. Their results showed a continuous distribution of pulse size, with two pronounced maxima. One maximum appeared at 100 Mev energy, the other at 72 Mev. The wide range of energies and apparently continuous distribution indicates that fission can occur in a great number of ways. Chemical identification of the radioactive products corroborates this, since practically every element between $_{34}Se$ and $_{57}La$ has been identified in fission products. More recently, Kanner and Barschall, at Princeton, have repeated the Columbia experiment and find similar results, their maxima occurring at 65 and 97 Mev, respectively. This means that the most likely mode of division gives a total kinetic energy release of 162 Mev. As a check on this Kanner and Barschall sputtered a thin aluminum foil with uranium and observed the total energy of the fission pairs. They obtain a peak at 159 Mev, in excellent agreement with the 162 Mev deduced above. If one assumes that the kinetic energies of the two fragments are inversely proportional to their masses, the above results infer that the most likely division would be into masses of 101 and 135, respectively (assuming U^{236} to begin with). Beck and Havas have calculated that more energy will be available to promote the separation of the fragments for an asymmetrical splitting than for a symmetrical one. Their conclusions are that the available energy will be greatest for a fission wherein one Z is 37, the other 55. It is clear that these values are well in line with the masses deduced above. A staggering amount of work has been done in identifying all the active bodies produced by fission, and the list is not even now completed. As mentioned, most of the elements between selenium and lanthanum are represented, and there is no good reason for believing that with sufficiently strong samples to work with all will not be found eventually.

It should be remembered that the figure of 162 Mev quoted above refers only to the kinetic energy of the fragments and does not represent the total energy liberated. Both fragments will, in general, be highly excited and will release further energy in the form of gamma rays, beta rays, or neutrons until both become stable nuclei. Take Xe^{139} as an example. As one-half of a fission this atom split off from the parent uranium nucleus with some 60 Mev of kinetic energy. After this has been expended, it proceeds to decay by the following chain:

$$Xe^{139(0.5\ \mathrm{min})} \xrightarrow{\beta} Cs^{139(6\ \mathrm{min})} \xrightarrow{\beta} Ba^{139(86\ \mathrm{min})} \xrightarrow{\beta} La^{139}$$

until it becomes stable lanthanum. Thus, to the 60 Mev must be added the energy of the three beta rays as well as any gamma radiation which might be involved. Henderson has measured the energy of fission by the calorimetric method, i.e., measuring the rise in temperature in a uranium solution exposed to neutrons. His technique would miss most gamma rays, neutrons, and the very penetrating beta rays, so his value of 175 Mev is probably still somewhat below the true average.

While discussing the radioactive products of fission, it is interesting to note that practically the same activities are found with uranium regardless of whether slow or fast neutrons are used. In the same vein, many of the uranium products are also detected whenever thorium is employed. Certain small differences have been reported, however. Since the splitting is a purely statistical phenomenon, no important differences in distribution of the products would be anticipated. Hence, the above conclusion is in line with expectations.

Neutrons are not the only agents able to induce the fission process. Gant, and Jacobsen and Lassen, found that energetic deuterons can produce fission in uranium. The observable threshold is at approximately 8 Mev.

The decay of the activity attributable to fission followed closely that of neutron-induced fission, thus accentuating our preceding remarks.

Haxby, Shoupp, Stephens, and Wells succeeded in observing fissions induced by gamma rays. The reaction $F(p, \gamma)$ served as the source of gamma radiation. The cross section for gamma-ray-induced fission in uranium is only about one-hundredth that for fission by thermal neutrons. Thorium also yielded positive results with gamma rays. Fission by alpha particles has been reported at Berkeley by Fermi and Segrè; and by protons by Dessauer and Hafner at Rochester.

As a fitting close to this chaper, it might be of interest to review the present state of the transuranic elements, which first served as red herring, drawn across the fission trail. The thin uranium layer experiment previously mentioned, wherein all fission products had sufficient energy to escape, left only a 23-minute beta activity behind, identified as due to U^{239}. It was finally proved by McMillan and Abelson that the resulting 93^{239} decays to 94^{239} via a 2.3-day beta activity. The fate of element 94^{239} is as yet unknown. The once-flourishing trans-uranic section of the periodic table has indeed fallen on evil times. Most physicists seem content to let it remain.

REFERENCES

L. A. Turner, "Nuclear Fission," *Rev. Mod. Phys.*, **12**, 150, 1940.

Karl K. Darrow, "Nuclear Fission," *Bell System Technical Journal*, **19**, 267, 1940.

CHAPTER 11

NUCLEAR THEORY

What we know here is very little; but what we are ignorant of is immense—*A quotation from Laplace seen on the bulletin board of a famous radiation laboratory.*

It is partially true that we have selected the title to this book with malice aforethought, because we would not have to expound on the theory of the nucleus. In spite of this we cannot bring ourselves to leave the reader without some idea of how the nature of the nucleus itself appears to the theoretical physicist. The reader may note there a little canny wording, for we have not made any claim about a description of the nucleus itself—only how it appears at present to the theorist. It is so likely that all the discoveries necessary to the founding of an adequate nuclear theory have not yet been made that any theory must be accepted as provisional and left at that.

Before we consider the nucleus, a glance at the atom as a whole is most instructive. It is generally described more or less as follows: electrons are moving according to the rules of quantum mechanics in the field of one another and of the charged nucleus, which nucleus is characteristic of the element. If the motion of the electrons is correctly calculated according to the required rules, supposing that the only type of force operative is the coulomb force between charges, then a very satisfactory theory of the atom results. The excellence of the agreement between prediction and findings based on this approach gives us great confidence in the validity of quantum mechanics and leads us to hope that it may be valid also in a region of nature which is several orders of magnitude smaller than the whole atom. This, however, is no more than a hope.

Now the nucleus itself offers a much harder problem in calculation for two reasons. The first, and more obvious, is that we cannot make the assumption that the only force operative is the coulomb force, because, if it were, the protons would blow themselves apart immediately. The second is that there is no such simplification as having the great majority of the force field due to a nucleus at the center of the atom with light electrons rotating around. Instead of this simplification we have the necessity of considering each particle in the nucleus to be as good as another, and we are therefore presented with a complicated "many-body" calculation for any but the simplest nuclei.

Nuclear Forces. The first of the difficulties above is intriguing as it sets us the task of determining the characteristics of some new forces of nature. Accordingly we can consider in the first place what evidence we have about the forces which operate in the nucleus, namely, those between neutrons and protons, neutrons and neutrons, and protons and protons. The neutron-proton "interaction" can be studied by considering the nature of the deuteron. The deuteron is a combination between a neutron and a proton. If the force between a neutron and a proton is very large the combination will be extremely stable, which means that a considerable amount of energy will be expended in separating the two. If the force is feeble, little energy is needed. Thus, by measuring the *binding energy*, some information regarding the neutron-proton force can be found. In nuclei this binding energy is very large, amounting to several Mev, and as the theory of relativity requires an equivalence between mass and energy the binding energy of a deuteron can be found by measuring the mass of the deuteron and finding the difference between the separate masses of the two components of the deuteron and the mass of the combination. Thus the relative mass of the deuteron is 2.0147, while the sum of 1.0081 and 1.0089, the separate masses of the proton and neutron, respectively, is 2.0170. The difference is 0.0023. In actual grams for a single deuteron this is $0.0028 \times (1.6 \times 10^{-24})$, and if we multiply by the square of the velocity of light to get the equivalent in ergs, according to the theory of relativity, we obtain 4.0×10^{-6} erg. In Mev this is 2.1.

In this way we can obtain an experimental value for the binding energy between the stable combination of a neutron and a proton. Now we are presented with the problem of using this to give a definite meaning to the interaction between the two. Remember that we are only at the very beginning of our work and that we expect no more than a part of the story from this one line of evidence. With this in mind it is not too difficult to see that the theorist represents the force between the neutron and the proton by a *potential field* as in Fig. 1, either A or B. The meaning of this form of representation is that we consider the motion of one particle in the field of the other and suppose that the potential energy due to this field can be represented by either a well or an indentation as shown in the two parts of the figure. Now the particle we consider will have a certain amount of kinetic energy as well as potential energy and will move so that its total energy is a constant. This total energy may be represented by a line as at G. The binding energy, the energy needed to separate the two particles so that they do not influence one another at all, is not the energy of the depth of the whole potential well, *OD* in the figure, because the kinetic energy of the particles helps this separation, but the amount of energy represented by the potential *OG* in the figure. We then have the experimental fact that *OG* is 2.1 Mev for the deuteron.

To use this information that the binding energy is 2.1 Mev we have to devise potential fields which will give the right value. If we choose the well type of field we can describe the well by two magnitudes, the

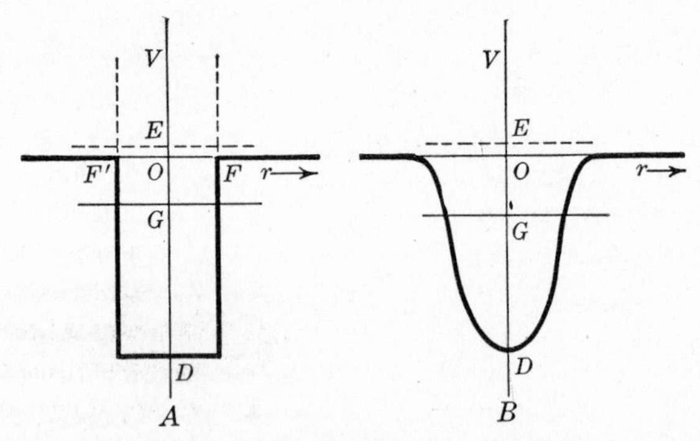

FIG. 1. Two ways of representing the potential field due to a force between a neutron and a proton, the force being that which makes possible the existence of a deuteron. Since the proton and neutron are in motion they possess kinetic energy, and the binding energy of the deuteron is determined by the position of the energy level, *G*, in the potential well. *GD* represents the total energy, kinetic and potential, inside the well, and *OG* the binding energy.

radius *OF* and the depth *OD*. Using this description we proceed as follows: We know from quantum mechanics that the motion of the neutron or proton is governed by a wave equation and that this has certain solutions which have physical meaning. These solutions can be obtained only for certain values of the energy difference, *GD*, and, if we can find a value of the two magnitudes *OF* and *OD* which make the first of these definite energy values (eigenvalues) such that *OG* is 2.1 Mev, we have obtained as much information as possible from the experimental value of the binding energy. It is not surprising that, within a range of values, we can choose several sets of radii and depths; we could hardly hope that one fact about one nucleus would give the complete story about this new type of force. We do, however, learn that the range of values requires the radius of the well to be about 3×10^{-13} cm and the depth about 20 Mev. The force is thus confined to an extremely small radius and is then of enormous size.

Before we continue to see what further we can learn about the nature of nuclear forces let us consider what types of forces we already understand and what factors affect these forces. The first type is the simple force, such as a coulomb force, or gravitation, which is simply a definite function of the distance between two particles. Adding more charge (i.e., more electrons or protons) simply increases the force proportionally. A second type is commonly found between atoms and has no counterpart in so-called ordinary forces. This force can be explained only by quantum mechanics and arises in a manner related to the peculiar nature of the waves associated with matter. In bare essentials quantum mechanics requires that the description of the motion of a particle be in terms of a wave equation in which the wavelength of the waves *depends on the energy* they have associated with them.

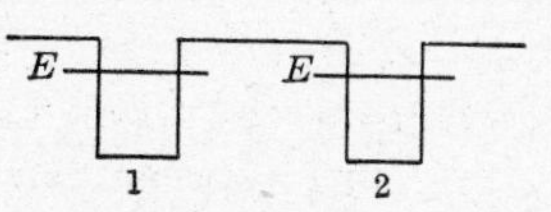

FIG. 2. Representation of the fields of two hydrogen nuclei with one of the energy levels of an electron indicated as at E. Since the wall between the two atoms is not infinitely thick there exists a chance that an electron in atom 1 find itself in atom 2. This fact requires a change in the wavelength of the waves describing the motion of the electron and gives rise to an "exchange" force.

To be more precise, if a particle moves with a total energy E, in a potential field represented by V, the wavelength of the waves describing the motion is $h/(2m(E - V))^{\frac{1}{2}}$. This means that, if a particle has operating on it some influence which causes the wavelength of these waves to change, it must suffer some change of $(E - V)$, and this cannot be done without the existence of a force. If, then, we find that the predictions of wave mechanics lead us to assert that there is a change in the wavelength of the waves describing the motion of a particle we are compelled to postulate the existence of a force.

Now consider two identical atoms each containing electrons, or, to simplify it more, consider two hydrogen nuclei, reasonably close to each other, with only one electron between them. We may represent each nucleus as a field of attraction, and for ease of drawing we may represent this field as a well. Then, as in Fig. 2 we have these two wells close together; and like the deuteron the electron has a definite energy E in each atom. The reader will recollect that there is always a finite probability that a particle can "leak" through any but an infinitely thick wall, and noticing that the wall between atom 1 and atom 2 is not infinitely thick he will see that if at any time the electron is in atom 1 it has a finite chance of being in atom 2. This conclusion is, on the surface, harmless enough—there is no reason why an electron should stay near one hydrogen nucleus when there is an alternative nucleus near by; but when it is followed up correctly it is found that the possibility of this "exchange" requires that the original wavelength of the waves describing the motion of the electron is altered. The amount of alteration depends, naturally enough, on the thickness of the wall separating the two atoms, which depends on their separation, and the alteration requires that a *force be exerted by one atom on the other.* This force is strong enough to make the hydrogen molecule ion reasonably stable in spite of the repulsion between the two protons, which is not balanced by any coulomb force of attraction. Such forces are called *exchange forces* or *resonance forces.* This explanation may or may not appeal to the reader, but it is designed to bring out one special feature of such a force, namely, that it is confined to a *pair* of hydrogen atoms. The proximity of a third hydrogen nucleus would undoubtedly affect the nature of the force, but not considerably, since it is only the fact of exchange between two atoms that causes the force. This type of force differs considerably from coulomb forces in that it has the feature of *saturation.*

With this preliminary discussion we can see where we may next look for information about nuclear forces. We may study the binding energy of more complicated nuclei, containing many particles, and observe whether the binding energy increases proportionally to the square of the number of particles as it would if forces acting were of the unsaturated type, or to the number itself if of the saturated type.* We quote the binding energies (difference between the masses of the neutrons and protons and that of the atom itself) for the first twelve stable nuclei. Figures are expressed in Mev.

H^2	2.1	He^3	7.6	He^4	27.6	He^5	unstable	Li^6	22.2
Li^7	29.1	Be^8	unstable	Be^9	48.3	B^{10}	54.5	B^{11}	66.3
C^{12}	82.3								

A continuation of these figures shows that the increase in binding energy is reasonably linear, so that the type of force we expect in the nucleus is the type which can be saturated and which would be of the exchange type. Now if we look more closely at the figures above we see that as far as the first three nuclei are concerned we are not so justified in dismissing the ordinary type of force. Thus the number of pairs in H^2 is one, and the binding energy is 2.1. The number of pairs in He^3 is three, and the binding energy is remarkably close to three times 2.1. In He^4 the number of pairs is twelve, and the binding energy, though not exactly twelve times 2.1, is still not far from it. It is after He^4 that

* If the attraction depends simply on the number of constituents, the energy will depend on the number of pairs we can form. This is $N(N-1)$, which is roughly N^2. If there is saturation a pair can be taken only once, and so the number of pairs effective is $N/2$, which is proportional to N.

the saturation feature begins to show up. *There is thus something inherent in the forces which requires that the saturation occur after four particles have been placed together.*

Before we continue this discussion of nuclear forces it is as well to look at all the known properties of elementary particles, particularly the neutron and proton. The obvious properties of mass and charge we can pass over; the property of *spin* requires consideration. To the chemist this property of spin is commonplace. He will have been waiting for it to be mentioned since he knows its importance in determining the nature of the elements. To those who are not so familiar with the idea we can say that in order to describe the behavior of an electron in an atom we are compelled to use four quantum numbers, three of which are related to the motion of the electron in the field of the atom and the fourth, the spin, is related fundamentally to the electron itself. It is a quantity which determines structure. This does not mean that there is any real meaning to be attached to the word "spin," in the sense of rotation; it means rather that the spin of a particle determines, among other things, in what condition we are likely to find it. The spin of both neutron and proton is $\frac{1}{2}$, which means that each contributes an angular momentum $\frac{1}{2}(h/2\pi)$ in some vectorial addition of angular momenta. The fact that this spin has this value means that both these elementary particles obey the Fermi statistics, requiring that only one particle have a particular complete set of four quantum numbers.

The application of this knowledge about spins at once sheds light on the saturation process and on the forces themselves. The fact that saturation occurs when there are four particles in the nucleus correlates perfectly with the fact that two neutrons can occupy a given quantum state, one with the spin one way and the other with opposite spin, and also two protons in the same way, making a total of four particles. The next particle, whether it be neutron or proton, is compelled by the operation of the Fermi statistics to go into a different level of energy, *a fact which prevents resonance forces from operating at all,* and the result is that no stable nucleus of five particles exists. If two particles are added there is some binding and it is possible to have stability. We therefore learn that forces operate only between particles in the same quantum state. We also learn rather more. In the first place these forces must not depend very greatly on the direction of the spins of the two particles relative to one another, for if we supposed that forces occurred only for parallel spins there would be no tendency for He^3 to have so great a binding energy since whatever is added to a deuteron must, by the operation of the Fermi statistics, have an opposite spin to the two previous particles which have like spins by our force requirement. In the second place we see that the forces between protons and protons, neutrons and neutrons, and protons and neutrons are much alike or the binding energy of He^3 would not be three times that of the deuteron and the binding energy of He^4 would not be twelve times.

This reasoning may seem so complicated to the reader that we may as well pause to summarize a little. We have found that new forces are necessary in the nucleus. These forces operate over an exceedingly small range of distance; they are of the "exchange type" in that they show saturation; they operate only between particles in the same quantum state; and they are not greatly affected by the direction of the spin of one particle relative to one another.

With this much information we can begin to look around for other lines of progress. We look to that favorite method of study of the nucleus, the scattering of particles by nuclei. Better yet, we propose to study the scattering of elementary particles by one another, and this can be done in two of the three possible cases. We can study the scattering of neutrons by protons and of protons by protons, but the third we cannot yet do. The scattering of neutrons by neutrons requires that we build a container for neutrons, and that has not yet been done. By far the best information exists for proton-proton scattering, and we can therefore treat it first. The first evidence for the action of nuclear forces in the scattering of protons by hydrogen was obtained by White using a cloud chamber to observe forked tracks due to collisions between protons and hydrogen gas in the chamber. He was able to analyze his data to show that the manner of scattering required a force at close quarters between the two protons concerned in the collision. The number of tracks he observed, however, though sufficient to show the reality of the effect of proton-proton forces, was not enough for a real idea of their nature to be obtained. The later work of Tuve, Hafstad, and Heydenburg, in a series of studies which is perhaps the most satisfying in the whole subject of nuclear physics, shows that as the energy of the protons from an electrostatic generator is varied the manner of scattering changes from that to be expected according to a coulomb force to one which corresponds to a sharply varying nuclear-type force. Their experiments, together with later work by Herb, Kerst, Parkinson, and Plain, are very thorough and permit an accurate determination of both the breadth and depth of the potential well due to proton-proton forces. When this is done it is found that although the force between these two like particles is not so great as the force between neutron and proton it is not very much less.

This agrees with the conclusion already mentioned in the last paragraph but one.

The scattering of neutrons by protons is a little different. We are not able as in proton work to obtain a sharply defined beam of neutrons of one energy only, and so the experiments cannot be as perfect as those of Tuve, Heydenburg, and Hafstad. However, two features of neutron scattering render its study informative. The first is the ease of detection of slow neutrons, neutrons having energies of the order of less than an electron volt; the second is the fact that neutrons are absorbed appreciably by hydrogen. Now when we make the simplest experiments on fast neutron scattering by hydrogen, for example determining how many neutrons are scattered right out of a block of paraffin by the hydrogen, we are able to predict how many *slow* neutrons are so scattered, and the prediction turns out to be many times too small. This discrepancy is of great interest, and its explanation has led to a considerable development of nuclear theory.

It was suggested by Breit and Wigner that the reason for the abnormal scattering of the slow neutrons is the existence of an energy level in the deuteron at about the energy of the slow neutrons. The scattering of neutrons by protons involves the temporary formation of a deuteron, which rapidly breaks up to form the neutron and proton again so that what is observed is scattering. Now, if it happens that for neutrons of nearly zero kinetic energy there is a stronger than ordinary chance of the formation of a deuteron, the scattering will be abnormally great. This greater than ordinary chance would be expected if an energy level existed in the deuteron of nearly zero binding energy, for then neutrons of zero energy would be favored in the formation of a deuteron. This is the suggestion made by Breit and Wigner. It is found to fit the experimental facts very well.

The interest in this suggestion is its implication regarding the nature of nuclear forces. A simple calculation shows that the force which accounts for the binding energy of the deuteron would not be great enough to allow an excited state which had other than zero angular momentum, for the necessary energy to permit the additional centrifugal force is not there. The excited state must therefore be one which differs from the ground state in that the neutron and proton have different relative spin directions from the ground state. This in turn requires that there be a difference between the force between the two fundamental particles according as their spins are parallel or antiparallel, in apparent contradiction to the conclusions we have already reached. A moment's reflection shows that the contradiction is not so bad as it seems, for the depth of the well is of the order of 20 Mev and the difference between the two energy levels is roughly 2 Mev, so that the fraction of the force which is spin-dependent is not very large.

A most ingenious use of the scattering of slow neutrons by hydrogen has been made by Brickwedde, Dunning, Hoge, and Manley. It is known that the hydrogen molecule can exist in two forms, *ortho-* and *para*-hydrogen. The difference between these two forms is in the orientation of the spins of the protons forming the nuclei of the molecule. In ortho-hydrogen the two spins are lined up in the same direction, giving a resultant spin of 1 for the whole molecule; in para-hydrogen the two spins are opposite, giving a resultant spin of zero. Now the lowest possible quantum state of all has a zero number, and this has the least energy content possible. This state cannot be occupied by ortho-hydrogen, where the resultant spin is 1, and so ortho-hydrogen has more energy than para-hydrogen. Now, if we imagine very slow neutrons passing in the vicinity of a hydrogen molecule, the energy the neutrons possess may not be sufficient to cause any transition in the hydrogen molecule, and the scattering would then be very small. However, since ortho-hydrogen has more energy than para-hydrogen it would be possible for an extremely slow neutron to cause a transition from ortho- to para-hydrogen and so have an extremely large scattering cross section. This possibility, however, is contingent on one important fact: there must be some force between the neutron and a proton which depends on the spins of the two. If this type of force is absent there can be no transition from ortho- to para-hydrogen and the scattering will be small. The four workers mentioned above produced very slow neutrons by surrounding a source of neutrons with paraffin cooled in liquid air and demonstrated that the scattering by ortho-hydrogen is roughly eight times the scattering by para-hydrogen, a very beautiful proof of the presence of spin-dependent forces.

We thus see how several lines of evidence lead to some idea of the nature of the forces between the elementary particles. The next procedure is to apply the information we have in order to see whether we can explain other phenomena. For example, it should be possible to derive a force from scattering information and the binding energy of the deuteron which will enable the binding energy of H^3, He^3, and He^4 to be calculated. The calculation can be made only approximately, but it has been carried out with results which can be classed as satisfactory or not according to how much of a perfectionist the critic is. At the present time the procedure is to suppose the forces between elementary particles to be of several kinds operating at once: "ordinary," spin-dependent, and spin-independent, being present in various proportions. No one constant set of proportions seems to fit all conditions; perhaps we should not expect that it should.

Ideas about Nuclear Structure. We have spent considerable time in discussing the evidence about nuclear forces and shown how a quantitative idea of their nature can be obtained. It should now be possible to embark on a reasonably satisfactory theory of the nucleus. The same considerations hold as in the electronic structure of the atom; we find the lowest states of energy and fill them with elementary particles at the rate of not more than one particle to a single state, as required by the Pauli principle. We thus expect that nuclei will exhibit shell structure as found in the atom itself, and to a certain extent this is true. One difficulty, which we have already mentioned, exists in the nucleus, namely, that we have no simple central type of field and the calculation of the lowest state of energy is not nearly so easy as for the electronic part of the atom, so that the operation of the Pauli principle is not simple to trace. Also we do not have the rich variety of properties to study as in the chemical properties of the elements; we are limited to a very few lines of evidence which bear on the nature of nuclei. The simple application of the principles which operate in the outer atom is thus not yet achieved, and nuclear theory is in the unsatisfactory position of having a set of ideas which should explain the whole subject and yet being unable to make the necessary calculations to verify their truth.

In order to overcome to some extent the limitations of calculation, statistical considerations have been applied to the nucleus which then appears much as a liquid drop appears to a molecular physicist. We can speak of the arrival of a neutron into a nucleus as raising the average energy of each constituent particle, or, in other words, the "temperature" of the nucleus, and the emission of a particle in a transmutation process or a scattering process is spoken of as "evaporation." Such ideas, which were first clearly presented by Bohr, are most valuable in explaining the great density of nuclear energy levels but are not very satisfactory since most nuclei have too few constituent particles to warrant the use of statistical methods. It may be that nuclear theory awaits the invention of mechanical calculation devices or of some new method of approximation.

Before we leave this subject a word about the possible nature of the "exchange" which is the basis of the nuclear forces is in place. The nature of the force binding the two protons in the hydrogen molecule ion may not be clear to those not versed in quantum mechanics, but at least it is categorically supposed that the force is due to the exchange of one electron between two nuclear fields. No such categorical statement is forthcoming regarding nuclear forces; in fact, the humility of the theorist shows the difficulty of the problem more clearly than anything else. It would be highly desirable if the force turned out to be due to the exchange of an electron and neutrino between a neutron and a proton, since this exchange is demanded by the theory of beta decay, but on trial this hypothesis fails as the force is far too small.

It occurred to Yukawa that a new particle of mass somewhere between that of the electron and the proton could explain the general feature of nuclear forces, and he made this suggestion in 1935. This appeared at the time to be very much of an *ad hoc* hypothesis, but the discovery by Anderson and Neddermeyer, and Street and Stevenson, of just such a particle in cosmic radiation has given much impetus to this explanation of nuclear forces. It requires about 100 Mev to be supplied to a nucleus to persuade it to part with a "mesotron," and when such energies can be developed artificially there is no doubt that the understanding of nuclear forces will begin to become more real. At present it is still true that we do not yet know what is in a nucleus, so our attempts at developing its structure are necessarily rather vague. In any event, to return to the "mesotron" theory of nuclear forces, it is suggested that a mesotron, which need not be stable, or even a particle at all, is capable of exchange between a neutron and a proton, or any other pair of nuclear particles. This exchange then causes the force of attraction much as in electron exchange between two hydrogen nuclear fields in the hydrogen molecule ion.

To leave on this rather unsatisfactory note gives us genuine pleasure. This is an age of vanishing frontiers, and it adds a touch of vigor to consider that here the frontier is very much present. We doubt whether the complete understanding of the atomic nucleus will be attained in our lifetime, and this adds considerable zest to existence. The feeling of zest is shared by workers in lab coats awaiting the 100-meter beam of the supercyclotron, by workers patiently amassing data about cosmic rays, by workers operating calculating machines and wearing down pencils. A little of it should have reached the reader.

APPENDIX 1

Dates of Some Important Developments

Discovery of alpha particle, *Rutherford*, 1904.
Scintillations, *Crookes, and Elster and Geitel*, 1903.
Cloud chamber used for nuclear-particle detection, *Wilson*, 1912.
Nuclear atom, *Rutherford and Bohr*, 1912.
Continuous beta-ray spectrum, *Chadwick*, 1914.
Rutherford-Geiger counter, 1908.
Isotopes of neon, *Thomson*, 1912.
Thermal diffusion predicted, *Chapman*, *Borelius*, 1915.
Transmutation of nitrogen, *Rutherford*, 1919.
Further transmutations by *Rutherford and Chadwick*, 1919–1923.
Mass spectrograph, *Aston*, 1919.
Radioactive indicators used, *von Hevesy and Paneth*, 1913.
Radio-autographs, *Lacassagne and Lattes*, 1924.
Physiological effects of x- and gamma rays discovered, 1898.
Genetic effect of x-rays, *Muller*, 1937.
Oil diffusion pumps, 1928.
Large water-cooled triodes, 1926.
Geiger-Müller counter, 1928.
Cyclotron first described, *Lawrence*, 1932.
Transmutation of lithium by artificially accelerated protons, *Cockcroft and Walton*, 1932.
Deuterium discovered, *Urey, Brickwedde, and Murphy*, 1932.
Van de Graaff machine, 1932.
Neutron discovered, *Chadwick*, 1932.
Positron discovered, *Anderson*, 1932.
Artificial radioactivity discovered, *Curie and Joliot*, 1934.
Cyclotron shimming discovered, 1934.
Large-scale separation of neon isotopes, *Hertz*, 1934.
Rubber gasket vacuum seals, 1936.
Discovery of Na^{24}, P^{32}, 1935.
Discovery of Fe^{59}, 1937.
Discovery of I^{131}, 1939.
Theoretical limit to cyclotron energy set at 10 Mev, 1938.
Crocker Laboratory beam found, 16 Mev, 1939.
In 1932, no artificial radioactive elements.
In 1934, 3 artificial radioactive elements.
In 1937, 190 artificial radioactive isotopes.

In 1939, 270 artificial radioactive isotopes.
In 1941, 370 artificial radioactive isotopes.
Uranium fission discovered, *Hahn and Strassmann*, 1938.
Chemical exchange method of isotope separation, *Urey*, 1936.
Thermal diffusion method of isotope separation, *Clusius and Dickel*, 1937.
Leukemia therapy tried, *J. Lawrence*, 1938.
Discovery of C^{14}, *Ruben and Kamen*, 1940.
"Betatron" developed, *Kerst*, 1941.

APPENDIX 2

Table of Atomic Species

In this section of the Appendix we give a table of atomic species. Of these, many are stable, many are radioactive with the emission of electrons, and many are positron emitters. These three categories almost cover the whole range of possibilities, and so we have attempted to make the table as compact as possible by indicating which of the three applies to a certain element, as follows. Stable elements are listed in **bold-face** type. If they are naturally occurring but radioactive, this fact is stated. Beta-ray emitters are listed in ordinary type, and positron emitters appear in *italics*. The atomic number is not explicitly stated for each element, but the range of atomic numbers is given at the head of each new column and as the order is consecutive it should cause little trouble to locate the value. The second column of the table shows either the abundance or the half-life according to whether the element is stable or radioactive. The last two columns show the energies of the radiations. Only if the categorical statement appears should it be assumed that a blank space means the absence of a radiation; it generally means that the information has not yet been obtained experimentally.

A few general comments on the table are desirable. In the first place it must be stressed that it is incomplete. This is due to the youth of the subject of artificial radioactivity. In ten years or so it will probably be true that the number of radioactive isotopes not well known will be like the number of unknown stable isotopes today, very small. At present there is probably insufficient knowledge about half the total radioactive isotopes. This being so we have included only those radioactive isotopes which have been reasonably well studied. For more complete information the article by Seaborg on artificial radioactivity in *Chemical Reviews*, August, 1940, should be consulted. Anyone intending to do serious research in artificial radioactivity should keep his own isotope table up to date with the aid of the current literature.

Not many general rules can be given about atomic species. One simple generality holds, namely, that practically no elements of odd atomic number and even mass number are stable. In addition, elements of odd atomic number are found with little diversity in mass number. The large numbers of isotopes are found with even atomic number. An interesting question concerns *isobars*, isotopes with different atomic numbers but the same mass number. Many such examples are known, but most of them differ in atomic number by more than one unit. This indicates that the change of one isobar into the other requires transition through a third isobar, and there may be insufficient energy available for the change. If, however, isobars existed with atomic number differing by one unit, one would presumably be more stable than the other, and the question arises why the transition does not take place. Actually several such isobars are known, for example, In^{113} and Cd^{113}, and both are stable. This fact is proof of the existence of strong selection rules which may greatly modify, or even prevent, an otherwise expected transition. In other words, one or other of these pairs of isobars is radioactive, but with a nearly infinite half-life.

Atomic Number 1 to 10

Atomic Species	Abundance or Half-Life	Particle Energies, Mev	Quantum Energies
H^1	**99.98%**		
H^2	**0.02%**		
H^3	31y *	0.013	
He^3	**10^{-5}%**		
He^4	**100%**		
	Mass five missing		
He^6	0.8s *	3.7	
Li^6	**7.9%**		
Li^7	**92.1%**		
Li^8	0.88s	12	
Be^7	*K*		*0.45*
Be^9	**100%**		
Be^{10}	>>10^3y	~0.5	<0.5
B^{10}	**18.4%**		
B^{11}	**81.6%**		
C^{10}	*8.8s*	*3.4*	
C^{11}	*21.0m* *	*0.95*	
B^{12}	0.022s	12	
C^{12}	**98.9%**		
C^{13}	**1.1%**		
C^{14}	1000y	0.145	
N^{13}	*9.93m*	*0.92, 1.22*	*0.28*
N^{14}	**99.62%**		
N^{15}	**0.38%**		
N^{16}	*8s*	*6*	
O^{15}	*126s*	*1.7*	
O^{16}	**99.76%**		
O^{17}	**0.04%**		
O^{18}	**0.20%**		
O^{19}	31s		
F^{17}	*70s*	*2.1*	
F^{18}	*112m*	*0.7*	
F^{19}	**100%**		
F^{20}	12s	5.0	2.2
Ne^{19}	*20.3s*	*2.20*	
Ne^{20}	**90.0%**		
Ne^{21}	**0.27%**		

* y = year(s); s = second(s); m = minute(s); h = hour(s); d = day(s).

Atomic Number 10 to 19

Atomic Species	Abundance or Half-Life	Particle Energies, Mev	Quantum Energies
Ne^{22}	**9.73%**		
Ne^{23}	40s	4.1	
Na^{21}	*23s*		
Na^{22}	*3.0y*	*0.58*	*1.3*
Na^{23}	**100%**		
Na^{24}	14.8h *	1.4	1.46, 2.0, 3.03
Mg^{23}	*11.6s*	*2.84*	
Mg^{24}	**77.4%**		
Mg^{25}	**11.5%**		
Mg^{26}	**11.1%**		
Mg^{27}	10.2m	1.8	0.9
Al^{26}	*7.0s*	*2.99*	
Al^{27}	**100%**		
Al^{28}	2.4m	3.3	2.3
Al^{29}	6.7m	2.5	
Si^{27}	*4s*	*3.7*	
Si^{28}	**89.6%**		
Si^{29}	**6.2%**		
Si^{30}	**4.2%**		
Si^{31}	170m	1.8	None
P^{29}	*$<$10s*		
P^{30}	*2.55m*	*3.0*	
P^{31}	**100%**		
P^{32}	14.30d *	1.71	None
S^{31}	*3.2s*	*3.8*	
S^{32}	**95.0%**		
S^{33}	**0.74%**		
S^{34}	**4.2%**		
S^{35}	88d	0.107	
S^{36}	**0.016%**		
Cl^{33}	*2.8s*		
Cl^{34}	*33m*	*2.5*	
Cl^{35}	**75.4%**		
Cl^{36}	$>10^3$y	0.64 (also K and positron)	
Cl^{37}	**24.6%**		
Cl^{38}	37m	1.1, 3.2, 5.0	1.7, 2.0
A^{35}	*1.9s*	*4.4*	
A^{36}	**0.307%**		
A^{38}	**0.061%**		
A^{40}	**99.632%**		
A^{41}	110m	1.5	1.37
K^{38}	*7.7m*	*2.3*	
K^{39}	**93.3%**		
K^{40}	**0.012%**	**Naturally radioactive, electron, positron and γ-ray**	

Atomic Number 19 to 26

Atomic Species	Abundance or Half-Life	Particle Energies, Mev	Quantum Energies
K^{41}	**6.7%**		
K^{42}	12.4h	3.5	
Ca^{40}	**96.96%**		
Ca^{42}	**0.64%**		
Ca^{43}	**0.15%**		
Ca^{44}	**2.06%**		
Ca^{45}	180d	0.2. 0.9	0.7
Ca^{46}	**0.0033%**		
Ca^{48}	**0.19%**		
Ca^{49}	2.5h	2.3	0.8
Sc^{41}	*0.8s*	*4.9*	
Sc^{42}	*13.5d*	*1.4*	
Sc^{43}	*4h*	*0.4, 1.4*	*1.0*
Sc^{44}	52h	Isomer	0.26
Sc^{44}	*4.1h*	*1.5*	
Sc^{45}	**100%**		
Sc^{46}	85d	0.26, 1.5, K	1.25
Sc^{48}	44h	0.5, 1.4	0.9
Sc^{49}	57m	1.8	None
Ti^{45}	*3.0h*	*1.2*	
Ti^{46}	**7.95%**		
Ti^{47}	**7.75%**		
Ti^{48}	**73.45%**		
Ti^{49}	**5.51%**		
Ti^{50}	**5.34%**		
Ti^{51}	2.9m	Isomer	
Ti^{51}	72d	0.36	1.0
V^{47}	*600d*	*K*	*None*
V^{48}	*16d*	*1.0*	*1.05*
V^{49}	*33m*	*1.9*	
V^{50}	*3.7h*		
V^{51}	**100%**		
V^{52}	3.9m	2.05	
Cr^{50}	**4.49%**		
Cr^{51}	26.5d	Also K	0.5, 1
Cr^{52}	**83.77%**		
Cr^{53}	**9.43%**		
Cr^{54}	**2.30%**		
Cr^{55}	2h		
Mn^{51}	*46m*	*2.0*	
Mn^{52}	*21m*	*2.2*	*1.2*
Mn^{53}	*6.5d*	*0.77*	*1.0*
Mn^{54}	*310d*	*K*	*0.85*
Mn^{55}	**100%**		
Mn^{56}	2.59h	1.2, 2.9	0.7, 1.7
Fe^{53}	*8.9m*		

Atomic Number 26 to 31

Atomic Species	Abundance or Half-Life	Particle Energies, Mev	Quantum Energies
$\mathbf{Fe}^{54}$	**6.04%**		
Fe^{55}	*4y*	*Also K*	
$\mathbf{Fe}^{56}$	**91.57%**		
$\mathbf{Fe}^{57}$	**2.11%**		
$\mathbf{Fe}^{58}$	**0.28%**		
Fe^{59}	47d	0.4, 0.9	1.0
Co^{55}	*18.2h*	*1.50*	*0.16, 0.21, 0.8, 1.2*
Co^{56}	*72d*	*1.2*	*1.05*
$\mathbf{Co}^{57}$	**0.17%**		
Co^{57}	*270d*	*0.26*	
Co^{58}	*72d*	*0.4*	*0.6*
$\mathbf{Co}^{59}$	**99.83%**		
Co^{60}	5.3y	0.16, 1.5	1.3
Co^{60}	10.7m		
Ni^{57}	2m		
$\mathbf{Ni}^{58}$	**68.0%**		
Ni^{59}	*36h*	*0.67*	
$\mathbf{Ni}^{60}$	**27.2%**		
$\mathbf{Ni}^{61}$	**0.1%**		
$\mathbf{Ni}^{62}$	**3.8%**		
Ni^{63}	2.6h	1.9	1.1
$\mathbf{Ni}^{64}$	**0.9%**		
Cu^{61}	*34h*	*0.9*	*None*
Cu^{62}	*10.5m*	*2.6*	
$\mathbf{Cu}^{63}$	**68%**		
Cu^{64}	12.8h	0.58	None
		Also positron, 0.66	
$\mathbf{Cu}^{65}$	**32%**		
Cu^{66}	5m	2.9	
Zn^{63}	*38m*	*2.3*	
$\mathbf{Zn}^{64}$	**50.9%**		
Zn^{65}	*250d*	*0.4*	*0.45, 0.65, 1.0*
$\mathbf{Zn}^{66}$	**27.3%**		
$\mathbf{Zn}^{67}$	**3.9%**		
$\mathbf{Zn}^{68}$	**17.4%**		
Zn^{69}	13.8h	Isomer	0.47
Zn^{69}	57m	1.0	None
$\mathbf{Zn}^{70}$	**0.5%**		
Ga^{64}	*48m*		
Ga^{65}	15m	K	0.054, 0.117
Ga^{66}	*9.4h*	*3.1*	
Ga^{67}	83h	K	0.18, 0.30
Ga^{68}	*68m*	*1.9*	
$\mathbf{Ga}^{69}$	**61.2%**		
Ga^{70}	20m	1.7	
$\mathbf{Ga}^{71}$	**38.8%**		

Atomic Number 31 to 37

Atomic Species	Abundance or Half-Life	Particle Energies, Mev	Quantum Energies
Ga^{72}	14h	2.6	1.0
Ge^{70}	**21.2%**		
Ge^{71}	11d	Isomer	
Ge^{71}	*40h*	*1.0*	
Ge^{72}	**27.3%**		
Ge^{73}	**7.9%**		
Ge^{74}	**37.1%**		
Ge^{75}	89m	1.1	
Ge^{76}	**6.5%**		
Ge^{77}	12h	1.9	
As^{74}	16d	1.3, also positron 0.9	
As^{75}	**100%**		
As^{76}	26.8h	1.1, 1.7, 2.7, also positron, 0.7, 2.6	3.2, 2.2, 1.5
As^{78}	65m	1.4	0.27
Se^{74}	**0.9%**		
Se^{75}	48d	K	0.50
Se^{76}	**9.5%**		
Se^{77}	**8.3%**		
Se^{78}	**24.0%**		
Se^{80}	**48.0%**		
Se^{82}	**9.3%**		
Se^{83}	30m		
Br^{78}	*6.4m*	*2.3*	*0.046, 0.108*
Br^{79}	**50.6%**		
Br^{80}	4.4h	Isomer	0.037
Br^{80}	18m	2.0	<0.5
Br^{81}	**49.4%**		
Br^{83}	140m	1.05	None
Kr^{78}	**0.35%**		
Kr^{79,81}	*34h*	*0.5*	
Kr^{80}	**2.01%**		
Kr^{82}	**11.53%**		
Kr^{83}	113m	Isomer of stable nucleus	0.049
Kr^{83}	**11.53%**		
Kr^{84}	**57.1%**		
Kr^{86}	**17.47%**		
Kr^{87}	4.5h		
Kr^{88}	3h		
Kr^{89}	2m		
Rb^{82}	*20m*		
Rb^{84}	6.5h		
Rb^{85}	**72.3%**		
Rb^{86}	19.5d	1.56	

Atomic Number 37 to 44

Atomic Species	Abundance or Half-Life	Particle Energies, Mev	Quantum Energies
Rb^{87}	**27.7%**	**Naturally radioactive**	
Rb^{88}	18m	4.6	
Rb^{89}	15m	3.8	
Sr^{84}	**0.56%**		
Sr^{85}	65d	Isomer	0.8
Sr^{85}	70m		0.17
Sr^{86}	**9.86%**		
Sr^{87}	2.7h	Isomer of stable nucleus	0.37
Sr^{87}	**7.02%**		
Sr^{88}	**82.56%**		
Sr^{89}	55d	1.50	None
Y^{86}	105d	K	2
Y^{87}	14h	Isomer	0.5
Y^{87}	80h	K	
Y^{88}	*2.0h*	*1.2*	
Y^{89}	**100%**		
Y^{90}	60h	2.6	
Zr^{89}	*78h*	*1.0*	*None*
Zr^{89}	4.5m		
Zr^{90}	**48%**		
Zr^{91}	**11.5%**		
Zr^{92}	**22%**		
Zr^{94}	**17%**		
Zr^{96}	**1.5%**		
Cb^{92}	11d	1.38	
Cb^{93}	55d	Isomer of stable nucleus	0.15
Cb^{93}	**100%**		
Cb^{94}	6.6m	1, 4	0.4
Mo^{92}	**15.5%**		
Mo^{94}	**8.7%**		
Mo^{95}	**16.3%**		
Mo^{96}	**16.8%**		
Mo^{97}	**8.7%**		
Mo^{98}	**25.4%**		
Mo^{99}	67h	1.5	0.4
Mo^{100}	**8.6%**		
Mo^{101}	19m	1.8	
43^{96}	*2.7h*		
43^{99}	6.6h		0.14
43^{101}	9m	1.1 (formed from Mo^{101})	
Ru^{96}	**5%**		
Ru^{98}	**?**		
Ru^{99}	**12%**		
Ru^{100}	**14%**		

Atomic Number 44 to 49

Atomic Species	Abundance or Half-Life	Particle Energies, Mev	Quantum Energies
Ru^{101}	**22%**		
Ru^{102}	**30%**		
Ru^{103}	4h		
Ru^{104}	**17%**		
Ru^{105}	20h		
Rh^{101}	**0.08%**		
Rh^{103}	**99.92%**		
Rh^{104}	4.2m	Isomer	
Rh^{104}	44s	2.3	
Rh^{105}	46d		
Pd^{102}	**0.8%**		
Pd^{104}	**9.3%**		
Pd^{105}	**22.6%**		
Pd^{106}	**27.2%**		
Pd^{107}	13h	1.03	
Pd^{108}	**26.8%**		
Pd^{110}	**13.5%**		
Pd^{111}	17m		
Ag^{106}	*24.5m*	*2.04*	*None*
Ag^{106}	8.2d	1.2	1.6, 0.69
Ag^{107}	**52.5%**		
Ag^{108}	2.3m	2.8	
Ag^{109}	**47.5%**		
Ag^{110}	22s	2.8	
Ag^{111}	7.5d		None
Ag^{112}	3.2h	2.2	
Cd^{106}	**1.4%**		
Cd^{108}	**1.0%**		
Cd^{110}	**12.8%**		
Cd^{111}	**13.0%**		
Cd^{112}	**24.2%**		
Cd^{113}	**12.3%**		
Cd^{114}	**28.0%**		
Cd^{115}	2.5d	1.11	0.55
Cd^{116}	**7.3%**		
Cd^{117}	3.75h		
In^{113}	105m	Isomer of stable element	0.39
In^{113}	**4.5%**		
In^{114}	48d	Isomer	0.19
In^{114}	72s	1.98	
In^{115}	4.1h	Isomer of stable element	0.34
In^{115}	**95.5%**		
In^{116}	13s	2.8	None

Atomic Number 49 to 54

Atomic Species	Abundance or Half-Life	Particle Energies, Mev	Quantum Energies
In^{116}	54m	0.85	1.8, 1.4, 1.0, 0.6, 0.4, 0.2
In^{117}	117m	1.73	
Sn^{112}	**1.1%**		
Sn^{113}	90d	K	0.085
Sn^{114}	**0.8%**		
Sn^{115}	**0.4%**		
Sn^{116}	**15.5%**		
Sn^{117}	**9.1%**		
Sn^{118}	**22.5%**		
Sn^{119}	**9.8%**		
Sn^{120}	**28.5%**		
Sn^{122}	**5.5%**		
Sn^{124}	**6.8%**		
Sn^{125}	9m		
Sb^{120}	*17m*	*1.53*	
Sb^{121}	**56%**		
Sb^{122}	2.8d	0.81, 1.64	0.96
Sb^{123}	**44%**		
Sb^{124}	60d	1.53	1.82
Sb^{127}	80h		
Sb^{129}	4.2h		
Te^{120}	**<0.1%**		
Te^{121}	125d	K	
Te^{122}	**2.9%**		
Te^{123}	**1.6%**		
Te^{124}	**4.5%**		
Te^{125}	**6.0%**		
Te^{126}	**19.0%**		
Te^{127}	9.3h		
Te^{128}	**32.8%**		
Te^{129}	72m		
Te^{130}	**33.1%**		
Te^{131}	25m		
I^{124}	*4.0d*		
I^{126}	13.0d	1.1	0.5
I^{127}	**100%**		
I^{128}	25m	1.2, 2.1	0.4
I^{130}	12.6h	0.83	0.6
I^{131}	8.0d	0.687	0.4
Xe^{124}	**0.094**		
Xe^{126}	**0.088**		
Xe^{127}	75s	Isomer	0.175, 0.125
Xe^{127}	34d		0.9
Xe^{128}	**1.90%**		

Atomic Number 54 to 64

Atomic Species	Abundance or Half-Life	Particle Energies, Mev	Quantum Energies
Xe^{129}	**26.23%**		
Xe^{130}	**4.07%**		
Xe^{131}	**21.17%**		
Xe^{132}	**26.96%**		
Xe^{134}	**10.54%**		
Xe^{136}	**8.95%**		
Xe^{139}	<0.5m		
Cs^{133}	**100%**		
Cs^{134}	3h	1	
Cs^{134}	1.7y	0.9	
Cs^{139}	7m		
Ba^{130}	**0.101%**		
Ba^{132}	**0.097%**		
Ba^{133}	30h		0.30
Ba^{134}	**2.42%**		
Ba^{135}	**6.59%**		
Ba^{136}	**7.81%**		
Ba^{137}	**11.32%**		
Ba^{138}	**71.66%**		
Ba^{139}	86m	1	0.6
La^{139}	**100%**		
La^{140}	31h	0.8	
Ce^{136}	**<1%**		
Ce^{138}	**<1%**		
Ce^{140}	**90%**		
Ce^{142}	**10%**		
Pr^{141}	**100%**		
Pr^{142}	18.7h		
Nd^{142}	**25.95%**		
Nd^{143}	**13.0%**		
Nd^{144}	**22.6%**		
Nd^{145}	**9.2%**		
Nd^{146}	**16.5%**		
Nd^{148}	**6.8%**		
Nd^{150}	**5.95%**		
61$^{?}$	12.5h		
Sm^{144}	**3%**		
Sm^{147}	**17%**		
Sm^{148}	**14%**	**Naturally radioactive**	
Sm^{149}	**15%**		
Sm^{150}	**5%**		
Sm^{152}	**26%**		
Sm^{154}	**20%**		
Eu^{151}	**49.1%**		
Eu^{153}	**50.9%**		
Gd^{152}	**0.2%**		

Atomic Number 64 to 73

Atomic Species	Abundance or Half-Life	Particle Energies, Mev	Quantum Energies
Gd^{154}	1.5%		
Gd^{155}	20.7%		
Gd^{156}	22.6%		
Gd^{157}	16.7%		
Gd^{158}	22.6%		
Gd^{160}	15.7%		
Tb^{159}	100%		
Tb^{160}	3.9h		
Dy^{158}	0.1%		
Dy^{160}	1.5%		
Dy^{161}	21.6%		
Dy^{162}	24.6%		
Dy^{163}	24.6%		
Dy^{164}	27.6%		
Dy^{165}	2.5h	1.9	
Ho^{165}	100%		
Ho^{166}	35h	1.6	
Er^{162}	0.25%		
Er^{164}	2.0%		
Er^{166}	35.2%		
Er^{167}	23.5%		
Er^{168}	29.3%		
Er^{170}	9.8%		
Tm^{169}	100%		
Tm^{170}	105d		
Yb^{168}	0.06%		
Yb^{170}	2%		
Yb^{171}	8.8%		
Yb^{172}	23.5%		
Yb^{173}	16.7%		
Yb^{174}	37.2%		
Yb^{176}	11.8%		
Lu^{175}	97.5%		
Lu^{176}	2.5%	**Naturally radioactive**	
$Hf^{172?}$	<0.1%		
Hf^{174}	0.3%		
Hf^{176}	5%		
Hf^{177}	19%		
Hf^{178}	28%		
Hf^{179}	18%		
Hf^{180}	30%		
Hf^{181}	55d		
Ta^{180}	17m	Isomer	
Ta^{180}	8.2h	<0.5	
Ta^{181}	100%		
Ta^{182}	97d		

Atomic Number 74 to 81

Atomic Species	Abundance or Half-Life	Particle Energies, Mev	Quantum Energies
W^{180}	**0.2%**		
W^{182}	**22.6%**		
W^{183}	**17.3%**		
W^{184}	**30.1%**		
W^{185}	77d	0.5	
W^{186}	**29.8%**		
W^{187}	23h	1.1	
Re^{185}	**38.2%**		
Re^{186}	90h	1.05	None
Re^{187}	**61.8%**		
Re^{188}	18h	2.5	
Os^{184}	**0.018%**		
Os^{186}	**1.59%**		
Os^{187}	**1.64%**		
Os^{188}	**13.3%**		
Os^{189}	**16.1%**		
Os^{190}	**26.4%**		
Os^{192}	**41.0%**		
Os^{193}	40h		
Ir^{191}	**38.5%**		
Ir^{192}	60d		
Ir^{193}	**61.5%**		
Ir^{194}	19h	2.2	
Pt^{192}	**0.8%**		
Pt^{194}	**30.2%**		
Pt^{195}	**35.3%**		
Pt^{196}	**26.6%**		
Pt^{197}	3.3d		
Pt^{197}	18h		
Pt^{198}	**7.2%**		
Pt^{199}	31m		
Au^{196}	13h		
Au^{196}	4d	0.36	0.41
Au^{197}	**100%**		
Au^{198}	2.7d	0.8	0.28, 0.44, 2.5
Au^{199}	3.3d		
Hg^{196}	**0.15%**		
Hg^{197}	25h		
Hg^{198}	**10.1%**		
Hg^{199}	**17.0%**		
Hg^{200}	**23.3%**		
Hg^{201}	**13.2%**		
Hg^{202}	**29.6%**		
Hg^{203}	54d	0.3	0.3
Hg^{204}	**6.7%**		
Tl^{203}	**29.1%**		

Atomic Number 81 to 93

Atomic Species	Abundance or Half-Life	Particle Energies, Mev	Quantum Energies
Tl^{204}	4.23m	1.6	None
Tl^{205}	**70.9%**		
Tl^{206}	3.5y	0.87	
Pb^{204}	**1.48%**		
Pb^{205}	80m		
Pb^{206}	**23.59%**		
Pb^{207}	**22.64%**		
Pb^{208}	**52.29%**		
Pb^{209}	3.0h		
Bi^{209}	**100%**		
Bi^{210}	5d		
Po^{210}	136d	α rays	
Po^{211}	10^{-3}s	7.5 α rays	
85^{211}	7.5h	6 α rays	
$_{90}Th^{232}$	**100%**	**Naturally radioactive**	
$_{90}UY^{231}$	24.5h		
Th^{233}	26m		
Pa^{231}		**Naturally radioactive**	
Pa^{233}	25d		
U^{234}	**0.006%**	**Naturally radioactive**	
U^{235}	**0.71%**	**Naturally radioactive**	
U^{237}	7d	0.26	
U^{238}	**99.28%**	**Naturally radioactive**	
U^{239}	23m		
93^{239}	2.3d	0.47	0.22, 0.27

APPENDIX 3

COMMONLY USED RADIOELEMENTS

In the table below we reproduce, with very little change, a table given by Hamilton in which the nature, method of preparation, and rough yields of the more commonly used radioelements are listed. The values for the yields are extremely rough and should be looked on merely as a guide in planning experiments or bombardments. We have decided that the average cyclotron which is used for tracer manufacture delivers 8-million-volt deuterons, and the yields we give are estimated for that energy. An error of a factor of 10 is not likely, but we wish to stress that we are here stating orders of magnitude rather than precise cross sections.

ELEMENT	HALF-LIFE	ELECTRON ENERGIES	QUANTUM ENERGIES	YIELD IN MILLICURIES PER MICROAMPERE-HOUR	PRODUCED BY
C^{11}	*21m*	*0.95*		0.5	B(*dn*)
C^{14}	1000y	0.15		5.10^{-8}	C(*dp*) or N(*np*)
N^{13}	*9.9m*	*1.2*	0.3	0.5	C(*dn*)
		0.9			
F^{18}	*112m*	*0.7*		0.001	O^{17}(*dn*)
Na^{22}	*3.0y*	*0.6*	1.3	0.003	Mg(*dα*)
Na^{24}	14.8h	1.4	1.5, 2.0, 3.0	10	Na(*dp*)
P^{32}	14.3d	1.7	None	0.2	P(*dp*)
S^{35}	88d	0.11		0.0001	S(*dp*)
Cl^{38}	37m	1.1	1.7. 2.1	1	Cl(*dp*)
		3.2			
		5.0			
K^{42}	12.4h	3.5		0.05	K(*dp*)
Ca^{45}	180d	0.9	0.7	10^{-5}	Ca(*dp*)
		0.2			
Mn^{54}	310d	K	0.9	0.001	Fe(*dα*)
Mn^{56}	2.6h	2.9	1.7	0.5	Mn(*dp*)
		1.2			
Fe^{59}	47d	0.9	1.0	0.00003	Fe(*dp*)
		0.4			
Cu^{64}	*12.8h*	*0.66*	None	3	Cu(*dp*)
Cu^{64}	*12.8h*	0.58	None	3	Cu(*dp*)

Element	Half-Life	Electron Energies	Quantum Energies	Yield in Millicuries per Microampere-Hour	Produced by
As^{76}	26.8h	2.7, 1.7, 1.1	1.5, 3.2	0.011	As(*n*-) Be(*dn*)
As^{76}	26.8h	*2.6, 0.7*	2.2		As(*n*-)
Br^{82}	34h	0.7	0.65	0.01	Br(*n*-) Be(*dn*)
Sr^{89}	55d	1.5	None	0.007	Sr(*dp*)
Sb^{122}	2.8d	1.6	0.5	0.005	Sb(*dp*)
I^{128}	25m	2.1 1.2	0.4	0.01	I(*n*-) Be(*dn*)
I^{131}	8.0d	0.7	0.4	0.02	Te(*dn*)
Au^{198}	2.7d	0.8	2.5, 0.4, 0.3	0.001	Au(*n*-) Be(*dn*)
85^{211}	7.5h	6.0 (α particle)		0.001	Bi(α2*n*) (32mvα)

APPENDIX 4

Absorption of Beta Rays

To understand the absorption of the continuous beta rays emitted by a radioactive substance two relations need to be known. The first is the energy distribution of the electrons themselves, and the second is the relation between the energy of an electron and the thickness of absorber which it will traverse. Neither of these is particularly simple if one aims at very rigorous consideration of absorption, but both can be approximated so as to be very useful in designing experimental equipment and technique.

We have stated in the text that beta rays have a maximum energy for any one element. Suppose that this is E_m Mev. Also suppose that the probability of emission of electrons of energies between the values E and $E + dE$ is W. Then the Fermi theory gives the following expression for W.

$$W = A(E)^{1/2}(1 + 2E)(1 + E)^{1/2}(E_m - E)^2dE \qquad [1]$$

This is not exact but is within 2 per cent. In this formula A is a constant for any one element. To the degree of approximation usually needed for radioactive tracer work this can be replaced by

$$W = B(E)(3 + 2E)(E_m - E)^2dE \qquad [2]$$

This can be relied on to about 15 per cent for values of E less than 2 Mev. The greatest deviation from this formula is introduced by the method of supporting the radioactive source. If the support is thick there is a considerable amount of scattering of the electrons by the support, and this changes the energy distribution. In the above equation B is again a constant for any one element.

In Chapter 7 we briefly discussed the absorption of beta rays and gave a rough beta-ray formula. This is approximately true for all kinds of absorbing material, but if aluminum is used a rather better accuracy can be obtained by using an empirical relation first given by Feather and improved by Widdowson and Champion. This is

$$R = 0.536E - 0.165 \qquad [3]$$

where R is the range, or thickness just penetrable, measured in grams per square centimeter. If the reader is prepared to use these two formulas he can get a reasonable idea of the relative counts for different thicknesses of absorbing material.

Where two groups of beta rays are found the correct procedure is to treat each group as having its own separate maximum energy and add the results. Actually a practical average can be taken by treating the element as if it had one maximum energy which is the average of the two most energetic groups.

APPENDIX 5

Absorption of Gamma Rays

If a series of absorbers is placed in the path of a parallel beam of gamma rays the absorption takes place exponentially according to the relation

$$\frac{I}{I_0} = e^{-\tau x} \quad \text{or} \quad \ln I_0 - \ln I = \tau x$$

where I is the ionization current or number of secondary electrons counted at a thickness of absorber x, and I_0 is the corresponding quantity with no absorber other than enough to give equilibrium ionization. τ is called the absorption coefficient.

In the following tables we give the absorption coefficients for several different substances and a large range of energy values. In addition we present a table of half-value thicknesses in aluminum and copper which may help in a quick rough determination of gamma-ray energies. Approximately, brass is the same as copper.

Gamma-Ray Energy	Absorption Coefficient				
Mev	*Carbon*	*Water*	*Aluminum*	*Copper*	*Lead*
0.25	0.26	0.124	0.29	0.91	
0.50	0.20	0.095	0.22	0.70	1.7
0.75	0.17		0.19	0.58	
1.00	0.15	0.069	0.16	0.50	0.80
1.25	0.13		0.146	0.45	
1.50	0.12		0.132	0.41	
1.75	0.114		0.122	0.38	
2.00	0.106		0.115	0.35	
2.50	0.087	0.043	0.105	0.33	0.475
3.00	0.083		0.100	0.32	
3.50	0.078		0.095	0.31	
4.00	0.069		0.086	0.30	
4.50			0.078	0.28	
5.00		0.030	0.075	0.27	0.480
5.50			0.073	0.28	
6.00			0.071	0.28	

Gamma-Ray Energy Mev	Absorption Coefficient				
	Carbon	*Water*	*Aluminum*	*Copper*	*Lead*
7.00			0.068	0.30	
8.00			0.065	0.30	
9.00			0.063	0.31	
10.00		0.022	0.061	0.31	0.61
15.00			0.061	0.32	
20.00		0.017	0.054	0.32	
30.00			0.058	0.34	
50.00		0.015	0.061	0.38	1.02

Half-Value Thickness for Different Energies

Aluminum		*Copper*	
$x_{1/2}$, cm	E, Mev	$x_{1/2}$, cm	E, Mev
2.0	0.15	0.50	0.12
3.0	0.47	0.75	0.25
4.0	0.92	1.00	0.52
5.0	1.40	1.50	1.20
6.0	2.00	2.00	2.10
7.0	2.95	2.10	2.50
8.0	4.00	2.30	3.80

APPENDIX 6

MASSES OF STABLE ISOTOPES

Isotope	Mass	Isotope	Mass	Isotope	Mass	Isotope	Mass
H^1	1.00812	C^{12}	12.00398	Na^{23}	22.99680	S^{34}	33.97974
H^2	2.01472	C^{13}	13.00766	Mg^{24}	23.99189	Cl^{35}	34.98107
He^3	3.01701	N^{14}	14.00750	Mg^{25}	24.99277	A^{36}	35.97852
H^3	3.01704	N^{15}	15.00489	Mg^{26}	25.99062	Cl^{37}	36.97829
He^4	4.00388	O^{16}	16.00000	Al^{27}	26.98960	A^{38}	37.97544
Li^6	6.01690	O^{17}	17.00450	Si^{28}	27.98639	K^{39}	38.97518
Li^7	7.01804	O^{18}	18.0047	Si^{29}	28.98685	A^{40}	39.97504
Be^8	8.00777	F^{19}	19.00452	Si^{30}	29.98294	Ca^{40}	39.9745
Be^9	9.01497	Ne^{20}	19.99881	P^{31}	30.98457	K^{41}	40.9739
B^{10}	10.01605	Ne^{21}	21.00018	S^{32}	31.98306	Ca^{42}	41.9711
B^{11}	11.01286	Ne^{22}	21.99864	S^{33}	32.98260	Ca^{43}	42.9723

APPENDIX 7

Energy and Range Relationships for Fast Charged Particles

We give here two tables relating the energy and range of various charged particles. These tables are intended for the following purposes: general information, quick calculation of the necessary target thickness in various cases, rough estimation of the range of a beam of particles, and estimation of the range of some group of particles evolved in a reaction. For serious measurement of nuclear energy levels the method of procedure given in the invaluable review article by Livingston and Bethe (*Review of Modern Physics*, April, 1937) should be followed.

A short word about nuclear energetics can be put in here. If a bombarding particle of atomic mass M_B has the energy E_B and produces a transmutation in which a nucleus of mass M_N and a particle of mass M_P, energy E_P, at an angle θ to the original direction of bombardment are formed, then if Q is the appropriate nuclear energy change there is a relation

$$\frac{M_N Q}{1.02} = (M_N + M_P)E_P - (M_N - M_B)E_B - 4(M_B M_P E_B E_P)^{1/2} \cos\theta$$

which holds and which can be used to determine any one of the unknown quantities. In the above it is assumed that only one product nucleus and one particle are formed. It is also assumed that the bombarding particle is captured. It is of interest that if the *maximum* value of E_B is considered then the formula also holds even if the bombarding particle is not captured, for where E_B is greatest the bombarding particle and the product nucleus move off together. All the above results from the application of the laws of conservation of momentum and energy to the process. Energies are in Mev.

In the tables we give *mean ranges*. The reason for specifying a particular type of range is that there is an element of chance in the penetration of a charged particle through matter. It may happen that a particle follows a path which involves a less than ordinary number of collisions that cause energy loss. The particle will therefore not lose all its kinetic energy until it has traveled farther. Its range is thus abnormally great. It is easy to see that this element of chance will cause a spread in the measured ranges of particles which have initially the same energy. This spread is called *straggling*. As straggling follows a definite law, it is quite possible to measure a quantity which can be related quite accurately to the initial energy. There are several such quantities, of which we select two, the "extrapolated numbers range" and the "mean range." The mean range is the range reached by one-half the particles; the extrapolated numbers range is obtained by plotting a graph of absorption versus numbers and extrapolating the steepest tangent to cut the axis of zero number. The two differ by about 2 per cent for protons and deuterons and 1 per cent for alpha particles. In all cases, of course, the mean range is less. For a thorough consideration of these two ranges the reader is again referred to the article by Livingston and Bethe.

Equivalent Thicknesses of Absorbers

In actual work, air is rarely used as the absorber. We here give the thickness in milligrams per square centimeter of surface area of a few standard absorbers which is equivalent to 1 cm. of air.

Al 1.53 Cu 2.10 Ag 2.72 Au 3.77

Energy-Range Relations

All ranges are in centimeters air equivalent, energies in Mev

Energy	Range				
	Proton	*Deuteron*	H^3	He^3	*α Particle*
0.2	0.29	0.28	0.24	0.16	0.17
0.4	0.65	0.59	0.57	0.26	0.27
0.6	1.10	0.90	0.87	0.35	0.38
0.8	1.65	1.30	1.20	0.45	0.47
1.0	2.30	1.72	1.53	0.55	0.57
1.2	3.06	2.19	1.95	0.63	0.66
1.4	3.91	2.70	2.37	0.74	0.74
1.6	4.88	3.30	2.83	0.85	0.84
1.8	5.92	3.92	3.30	0.96	0.94
2.0	7.20	4.61	3.90	1.09	1.05
2.5	10.40	6.51	5.22	1.46	1.35
3.0	14.10	8.78	6.90	1.86	1.70
3.5	18.30	11.32	8.79	2.35	2.08
4.0	23.10	14.40	10.81	2.87	2.49
4.5	28.30	17.30	13.17	3.38	2.97
5.0	33.90	20.80	15.60	4.10	3.48
6.0	46.7	28.2	21.6	5.50	4.52
7.0	61.2	36.6	27.5	7.09	5.90
8.0	77.3	46.2	34.8	8.80	7.35
9.0	95.3	56.6	42.3	10.60	8.89
10.0	114.8	67.8	50.2	12.85	10.55
11.0	136.1	80.2	59.5	15.2	12.40
12.0	150.4	93.4	69.3	18.0	14.18
13.0	183.1	107.4	79.0	19.8	16.24
14.0	209.1	122.4	90.3	22.3	18.35
15.0	238.5	138.2	101.7	24.3	21.17
20.0		229.6	169	39.5	32.5
25.0		343	260	62.5	51.0
30.0		477	344	87	71.0
35.0				114	92.5
40.0				144	115.7

Range-Energy Relations

Range	Energy				
	Proton	*Deuteron*	H^3	He^3	α *Particle*
1.0	0.56	0.64	0.63	1.81	1.92
2.0	0.92	1.23	1.21	3.15	3.39
3.0	1.18	1.50	1.63	4.12	4.52
4.0	1.42	1.82	2.03	4.94	5.47
5.0	1.62	2.11	2.41	5.68	6.31
6.0	1.82	2.37	2.75	6.34	7.07
7.0	1.98	2.61	3.03	6.92	7.76
8.0	2.15	2.84	3.31	7.52	8.43
9.0	2.31	3.05	3.55	8.08	9.07
10.0	2.45	3.24	3.80	8.64	9.67
15.0	3.11	4.10	4.83	10.8	12.3
20.0	3.68	4.88	5.72	13.0	14.5
25.0	4.20	5.58	6.51	15.2	16.9
30.0	4.66	6.21	7.33	17.0	19.1
35.0	5.08	6.81	8.02	18.7	20.7
40.0	5.49	7.34	8.72	20.1	22.2
45.0	5.87	7.89	9.33	21.3	23.4
50.0	6.24	8.38	9.95	22.4	24.7
60.0	6.93	9.32	11.02	24.4	27.2
70.0	7.55	10.2	12.0	26.5	29.8
80.0	8.06	11.0	13.1	28.4	32.1
90.0	8.72	11.7	14.0	30.6	34.4
100.0	9.25	12.5	14.8	32.4	36.6
150.0	11.61	15.7			
200.0	13.65	18.6			
300.0		23.3			
400.0		27.3			
500.0		30.7			

APPENDIX 8

THE MESOTRON

In Chapter 2, while supposedly describing the elementary particles, we made only very brief mention of the mesotron. The reason was that the mesotron can play virtually no part in the application of nuclear physics to other purposes. In fact, the only possible excuse for introducing it under that guise would be to point to the fact that a considerable part of the ionization in the air is due to mesotrons and that they probably produce a finite number of mutations and so affect the distribution of species. Without making such a thin excuse, however, we can include here a little about the mesotron for no other reason than general interest.

Like the neutron the mesotron was discovered as a result of an anomalous behavior in a radiation which was thought to be nearly understood. The neutron was first mistaken for a quantum, and its identity was betrayed by the fact that it carried far too much momentum for its energy. When considered as a heavy neutral particle this appeared natural. The mesotron appeared in the field of study of cosmic rays. If careful cloud-chamber pictures of the particles designated as the charged component of cosmic rays are taken, with the cloud chamber in a magnetic field, then we have two separate methods of estimating the energy of the particle. The first is the curvature of the track seen in a known field, the second is the ionization produced per centimeter of path. Both these methods require one further thing—*knowledge of the nature of the particle, that is, its rest mass and charge.* One very persistent finding involved a particle, sometimes assumed to be an electron, sometimes a proton, which ionized far too much if an electron and far too little if a proton, for the energy as deduced from the bending in the magnetic field. Stated baldly thus it appears strange that such a contradiction was not seen to exist earlier, but a great uncertainty is always involved in extrapolating a theory from low energies to energies in the hundreds of Mev as involved in cosmic rays. The necessary time had to elapse before it was clearly realized that an energetic electron should definitely ionize but little and an energetic proton still ionize considerably. The nature of the contradiction mentioned above was most clearly shown and the interpretation given almost simultaneously by Street and Stevenson at Harvard and Anderson and Neddermeyer in California. The explanation is that the particles are *heavy electrons,* which may be either positive or negative and have a mass which has the most probable value of 180 times the rest mass of the electron. It is not yet certain that there is not a distribution of masses. The name *mesotron* is gradually becoming adopted for these heavy electrons, though "meson" is still used.

The mesotron is not stable. It reverts to an ordinary electron, an event which has actually been photographed by Williams and Pickup. Its half-life has been estimated by a rather simple method as follows. The number of coincidence counts observed by a certain pair of counters with appropriate absorption between them to ensure that the recorded coincidences are mesotrons was recorded at low altitude and high altitude. Two differences exist between the two experiments, the one the *absorption* of the air and the other the *sheer height*. The equivalent of the absorption of the extra air at low altitudes was placed above the counter system while it was at high altitudes and the counts recorded. The numbers did not agree with those recorded while at low altitude but were, though less than when not covered by absorber, still greater than the low level values. This means that there has been a loss of mesotrons on the way down which is not the kind of loss introduced by encountering so many atoms. The absorber contained as many atoms as the thin air on the way down but was not so effective. The conclusion is that the mesotrons decay on their way down, and from their number and speed it is possible to deduce the decay constant. Their speed tells the time it takes to reach the lower level, and the difference in the counts the number decaying. The actual count gives the number available to decay, and so the complete decay formula can be filled in with the unknown the decay constant. The half-life depends on the mass chosen for the mesotron, but estimates now indicate somewhere between 1 and 2 microseconds.

The part played by mesotrons in the nucleus is not yet known. Most exciting future experiments involve the supercyclotron and bombarding particles of energies in excess of those necessary to eject a mesotron out of a nucleus —if it is there. Until such experiments have been made we are not out of the age of speculation.

REFERENCE

KARL K. DARROW, "Particles of the Cosmic Rays," *Bell System Technical Journal*, **18**, 190, 1939.

APPENDIX 9

A Few Problems

1. Estimate the number of neutrinos per hour passing through the anatomy of an average New Yorker when the Crocker Laboratory cyclotron is bombarding a target with 300 microamperes of deuterons at 16 Mev. (Order of magnitude is all that is expected.) *Our guess, 30.*

2. Five miles away from a cyclotron recording apparatus is set up to detect: (*a*) counts due to slow neutrons, (*b*) counts due to gamma rays, (*c*) counts due to fast neutrons. The recording apparatus includes some very fast oscillograph sweeps. The cyclotron is suddenly stopped. Describe the behavior of the recording apparatus immediately after the stoppage.

3. A beam of 100 microamperes of 10-Mev deuterons hits a copper target of mass 0.1 gram which is thermally insulated. How long will it take to melt? (Give answer within a factor of 2.) *Our estimate,* $\frac{1}{25}$ *sec.*

4. A beryllium target whose area is 1 sq cm and thickness 1 mm is bombarded by a deuteron beam of equal area and intensity, 100 microamperes at 10 Mev. How long will it take to use up one-tenth of the beryllium by transmutation? (Only order of magnitude needed.)

5. Calculate the Q-value for the reaction $Be^9(\alpha n)C^{12}$.

6. Assuming that the range of a very fast deuteron is proportional to the square of its energy, and that the cross section for transmutation of the atoms of air is 10^{-26} sq cm, calculate the energy of deuteron beam which would be 100 per cent effective in causing transmutation. (Answer to within a factor of 2.) *Our estimate, 2600 Mev.*

7. One cubic centimeter of a solution of NaCl containing radioactive sodium and giving 1000 counts per minute 1 meter from a Geiger counter shielded by 2 mm of lead is injected into a man's blood stream. After a few minutes 1 cc of blood is withdrawn and gives 25 counts per minute 10 cm from the same counter. What is the volume of blood in the man?

8. A cyclotron beam is observed to be 1 meter long. A strong draft of cold air is then blown across its path. Will the beam show any change in appearance?

9. A cyclotron of dee radius 50 cm, magnetic field 14,000 gauss, is used to accelerate deuterons. What is the energy of the beam? If a foil of aluminum of thickness given by 7 mg per sq cm is used to seal off the exit slit, what will be the length of the emergent beam?

10. How many electrons are given off per second from a microgram of pure P^{32}?

11. A solution of boric acid containing 100 grams of boron per 500 cc is thermally insulated and exposed to slow neutrons. How many neutrons would be necessary to cause the solution to boil, and what would be the increase in mass of the solution when it did? (Order of magnitude only.)

12. Some material containing 1 per cent carbon, 1 per cent sodium, and 98 per cent phosphorus is bombarded for 1 minute by a beam of 10-Mev deuterons. After one week a thin-walled Lauritsen electroscope gave 10 divisions per minute. What is your estimate of the activities 5 minutes and 5 hours after bombardment? No radioactive material is lost. (Give answer to within a factor of 5.)

13. A radioactive element emits gamma rays of 0.5 and 2 Mev in equal numbers. With 8 cm of copper interposed a Geiger counter gives 20 counts per minute. What count would be expected with only 1 cm interposed?

AUTHOR INDEX

SUBJECT INDEX